IN PURSUIT OF
SCIENCE AND TECHNOLOGY
JOHN C. KIM

A Journey through Four Capitals:
Tokyo, Pyongyang, Seoul, & Washington

A MEMOIR

Table of Contents

1

The Office of Naval Research Unveils the "Matchbox" Atomic Clock

One highlight of my career during the past half-century was my work on the development of miniature atomic clocks. I managed the development of the atomic clock when I was with the Office of Naval Research (2001-2013) as a Program Officer in charge of the U.S. Navy's basic research in the Navigation and Timekeeping Program. What follows is the news release on the atomic clock by the Public Affairs Office of the Office of Naval Research (ONR) on September 9, 2003.[1]

How accurate is your kitchen clock? Probably good enough to get you to work on time, but perhaps not good enough for extremely precise ship and aircraft navigation, ground-to-outer space communications, or missile guidance.

In October 2003, the Office of Naval Research will unveil the performance of the next-generation, super-accurate clock no bigger than a matchbox. The Ultra-Miniature Rb CPT Atomic Clock, 40 cubic centimeters in volume and using a minuscule one watt of power, doesn't weigh much more than a matchbox either. And it will lose only about one second every 10,000 years. Dr. John Kim, who oversees Navigation and Timekeeping Technology Programs at ONR, points out that, while commercial atomic clocks already are available, they're relatively large and bulky. A typical Cesium beam atomic clock measures about 4,800 cubic centimeters in vol-

ume (about the size of a large backpack) and consumes up to 50 watts of power, and costs $20,000.

Kernco, Inc., of Danvers, Mass. is a longtime builder of precision timing devices. In October, Kernco will deliver a field-tested unit of the Ultra-Miniature Rubidium (Rb) CPT (Coherent Population Trapping) Atomic Clock to ONR that, Kim points out, is about half the size of the current commercially available ones, but improves on power needs by a factor of four. The tiny size of the Kernco clock, he says, will permit new degrees of design flexibility for systems, especially aircraft, which places a high premium on size and weight. ONR awarded Kernco a contract in Nov. 2000 for the development of the 40 cubic-centimeters clock.

The Kernco laser-based Ultra-Miniature Rb CPT Atomic Clock, which is entirely optical, is a critical breakthrough for miniaturizing atomic clocks. The fiber-optic communications industry developed extremely compact lasers to meet the needs of its optical transmission device. That device is the Vertical-Cavity Surface Emitting Laser (VCSEL). The difference between this new clock and other atomic clocks are the size, the weight, the power consumption, the transportability, and the price. The Kernco clock is a tactical grade atomic clock. Kernco has already begun their work for ONR on an even smaller ten cubic centimeters Rb CPT Atomic Clock, but also that will not be the last word: other agencies are developing still a more accurate atomic clock.

In the 1980s, atomic clocks were expensive and bulky, and they consumed considerable battery power. Only a few essential military platforms could use such an atomic clock. The size has been an important consideration as the atomic clock needs to be embedded into small weapon systems. The battery power consumption also has been another critical factor for an underwater application, since the atomic clock must operate in underwater environments for long periods of time.

One solution to an affordable atomic clock was to place the time standards on orbiting satellites and use the downlink signals to update less accurate clocks in user equipment by transmitting one pulse-per-second updates. Such satel-

lites became known as the Global Positioning System (GPS). Many ground users could share one super-accurate atomic clock onboard the GPS satellite. GPS relies on clock stability of onboard Cesium and Rubidium clocks for its position accuracy. GPS relies on clock stability of onboard Cesium and Rubidium clocks for its position accuracy.

I recently found an online course[2] on GPS, published by the Warnell School of Forestry and Natural Resources of the University of Georgia, Athens. The Forestry School included my portrait (see photo 1). My children called the Rb CPT atomic clock "Dad's Electronic Mustache."

One day I posted this online course to Facebook with the following caption:

"Here is a portrait of mine, circa 2003, holding an atomic clock."

Then, a blogger read a note from the online course, which stated that, the cost of an atomic clock onboard the GPS satellite is $100,000. The blogger responded:

"That's $100K! Hmmm?"

I responded:

"One atomic clock (which costs $100K) is shared by several hundred million users. I call it economical."

I think I made my point successfully as the blogger replied with a *"thumbs-up"* emoji message.

Unfortunately, for all of its promise, all was not well with the GPS atomic clock and the GPS navigation system. It turned out that GPS is vulnerable to intentional and unintentional interferences. Attempts to jam U.S. GPS-based weapons and navigation systems in the recent Iraq War (2003-2011) were a reminder of just how vulnerable technology can be.[3]

While work continues, new atomic clock technology developed by ONR offered an opportunity to place an affordable atomic clock in the hands of individual users. Thus, the precision clock industry came full circle from an individual user to a single atomic clock on the GPS and back to an individual user.

In 1927, the first physics-based clock similar to the Ultra-Miniature Rb CPT atomic clock was invented by Warren Marrison and Joseph W. Horton of the Bell Laboratories. They developed a quartz crystal clock, which used the piezoelectric properties of quartz crystals.[4]

What is the piezoelectric effect?

"When a quartz crystal receives electric energy, it vibrates at 32,768 Hz in the quartz clock with the accuracy of 10^{-8}. This vibration provides the accurate time reference."

"This clock was good enough for applications in non-military systems."

The accuracy of atomic clocks is three orders of magnitude better than that of quartz clocks: At the time, there was a growing need for miniature, low power consumption, and high-precision atomic clocks for tactical platforms such as the Tomahawk cruise missile, Unmanned Aerial Vehicles (UAV), sonar, and Unmanned Underwater Vehicles (UUV). The size of the tactical grade atomic clock was about 200 cubic centimeters, with a power consumption of about 5 Watts. Such an atomic clock delivered performance accuracy in the Allan deviation of 5×10^{-10} after 10 seconds integration. The Allan deviation is a measure of frequency stability in clocks and oscillators.

Such success of these clocks also brought unintended consequences to the atomic clock industry. Due to the success of GPS as a time source, GPS caused the decline of the atomic clock industrial base. In the 1980s, there were a dozen atomic clock manufacturers in the U.S. The surviving atomic clock industry in 2012 included Symmetricom, Beverly, Mass.; Frequency Electronics Inc. (FEI) Government Systems Inc., Mitchel Field, Long Island, N.Y.; and Stanford, Sunnyvale, Calif.

In 2009, Dr. Mike Garvey and Dr. Robert Lutwak of Symmetricom proposed a Cesium CPT atomic clock for applications in tactical platforms in response to an ONR Broad Agency Announcement (BAA). The size of the resulting device would be three cubic centimeters, the power consumption 500 milliwatts, and performance regarding the Allan deviation 10^{-12}. This atomic clock would be named the Tactical Grade Atomic Clock (TGAC).

So you saw a glimpse of my career of more than half a century in a brief public affairs announcement of the Office of Naval Research. What follows in the rest of this memoir is a remembrance of my personal life, journeying through four capitals, and a chronicle of my professional life, pursuing science and technology.

The world we live in is increasingly dependent on science and technology.

It is essential to understand not only the individual disciplines in science, but also how science interacts with technology, engineering, and mathematics. I pursued science and technology throughout my career of over 60 years. At Kyunggi High School in Seoul, I studied basic science such as physics, mathematics, general chemistry, and biology. At Seoul National University (SNU), I specialized in electrical power engineering, which was the classical electrical engineering curriculum in the 1950s. When I entered Trine University, I had shifted my emphasis to electronics and communications engineering. In 1959, when I enrolled at Michigan State University (MSU), I had taken the latest electrical engineering courses, which included the study of transistors, electronics, computer engineering, and numerical analysis. At the time, I was ill-prepared to tackle such coursework. When I began working in the American industries, like Honeywell, Raytheon (Melpar) and Northrop-Grumman (TRW), I had jumped into military technologies such as sonars, radars, computers and communications, and radio technology, each of which I have always studied to catch up with latest developments. And catch up I did to survive in the industry. At ONR, the job shifted my emphasis to other areas of science (fiber optic gyroscopes, laser cooling devices, quantum devices, etc.) These challenges became my opportunity.

One challenge was super-precision atomic clocks, which could alleviate collateral damage by making surgical bombing possible. Another example was wireless radio communications devices. The signal quality of military radios has improved through digitization, modulation, and multiple-access technologies, cellular and space communications developed into the ubiquitous wireless telephone technologies today. The vacuum tube and later transistorized computers changed our lives and created another revolution, perhaps equal to or more significant than the industrial revolution.

I do not claim that I had anything to do with the invention of the digital computer, but in 1963, I helped Howard Aiken's initiative to create a computer with a somewhat different number system called the residue number system, which he explored through a U.S. Air Force contract. I also had been present when the most primitive programming language was used in the Michigan State University's MISTIC computer, which Professor Larry Von Tersch constructed two years before I arrived in East Lansing. I was fortunate to study under these pioneers of computer technology. Later, in 1973, I was personally

acquainted with Judge Earl Larson of the District Court of Minnesota, who invalidated the 1964 patent right for the Sperry-Rand's ENIAC computer, thus putting the invention of the digital computer into the public domain.

PART ONE
GROWING UP IN JAPAN AND KOREA
(1935–1958)

2

The Beginning

My children often asked me,

"Dad, why did you come to America?"

I would answer,

"There was no reason. It just happened."

However, when I thought about it more, it had not been as simple as that. My journey started when a wave of immigration swept me upon the American shore. Out of the 423 graduates of my high school class of 1954, more than a quarter—122 of them—went abroad, mostly to America. Their families sent them overseas to find safety from the shooting war in Korea, and more importantly to obtain a better education in American colleges. I was not an exception to this phenomenon. I joined the mass migration of my classmates from South Korea to America in the 1950s during and after the Korean War. If there were no wars and no Americans in South Korea, I would have charted my course to Japan for further study, but the course was set to American for the better. This migration was pushed along by the political changes in Korea. Why did I come to America? I think it was fate.

Fate, or the course of the life, is stochastic; it has a pattern, which might be analyzed but not be predicted precisely. I made several momentous travels in my life: I was born in Tokyo, where my parents immigrated a decade earlier as a result of political changes in Korea. The next move was from Tokyo to Pyongyang in 1941 and third from Pyongyang to Seoul in 1945. Finally, I moved from Seoul to Washington in 1958. These journeys through four capitals added uncertainties into my life, but also enriched and shaped my life.

Born in Tokyo

My parents kept a sheet of red bond paper, which was the certificate of my smallpox vaccination, issued by the City of Tokyo on November 28, 1936. This piece of paper summarized my vital personal data: my name, Chan Kyu Kim; my place of birth, No. 13, First Street, Horinouchi Precinct, Suginami Ward, Tokyo, Japan; and my date of birth.

In 1967, after my naturalization as an American citizen, I changed my name to John Chan Kyu Kim at the Fairfax Circuit Court. I adapted my name four times according to political changes around me; I became a multilingual person speaking and reading five languages, according to the places I lived, in the schools I attended, and for companies I worked.

My high school friend Hee-young Chae, who also lived in Tokyo for so many years and later immigrated to Baltimore, nicknamed me Suginami. That was the name of the borough where I was born. Suginami is now the demographic center of the metropolitan area of Tokyo. Until the 1920s, cedar trees lined the main road in the village. When I was growing up in Suginami, there had been rice paddy fields and thatched-roof houses scattered in the village. Village women washed their laundry on the bank of the Zenpukuji River. Today, a four-mile long river bank laid with stones is a municipal park, in which 400 cherry trees stand. There was an old Buddhist temple, Myohoji, hidden in the grove of cedar trees. Gradually, this rural scene was transformed from a village into a residential suburb for middle-class commuters to downtown Tokyo. When I visited our old homestead in Horinouchi, black chimneys had replaced rice fields in the 1950s and the borough was packed with both residential houses and offices.

My Parents

In the spring and the fall each year, Rahn and I have been visiting the tombs of my parents in Parklawn Memorial Park in Rockville, Maryland. From the main gate at Viers Mill Road, we drive over a quaint narrow stone bridge and arrive on their grave site. A stone bas-relief sculpture of the Last Supper is at the top of the hill. We fill a bucket of water at the water spigot below, and Rahn

usually lays fresh cut flowers on my father's and mother's tombstone, as my mother so much loved gardening. On my father's bronze plaque, we engraved a simple summary of his life, that his name was Ke-jun Kim (1909-1984), his surviving family member's names, and a Christian cross.

He was born in Yongbyon, now in North Korea, as the second son of his father, Seong-ok Kim (1869-1941), and his mother, Shin-sil Kang (1876-1948). My paternal grandfather was landed gentry, as I remember, a lean, scholarly looking gentleman, more interested in the cultivation of his orchard trees as a gentleman farmer. He grafted a unique pear tree called "Chi-yang-no" in his orchards.

Next to father's grave is my mother's. On her bronze plaque, we also engraved a summary of her life, with her name, Young-seok Kim (1915-1994), and the names of her five children, and a Christian cross.

She was born in Seoul, Korea, as the second daughter of her father, Seong-hyeon Kim (1872-1948), a military officer in the Yi dynasty, and her mother Sang-chun Park (1882-1967). I remember my maternal grandfather was a tall gentleman of the old guard, with the stern military bearing.

My mother preserved my pin-striped sailor suit, which I wore when I was four years old (see photo 6). Later, this was handed down to my younger brothers. She bought this suit at a Tokyo department store, called Daitetsu, almost 80 years ago. I also have a photograph of me sitting on my maternal grandmother's lap, wearing the blue pin-striped sailor suit (see photo 5). My mother must have kept it and brought it to America. In 1983, my mother gave the suit to my wife, Rahn. When she received it, Rahn did not ask my mother how it had found its way to Washington. I wished she had asked my mother, but it was too late, and it would stay as a mystery. Much like me, my blue sailor suit traveled half-way around the world as the winds of political change blew it here and there like an autumn leaf. In the photograph of me on my grandmother's lap, I was wearing a cap with a blue star, leggings, and a pair of wool socks which my mother had knit. They made my legs itchy as they were made with coarse wool. The suit travelled from Tokyo, to Pyongyang, and continued to Seoul, and finally found the original owner in Washington.

All the places the suite and I traveled were different and distinct in culture and environment. In retrospect, I found it remarkable that I adapted to these names, places, languages, and environments, while I tried to preserve my identity.

I heard that one's hometown is the place where one has the most friends. I have more friends in Washington than in any other place. On that account, I claim Washington as my hometown. I undertook some of my travels by my own choice, and some not. I found my journey exciting as it covered the Korean Strait, the Thirty-Eighth Parallel North, the Pacific Ocean, and the North American continent. Also, during those journeys, I found myself trapped in the middle of the Second World War and the Korean War. I would not call my journey a wandering odyssey but rather a pilgrimage full of purposes.

MY FATHER'S HOMECOMING TO YONGBYON

In 1939, my father made a homecoming trip with my mother and three children Jeong-kyu, Phil, and me from Tokyo to Yongbyon, crossing the Korean Strait, covering the distance of 1,500 miles. As I was a young boy of four years old, I remember only two things about that travel. One was a small mishap on the train. When the train reached Pyongyang station, I was looking out the window with my chin resting on the window sill. Alas, the train lurched suddenly, and I cut my chin. I still have the faint scar on my chin. The other thing I remember from that train trip was the public announcement in the railroad station in a rhythmic voice in Japanese. I asked my mother what was being said. She answered:

"The next station is Pyongyang! Pyongyang! Please check your belongings."

I was fascinated by the sonorous sound and still remember that after all these years.

YONGBYON

In October 1944, during the Korean Thanksgiving holidays, I traveled with my father and my uncle to Yongbyon from Gaecheon. We paid homage to my grandfather. We started from our home, on foot, and walked 15 miles as there was no public transportation available. We crossed the Cheong-cheon River, which borders two counties of Gaecheon and Yongbyon. Yongbyon was in the north of the River and Gaecheon in the south. Yongbyon was a pristine and quiet town on the bank of the Cheong-cheon River.

From the 1980s, Yongbyon attained notoriety as North Korea constructed nuclear reactor.[5]

"Why did they choose Yongbyon as the site for nuclear research laboratories?" In 1962, North Korea obtained a Russian-made two-megawatt experimental atomic reactor in Yongbyon.[6] There were two things in Yongbyon which attracted Russian nuclear engineers. One was the river, which encircled the city and provided the lagoons for the reactor. The other was a technical college in the city, which offered skilled technicians for operating and maintaining the reactor.

"How did a technical college come to being in Yongbyon?" The answer to this question is a long story, which started with a hardworking Irish Methodist missionary, Rev. Charles Morris (1869-1927), who started a small mission school in 1901. He arrived in Korea in 1901 and later married Louise Ogilvy,[7] who, at the age of 18, had also moved to Korea from Kansas to be a missionary. The two of them met, married in Kobe, Japan, in 1903, and lived in Yongbyon in 1905-1912.[8] During the period, Charles Morris established the area's first church and went on to build five more churches in the province. In 1907, Morris found a mission school, and in 1925, he built Yongbyon Methodist Church, which later became known as Morris Memorial Methodist Church.[9] In 1922, Morris rechartered the school as Soong-deok Mission School and expanded the high school with an endowment of ¥1,800 from prominent citizens of Yongbyon, including Rev. W. Arthur Noble and my grandfather.[10]

When the World War II broke out in 1941, the Japanese Colonial Government in Korea had begun the persecution of Christian missionaries. The colonial government took over the Soong-deok school and renamed it to Yong-moon Technical High School in Gu-jang, located three miles east of the

old mission school. After the Korean War, in 1953, the North Korean regime expanded the high school as Yong-moon Technical College. When the regime planned on building a nuclear generating station with the help of the Russians, they had been looking for a nuclear research and reactor site. As North Korean nuclear development began in earnest in 1965, they established the College of Physics in Yongbyon to train specialists necessary for the operation of the Yongbyon IRT-2000 Research Reactor (with the power rating of two megawatts).[11]

What started as a missionary school 90 years ago helped Yongbyon become a highly publicized nuclear reactor site and contributed to the nuclearization of the Korean peninsula. The missionary, Rev. Charles Morris, who built the mission school in Yongbyon, could not have imagined that one day his school would become a hornet's nest for a nuclear weapons production facility. It was an unintended outcome for his work.

MY GREAT-UNCLE SANG-YU PARK AND HIS COUSIN SANG-JUN LUTHER PARK

During the Japanese colonial occupation period in Korea, one of the most oppressive policies which Japan imposed on the Korean people was an attempt to annihilate the Korean national identity. In 1941, Japan promulgated a law, which required all Koreans to adopt a Japanese surname. Our clan was forced to change our surname, and our clan elders took the name of Kaneyama. There were a few exceptions, one of which was my Great-Uncle Sang-Yu Park (1889-1977), who refused to adopt a Japanese surname. He kept his surname Park for all of his life. Ironically, he had a cousin, Sang-Jun Luther Park (1876-1945), who was a pro-Japanese politician. During the Japanese colonial period, Luther Park became Governor of Hwanghae Province, and later a member of the Japanese House of the Councilors,[12] in 1940. In 1942, he became the first President of Myeong- Ryun College (later Seong-gyun-gwan University), Seoul, Korea.

Great-Uncle Sang-Yu Park was the only person of my grandparents' generation with whom I had meaningful dialogues. He had received a traditional Korean classics education and was an expert in Korean classical music. From him, I learned about the Korean and Chinese classical music, which has the similar terminologies to Western music, that is, the scale, the key, and the

strength. The scale has five notations, Gung, Sang, Gak, Chi, and Wu (or C, D, E, G, and A) from which the Korean pentatonic music is composed. There are several cultures in which the pentatonic scale has been used. For example, *Ol' Man River* by Jerome Kern and Oscar Hammerstein in the musical *Show Boat* was composed in pentatonic scale taken from African folk songs. The Western musical scale definitely uses the fundamental and its harmonic frequencies to designate the scale; thereby, the resultant music is harmonious or pleasing to ears. As my great uncle explained, the Asian music scale was less concerned with the frequencies associated with 12 notes, which included the major and minor keys. Whether they were a string, a wind, or percussion, an instrument was built by the linear dimension, which caused the resultant music to become somewhat dissonant, typical of Asian music. Great-Uncle Sang-yu Park expounded on the theory of music to me. What I remembered from his lecture on Asian music theory was that it put the emphasis on the form, but not as much on the harmonics; music sounds dissonant to my ears. But remembering many conversations I had with him, I am thankful for his lectures. I only wished that I had delved into the subject more deeply. Alas, it was a lost opportunity.

When I was ready to leave for America, my father and I went to my great uncle's house to bid farewell. After the usual farewell, he asked me to do him a favor

"What can I do for you, Great-Uncle?"

"It is about the sunrise and sunset. In America, please tell me if the Sun rises in the East or the West?"

"According to the Ying-Yang Theory, the Sun must rise in the West."

"Yeah, but it must rise in the East wherever you are, that is, in Korea or America."

When I was about to explain to him the helio-centrism and the geocentrism, my father nudged me with his elbow and told me to say just "yes." I often thought about the question, and I said to myself, the old gentleman could be right. Regarding relativity, his West could be our East. The concept of Yin and Yang was so deeply embedded in Eastern philosophy. It successfully explained almost everything like cosmology, medicine, philosophy, etc.

Phyllis Hall King, and an American Missionary Family

My great uncle's cousin, Governor Luther Park, had known a Christian missionary and physician, Dr. Sherwood Hall when both of them were young men. Dr. Rosetta Hall and her son Sherwood Hall had once been frequent guests in Luther Park's home in Jinnampo, where Luther Park's father was the Magistrate.[13]

Fifty years later, Rahn and I met Phyllis King, the daughter of Drs. Sherwood and his wife Marian Hall. Phyllis and her husband Dr. Edward King were members of Trinity United Methodist Church (UMC), McLean, which was our church for many years. In 2012, Phyllis and Edward gave me an old photograph (see photo 8) of the Hall and Park families, vacationing in 1928 in Little Diamond Mountain near Haeju, Korea. Two Park brothers, Moonhyeok and Moon-ok, were my mother's cousins. In 1981, Dr. Sherwood Hall published an autobiography, *With Stethoscope to Asia: Korea.*[14] In this memoir there was a photo insert of Governor Luther Park,[15] who was wearing a full-dress, embroidered Japanese court uniform, holding a feathered two-cornered hat and carrying a side-sword.

In January 2012, Rahn and I invited Phyllis and Ed King to a Korean restaurant and talked about the fellowship and the connection between the two families. I was grateful for the kind letter and a photograph, which Phyllis and Ed subsequently sent to us:

McLean, Virginia
January 17, 2012

Dear Rahn and John,

> We so very much enjoyed your luncheon treat for us at Woo-Lae-Oak Restaurant, and seeing the lovely picture of your beautiful family and being introduced to such delicious Korea food. Thank you so very much for the most enjoyable time and also for learning about John's detective work in finding his relationship with Governor Sang-Jun Luther Park.

I returned with a new enthusiasm for trying to locate that original photograph on page 314 of Sherwood Hall's autobiography,[16] but although I've been going through many boxes, I have not yet found it. However, I was very excited to find the enclosed photograph with my grandmother's note:

Governor Luther Park's wife & two sons, Dr. Sherwood and myself, Mrs. Susan Noh a mutual friend of the Parks, and ourselves—out for a picnic at the Mt. So-keum-kang (The Little Diamond Mountain). Governor Park was too busy to go.

So here you have two more family cousins to confirm the looks and the height of your relationship to this family, John, and if you would like to keep this photo, we are happy for you to have it. You have been such a good detective; you deserve to have this "find" to reward your efforts.

When Rosetta Hall describes the destination of the picnic as the "Little Diamond Mountains," I'm assuming they were in Haeju,[17] maybe overlooking the harbor? Also, I'm enclosing a photocopied page from Dr. Rosetta Hall's guestbook, which Ed was describing to you. In the letter beneath Samuel A. Moffett's signature on January, 21st, 1915, was Lucia H. Fisk's signature, whom he later married. Many years later at the dinner with the Korean group in my house in Virginia, Samuel Moffett, Jr. told us that Samual and Lucia were his parents. We teased him about being a "honeymoon baby." Well, I better get this mailed off to you, and then come back to more searching for Governor Park!

Thank you again for your generous luncheon treats. We very much enjoyed our time with you.

Very appreciatively
Phyllis and Ed King

When I received the photograph of the Park and Hall families, only a few of the faces were familiar to me, but I had to do some research to verify Great-Uncle Luther Park's wife and two sons in the photograph. I knew a person who could help me do that. That person was my Aunt Yim-Soon Yi, who was in her 90s and living in Flushing, N.Y. In the summer of 2014, Rahn and I visited my aunt and met at a Korean restaurant where I showed her the photograph and asked:

"Aunt, I want you to take a look at this photo. Do you know who these people are?"

After a long gaze at the photo, she responded,

"I don't know anyone. Who are they?"

"This is an old photo I have received recently from an American missionary who used to live in North Korea in the 1930's and the 1940's. Do you know who this elderly woman is?"

Again, she examined the faces and there appeared a twinkle in her eyes, and she finally said:

"Yes, I remember the lady. She was Sam-cheong-dong grandmother. She was the wife of Governor Park."[18]

"Well, you remembered. That is right. Now, how about these two young men?"

"Now I can tell you who they are. The one on the left is Moon-ok, and the one on the right is his younger brother, Moon-hyeok. They were two sons of Governor Park. The lady on the left is Mrs. Susan Noh. I remember the high heels she used to wear, which were fashionable footwear in those days."

And we all chuckled for a while as I found a bit of the family history from this faded photograph and my aunt's memory.

Then, what happened to Sherwood Hall, his wife Marian Hall, and their daughter Phyllis. In 1940, they were forced to leave Korea. The American Consul-General in Tokyo advised them to evacuate at the port of Inchon. Subsequently, the Methodist Mission Board in New York ordered Sherwood and Marian Hall to proceed to Madar Union Tuberculosis Sanatorium in Ajmer, India[19] where these two good doctors served as a medical missionary team for the duration of the War II.

Our Family Returns to Korea

While the Empire of Japan was forcing American missionaries to leave Korea, my family returned from Japan to Korea. It was an unsettling time in East Asia as Japan and China began waging the Sino-Japanese War in 1937, which then extended throughout East Asia and the Pacific region after the Japanese attack on Pearl Harbor. My father sensed danger and decided to return to Korea. I read newspaper articles from 1943 reporting burning houses caused by dreaded incendiary bombs dropped by American B-29 bombers on Tokyo and other cities in Japan. Also, my father was discouraged by ever worsening racial discrimination against the Korean people in Japan. We would live as a minority. No matter how much we could benefit from the better living standards and schools in Tokyo, it was not worth it.

Life in a Small Finishing Town Jumunjin

In 1941, my family returned to the small fishing town of Jumunjin on the East Coast of Korea, where my maternal grandparents lived. It was a small village with a white sand beach where many sweet briars bloomed. Three months after our arrival in Korea, however, my two brothers and I contracted measles, as we had no immunity for it. The three of us had high fevers, and my parents wrapped us in blankets and carried us to a clinic, where the medical authority quarantined us. My mother said that, during the quarantine in the clinic, I asked for oranges, and, after we had eaten them, our fever broke. Phil and I recovered, but my middle brother, Jeong-kyu did not survive. My parents buried him in Jumunjin, and I remember my mother silently weeping whenever she crossed the bridge, called the Sadari, saying: "Over there on the sunny hillside I can see my son's grave."

The last time I saw Jumunjin was in January 1972, when I was there on a TDY assignment to work on a U.S. Defense Department project in South Korea. The U.S. Army provided a helicopter on which I flew over the town, and I had a good view of the harbor. I saw a natural port on the coast, which provided a home for many fishing boats and saw a lone lighthouse, guiding fishermen from the dark sea to the land. I remembered, in the squid season,

how all spaces in town, including rooftop, were occupied by drying squid. I also remembered the long line of fish stalls in the oceanfront and, women divers carrying wicker baskets of harvested seaweeds, sea cucumbers, and abalones in the spring, summer, and autumn months,

There is a story about me in my family, which I have heard over and again. It had happened one day when I visited my grandparents' house I must have wandered away and got lost, or my grandmother lost me, near the beach. The whole family and our neighbors searched me on the beach and the neighborhood. Then, my grandmother spotted something brown afar on the beach, and, as she approached, she discovered me playing on the sand. My grandmother and I joined the search party. When I saw my father, I loosened my grip from grandmother's hand and dashed to my father. She was quite miffed. My father had been riding a bicycle to search for me, and I rode back home with him.

My father joined the Jumunjin Fishery Cooperative as an investor. The cooperative owned and operated a fleet of commercial fishing boats. The cooperative hired fishermen to catch sardines in the East Sea. During the war years, Japan was short of lard supplies and food. They promoted the fishery industry to produce fish lard. The cooperative had a fish lard plant and a cannery on the south side of the town. Fish were boiled and squeezed by a sizeable fish-oil press. The dried lees made excellent organic fertilizer.

My father bought a motorbike with a sidecar. He was the only private person in town who owned such a contraption. I remember riding in the sidecar as he drove the motorcycle around town. He also owned an air gun. He and I went around the countryside looking for game birds like quail and pheasant. My mother and grandmother made meat patties from these birds. I would watch them use a heavy butcher knife to pound bird meat, including small bones until it became very soft. My mother made kebob on skewers and cooked them on an open charcoal fire. I liked the smell of sizzling pheasant meat. My grandmother prepared dumplings with pheasant meat. They were delicious.

When my parents moved from Tokyo to Jumunjin, they had brought a Yamaha organ, as it was my aunt Young-Souk's favorite instrument. She played

it by pedaling to produce wind. My aunt played her favorite songs of the day. The one I remember and sing even today is "Moon over the Ruined Castle," which is quintessential Japanese folk music.

*The Moon over the Ruined Castle*endnote[20]
(Translated by John Kim)

There once was a flowery spring feast high up in the castle.
Cups were passed around with moonlight reflected on "sake,"
The moonlight shined through the old pine branches,
But, where is that old moonlight now?

In the fall of 2012, there was a small musical concert in the Masonic Memorial Hall in Alexandria, Virginia. A Japanese cellist, Masatoshi Mitsumoto,[21] played this beautiful but melancholy song. It brought back my memories of the old days, and brought me to tears.

Since both my parents were fluent in Japanese, they had been very comfortable in the Japanese community in Jumunjin. The Japanese community consisted of credit union staffs, elementary school teachers, and township officials. In 1941, a Japanese friend of my father, Mr. Yasuda, offered to sell to my father a very prosperous general store with a tobacco monopoly outlet. Mr. Yasuda had decided to return home to Japan, as the World War II was raging in the Pacific. He sensed that he would be better off returning to his homeland than staying in Korea. During Japanese Colonial Government rule, all tobacco and ginseng products were controlled by the Government Monopoly Bureau. The Yasuda general store was on the main street of the town, and across the tree-lined street was the credit union. In a small town like Jumunjin, a credit union was a hub of commerce. My friend Peter Choe, who was born and raised in Jumunjin, remembered the Yasuda store.

3

Old Pyongyang as I Remember it During the World War II

My parents moved to Pyongyang from Jumunjin in 1942. This move would put our family in grave danger three years later when the political change boxed us in the wrong side, the Russian-occupied side, of the Thirty-eighth Parallel.

In 2002, I saw an advertisement for an auction of old books on the Internet. Among items I found a set of tourist brochures and maps of Pyongyang circa the 1920s. The auction started with a suggested opening bid of $50, to which I offered $25. On the deadline, my bid of $25 was the highest, so that I got the brochure and the maps. The brochure, which included a map of Pyongyang, was published in 1922 by South Manchurian Railway Co. The brochure spelled the city, Pyongyang as "Heijo" in Japanese. The brochure must have been prepared for American tourists of the early 1920s, as it mentions two comparable cities in size to Pyongyang: Detroit and Kansas City. This guide and map were kept by an unknown tourist all these years and found their way to my collection.

My story of old Pyongyang comes from events and scenes according to the memory of a fourth grader. I have many nostalgic memories of my family's life in Pyongyang in the 1940s.

The tourist brochure listed tram fares of ¥0.5 and jinrikisha fares of ¥4.00 for a half day rental with manpower provided by a coolie. Room rates at the best hotel, the Yanagiya (Willow) Hotel, were ¥80 per single room without bath and ¥120 per double room without bathroom. The brochure noted that rates for the American plan, meaning the meals are included in the fares. Oh, yes, there was also the European plan available for less than prices of the American plan. Breakfast, lunch, and dinner charges cost ¥4, ¥6, and ¥7, respectively.

The Willow Hotel was maintained by South Manchurian Railway Co. and was a five-minute ride from the railroad station by taxi. Today, the same Willow Hotel stands at the same location and enjoys the reputation of being the best hotel in Pyongyang. Notes in the brochure give the exchange rate of dollars to yen in 1920 at $1 to ¥33.

In 1942, we moved to Pyongyang and lived there for three years. We lived in a house in Gyogu Precinct near Pyongyang Train Station. We had a near-fatal carbon monoxide incident in the house. Like most people in Pyongyang, we used anthracite coal for heating our home. The heating system was a hypocaust (an under-floor hot-air heating system). One day, carbon monoxide seeped into the house through cracks in the hypocaust, and all of us became unconscious except for my Aunt Young-Sook. She quickly carried everyone to the courtyard and made us drink pickled radish juice, which apparently detoxicated carbon monoxide. Fortunately, we all recovered from poisoning. Thanks to her quick action, we averted a disaster.

THE CENTRAL DISTRICT OF PYONGYANG

In 1975, I found an old military map (scale of 1:12,500) of Pyongyang published by the U.S. Army Map Service,[22] during the World War II. With this map, I was able to locate familiar streets and sites such as our old house —a traditional Korean tiled house at No. 34 Gyogu Precinct — my elementary school, the railroad station, and other landmarks of Pyongyang. I was able to memory-jog around the old Pyongyang neighborhood. The degree and amount of detail in the map probably indicated of the American military's strategic interests of the city, way back in the 1930s before the World War II.

My memory-jog started from the railroad station, which was the terminal of two tram lines in the city. One went to West Pyongyang Railroad Station through the downtown, and the other crossed over the Daedong River to Dongdaewon District. Our house was in the new district of Pyongyang.

On the map, I saw many landmarks in our neighborhood; the fire station with a 30-foot tall watchtower, the baseball diamond with its rough grass and gray dirt mound, and my South Fortress (Seong-nam) Elementary School and the playground with monkey bars. The map also identified the Prefectural

Government, the Japanese girl's high school, Wakamatsu, and the Post Office. When our family lived in the city, we rode on a tram from the main railroad station to Yellow Gold (Hwang-geum) precinct, the central business district, where Mitsukoshi department store and other modern shops were lined up.

Two Islands in the River and Dongdaewon District

In the summertime, my family would sail on a boat cruise on the Daedong River. The boat we took was a single-mast junk sailboat, with the mast about 24 feet tall. It was propelled by the wind on the sail and by sculling an oar at the stern. The sail was washed with muddy clay water and became yellow, hence the name, "the yellow sailboat."

The junk boat could move fast downstream at full sail, powered by the wind. The river was blue and cold, contrasted by the yellow sail. I would dip my hand in the water so I could feel the flow of the cold water even in the summertime. Our view of Pyongyang from this junk boat was like a watercolor painting. Even today, I can almost see in my mind's eye the rock cliffs of Peony (Moran) Hill, some 300 feet high above the river.

The boat would start from the Silk (Reungra) Island pier, at the foot of Peony Hill. The first stop of the boat was at the Daedong Gate pier on the right bank of the river. The Daedong Gate faced the river; the tip of the roof seems flying in the air. From the riverboat, we could see the planned new town on the left bank of the river. This part of the town was Dongdaewon District, designed with modern city planning in the rectangular street pattern. The second stop was at the Customs House pier, whose imposing red brick Western building told passerby of thriving commerce of Pyongyang. The last stop was at the dock at Willow Market, from which we could see the Goat's Horn (Yang-gak) Island on the left bank. For this annual family outing, my mother packed lunch bags with sushi rolls and marinated Mongolian kebobs.

SOUTH FORTRESS ELEMENTARY SCHOOL

My father enrolled me in South Fortress Elementary School, which was ten blocks from our home. I remember the cold winter weather in Pyongyang bit us with the harsh Siberian wind. There was no school bus in the school system such that we walked to the school on foot, rain or shine, and even on snowy and icy roads.

There were many Japanese teachers, with a few slots filled with Korean teachers. My homeroom teacher was a Japanese lady, Yuriko Nakayama Sensei, who was in her mid-twenties. One day my parents and I visited her house with a basket of fruit. She lived in the Government-built teachers' housing quarters near our home. My parents told her that they had lived in Tokyo for many years. She was surprised to meet Korean parents who were well-informed on Japan; she became a good friend of my parents. In school, she remarked,

"Masahira (by then I was called by my new Japanese name), how delightful it is to hear you speak a perfect Tokyo dialect."

Lessons learned from my parents' friendship with Nakayama Sensei were that Japanese people became ordinary friends when we meet as individuals. But they could become confrontational as a group, and they could become chauvinistic. I once asked my father:

"Why are they like that?"

"Until recently, Japan was an island nation with strong cliquishness within their prefecture, which was ruled by *Daimyos* (war barons).[23]

"This cliquishness fostered a chauvinistic attitude toward any outsiders, and these countrymen marched in lockstep. That was one of their national characters, and, could have been the cause of their downfall in the 20th century."

About that time, there was a Chinese youngster of my age in our neighborhood. I got acquainted with him, and we became good friends. His family lived in a Manchurian-style adobe with mud walls, which was well-suited for the cold weather in Pyongyang. Their house had a raised wooden floor, a low dinner table, and large and small chests. His mother served us large pita bread with sweet sorghum as a snack. My Chinese friend was a heavy-set, ruddy complexioned boy. He spoke Korean with almost no accent. Many Chinese lived in Korea as they freely emigrated across the Yalu River. Koreans being a homogenous race in the peninsula for several millennia, the people seldom

had contact with foreigners, unlike America today. There was almost no racial diversity in the peninsula. This homogeneity tended to foster a chauvinistic attitude in many Koreans. Today, however, South Korea has become home to many foreign workers, currently more than 1 million, as the Korean industry experienced labor force shortages. South Koreans accept foreigners in their workplaces, but not in their homes and society.

EVACUATION TO A RURAL VILLAGE DURING THE WORLD WAR II

In early spring 1945, my family moved from Pyongyang to the rural County of Gaecheon. Why did we move from Pyongyang to the rustic hinterlands? The Japanese Colonial Government urged citizens to disperse from Pyongyang and other large metropolis to avoid bombing from American aircrafts. As a result, my family moved to Gaecheon, 60 miles north of Pyongyang. The World War II had another impact on us. But this relocation gave me unusual experience of living in the countryside.

My uncle had an estate farm in Gaecheon. The house stood at the foot of Mt. Gaema, the elevation of which was 500 feet. A mountain creek fed the irrigation network down the plain in Gaecheon. Across the street from the farmhouse, there was an irrigation ditch, five-feet deep, through which clean and cold water flowed. Mulberry trees lined the bank of the irrigation ditch. My grandmother and aunt raised silkworms; mulberry leaves were food for silkworms. They ran a small cottage industry of sericulture (silkworm), producing silk yarn from their cocoons. There were a dozen plum and apricot trees on the back hill. The house was spacious, rectangular building with a dozen rooms of various sizes and clay courtyard. Photograph 9 is an artist's rendition of this bucolic country estate farm.

THE CHOYANG COLLIERY RAILWAY[24]

There was a depot of a narrow-gauge railroad a half-mile away from our house. The railroad carried coals from the Choyang District to the mainline railway station in Cheondong. The Mutsui Mining Company of Japan built this railway in 1933, which became known as the Choyang Colliery Railway. The colliery railway supplied high-quality anthracites to Japanese Naval ships in the Yellow Sea. The railway company ran a telegraph line along the narrow-gauge track, which was used for communications for the Mitsui Mining Co. It was the only piece of the modernity in that rural village. (see photo 10)

The train was not meant for passengers, but we would hop on a hopper car to get a free ride from the depot to the village, where my elementary school (Choyang Elementary School) was located. The railroad company prohibited us from riding in the hopper car for safety reasons, but engineers would turn a blind eye to our rides. The top speed of the train was 25 mph, but it left the station, of course, at a much slower pace. It was an exciting adventure for us to hop on-board. Colliery hopper-car trains ran on a narrow gauge (3-foot) track, while mainline trains from Seoul to Northeast China, Siberia, and Europe ran on the broader, standard gauge (4 feet, 8-1/2 inches) track. The colliery train was powered by the meager carbide fuel, which generated acetylene gas by mixing with water. The carbide was used because of the shortage of coal during the War.

One day in the early summer, my uncle suggested to my parents that they start a vegetable garden behind our house and grow cabbages and radishes. All summer long my parents tended the garden and pulled out weeds. During dry spells, they carried buckets of water from the irrigation canal and watered the garden. In the fall, they harvested the cabbages and radishes, but to their dismay, the radishes were not long but round hard balls. They were so hard that it was difficult to sink one's teeth into them, and they tasted bitter but not sweet. We were disappointed with our summer-long farming. What a bitter-sweet experience!

VJ Day and the End of the War

My family led a relatively comfortable life during the war, in this remote rural area. My uncle owned considerable farmland, and a dozen tenant farmers worked there. When we lived on the farm, my uncle provided us the dwelling, the food, and other essentials of daily living. My father enjoyed his life as a country gentleman during our evacuation. All of us were almost oblivious to what was happening in the outside world.

Then, in the late summer of 1945, our lives suddenly changed from tranquility to chaos in our village by a sudden political change in Korea, following the collapse of the Empire of Japan. The Japanese surrendered unconditionally to the Allied forces after the atomic bombs destroyed Hiroshima and Nagasaki. On August 15, 1945, the news of the end of the war came unexpectedly to our village. With the end of the War, Korea was split into two political entities in the Korean Peninsula, which continued until today. I was then a fourth grader. One week after VJ Day, I saw Russian Red Army soldiers passing through Gaecheon on trains. For the first time, I heard about the Thirty-eighth Parallel North, which became the border between the two Koreas. The separation had profound effects on our lives as well as on the country and the region.

Earlier, in the 1930s, my father had seen political turmoil in Tokyo caused by hard-core Japanese Communists. When North Korea was occupied by the Red Army, he told us:

"They would brand our family as the so-called bourgeois class. We cannot survive under the Communist regime."

He foresaw troubles well ahead of any North Korean Communist regime revealed its true color. How lucky our family was, that my father foresaw what would lie ahead of us if we stayed in North Korea. One evening, he told us that he had made up his mind to go south alone to assess the situation. We would stay in Gaecheon with my uncle. My father was able to cross the porous border, mingling with Japanese refugees from Manchuria. At that time, the Russian Red Army allowed nearly four million Japanese civilian refugees and disarmed soldiers to return to Japan.[25]

A week later, my mother bought me a beginner's Russian language book in the marketplace. I still remember Russian numbers that I had memorized:

"*Odin, dba, tri, tchetri, pyeatye* (one, two, three, four, five in Russian), and

other words like *Kareyskii, Japonskii, Russkii* (Korean, Japanese, Russian in Russian) and *karandash and kniga* (pencil and book in Russian)."

That language book was my first exposure to a European language. I never studied Russin beyond that level. I thought about my little beginner's Russian textbook and considered myself fortunate not to be forced to learn Russian beyond that. I had already lived through ten years of my life without really knowing my mother tongue, Korean. How confusing it has been.

Normal life continued in the village for several months, but then, one night in November 1945, my father returned to our home and told us,

"Let's pack essential clothing, which each of us can carry. We'll leave the house at the crack of dawn to go to the train station."

He urged my uncle and the family to come with us to South Korea. My uncle had a significant amount of land and properties in Gaecheon, and it was impossible for him to leave his house overnight. He simply could not abandon the estate.

Before dawn, we bid farewell to my grandmother, uncle, and cousins, and we began our escape to South Korea. It was the last time I saw them. Two days earlier, my father had met an old friend of his in Gaecheon who had been a police officer in the old system. He had become an officer in the Peoples Public Safety Department in the new regime. With his help, my father obtained a fake transit pass, which allowed my family to travel to South Korea. We disguised ourselves as refugees from Manchuria, returning to our hometown of Jumunjin in South Korea. My father made a cover story for us:

"We lived in Anshan, Manchuria. We are Korean refugees returning to our homeland in the south."

We had our fake transit pass to prove it. We walked four miles to the railroad station and boarded a train to Pyongyang, and then on to Haeju, which was the southernmost city in North Korea. I saw my reflection in the glass window of the third-class train car, and quietly repeated to myself,

"Anshan, Manchuria. Anshan, Manchuria."

When we arrived at the Haeju railroad station, we found several thousands of refugees, mostly Japanese and some Korean, gathered there. All of them wanted to cross the border. Some Japanese soldiers, still wearing their tattered uniforms without an insignia or a unit badge, huddled in the corner of station plaza. In front of them were Red Army MP's with their PPD-40 submachine

guns. What a contrast it was between the victors and the vanquished!

In the town square outside the Haeju station, a large crowd of refugees was milling around. My father hired two porters to carry my younger brothers and a guide to lead the border crossing. As my father organized a border crossing party, an old acquaintance of my father appeared. He was trying to escape to the south as he was a former clerk of the District Attorney's office in Pyong-yang. This fugitive begged my father to include him in our party. My father reluctantly allowed him to join us.

Then, our party followed the guide in the cold November night and marched on rough country roads, sometimes crossing small creeks. After we hiked about an hour, we came out of the woods. Suddenly, the two-man border patrol appeared and stopped us. One of the patrolmen was a Russian Red Army (*Ruskii*, as we called them) MP and the other was a North Korean policeman; both were armed with semi-automatic machine guns. They questioned us. My mother was carrying my younger brother Dong-kyu on her back; she had a few valuables which she had sewed in the inner lining of a quilt blanket. Those hidden valuables were the entire assets of the family, and we prayed the policemen would not find them. They frisked us one-by-one. When it was my mother's turn, the North Korean policeman looked at her, who was carrying an infant on her back and a bag on her side. He politely told her to move on! What a relief it was. The two policemen paid most of their attention to my father's friend, who aroused suspicion with his nervous behavior. They detained him for further questioning, but my family, the porters, and the guide were allowed to cross the border. In retrospect, my father's Good Samaritan gesture to let the gentleman join our border crossing party saved our family from a potential disaster. We never heard of the gentleman again.

When we finally arrived at the South Korean border town, we let out a sigh of relief. At the border checkpoint, friendly South Korean policemen and U.S. Army MPs welcomed us to the south. The first welcoming act at the border control was a South Korean Public Health official spraying DDT powder through our sleeves as we lifted our arms to disinfect us.

My father found a room in an inn, which was packed with refugees. We had hot food for early breakfast. At noon, we took a train to Seoul and arrived in the evening. The night scene of Seoul was bright with lighted buildings. We arrived at the house of my mother's cousins. We surely surprised them. After

we stayed overnight at my uncle's house, my father led us to our new home, which he had purchased a month earlier for us, when he came to Seoul. This safe crossing to the south brought freedom to us from the shackles of Communist Korea. We traveled 220 miles from Gaecheon to Seoul in four days in all.

ON MY MULTILINGUALISM

Up until August 1945, I only spoke Japanese as my primary language, even at home. I spoke Korean occasionally with my parents or our relatives. After the end of the war and the political upheaval in Korea, I evidently switched my primary language to Korean. The strange thing was that I had no recollection of the time when I started to speak Korean, exclusively.

I know how to read and write Chinese letters because of my classics language education from elementary school until my college years. I began to study English in the seventh grade. Then, in high school, I learned French and German as secondary languages. Altogether, I learned to read and write in five languages with varying degrees of fluency.

In the 1990s, there was a Japanese language institute in Washington, known as Reitaku University Institute of Cultural Exchange (RICE). The Japanese Ministry of Education subsidized RICE. I enrolled in the advanced class for four years. One of the teachers was Norimitsu Tomotsune, a graduate of Doshisha University in Kyoto. He was a young, energetic teacher. Tomotsune Sensi[26] selected reading materials from best-selling novels and excerpts of current events in newspapers, mostly from Asahi Shinbun, a widely circulated Japanese daily newspaper. It was an excellent program for me to brush up on my Japanese.

After 1945, I seldom had the opportunity to speak Japanese in Korea. However, I continued to read Japanese books. At RICE, when I read Japanese books and newspapers, I instantly recalled words and phrases that I thought I had forgotten. It is remarkable that I have such a recalling ability, after six decades, of words embedded deeply in the hidden memory lanes in my brain.

UNCLE HEON SUNWU

I had an uncle, Heon Sunwu (1923-1965), a Presbyterian minister, who experienced the life faced by many Korean youths during the World War II. In 1941, he was forced to enter the Japanese Imperial Army (JIA) Ordnance School, Sendai, Japan. In 1945, the JIA transferred him to a post in Harbin, Manchuria. On August 15, 1945, when Japan surrendered, Russian soldiers captured him. He became a prisoner of war and was interned in a camp in Inner Mongolia. During his internment, he became interested in Mongolian culture. I learned a lot about the Korean people as a sub-race in the Asian continent from what he told me about his Mongolian experience at the end of the Second World War:

"John, one day, our regimental headquarters announced that the war was over. Our regiment surrendered to the Russian Army one day after VJ day."

"Uncle, where was the regiment stationed?"

"We were in a place called Handangi Sumu in Manchuria.

"It was near the Russian border.

"The Russian Army moved us to Khalgol area in Outer Mongolia.

"They transported all 800 of us by trucks and trains to a makeshift POW camp."

"So what was the camp life like?"

"The Russian soldiers were friendly with Korean POWs. We also met some Russian soldiers, who came from Kazakhstan.

"Some of them looked like Koreans with Asiatic faces.

"Three weeks later, our Russian captors let Korean prisoners go to the Sunday service in the Russian Orthodox Church.

"We were free to roam around the village.

"We never thought of escaping as Outer Mongolia was far from Seoul."

"So how did you spend your time?"

"I met very friendly Mongolians. They were very curious about us Korean prisoners.

"Then, one elderly gentleman invited us to his home."

"What was their house like?

"Did they stay in a tent?"

"No, they did not stay in a tent.

"The Mongolians were nomads, but they lived in houses in a shanty town.

"They used cardboard and corrugated sheet metals as building materials.

"I was interested in their customs and their way of life."

"Did you find anything interesting?"

"Yes.

"One day there was a funeral procession in the village.

"They surprised me with their funeral songs.

"The rhythm of Mongolian funeral songs was quite similar to those of Korea.

"I even felt a kinship with Mongolians."

"Can you describe it, or, sing it for me?"

"No, I cannot sing.

"But the rhythm was like what I've heard in the countryside of Korea when mourners in the funeral procession sing.

"They wail ritually, '*Aigo….. aigo…..*'

"When I heard their singing from afar, the lyrics or words were indistinguishable, but the only thing I could hear was the rhythm fading in and out, wailing '*Aigo….. aigo…..*'

"Then, I realized Mongolians and Koreans had shared common ancestors.

"I later found out that the subrace of Mongols and Koreans were known as Ural-Altaic."

"You mean the two mountain ranges in Russia and China?"

"Yes, the Ural Mountains divide Asia from Europe and the Altai Mountains divide China from Russia."

"So how long did you stay in Khalgol?"

"Not much longer.

"Our Russian captors wanted to get rid of us.

"After two months of internment, they released all of us.

"I received a pardon paper, with which I could ride trains from Outer Mongolia to Pyongyang.

"It took me a month to reach South Korea."

A ROADSIDE PHOTOSHOP

In the fall of 1950, the South Korean government decreed that all citizens in South Korea had to obtain an identification card at their local government office. To get an ID, everyone needed two copies of a passport-size photograph with their application. As there was a sudden demand for photos, Uncle Heon and I opened a roadside photoshop in front of the borough office; to take pictures, we used my Olympus camera. Our business went well until one day my mother saw our street photoshop. She was appalled to see us becoming paddlers. She seized the camera and the black box on the spot and scolded uncle, "Your nephew should be busy with his school work. You should have set a good example for your nephew." It was as much of my idea as my uncle's. A few days later I recovered my camera after swearing to my mother that it will not be repeated. It was a tempest in a teapot, passed after a few days.

In 1951, Uncle Heon entered Jung-Ang Presbyterian Theological Seminary in Seoul. He was ordained as a Presbyterian minister and then was commissioned as a Second Lieutenant in the South Korean Army Chaplain Corps. During the Korean War, and afterward, Uncle Heon and I would meet from time to time. During our conversations, he would expound on Western philosophy and Christianity and on books he had recently read or studied in the seminary. He found in me a captive audience, mostly unchallenging his thoughts and lectures as I was being introduced to these topics for the first time. In retrospect, I could see these discussions were mutually beneficial but more so for me. Also, as he knew of my erratic church attendance at East Gate Methodist Church, he urged me to attend church services more regularly. He believed that one day I would become a steady church-going Christian; his prediction proved to be right.

4

The Family Settles Down in Seoul

Enrolled in an Elementary School in Seoul

My family started a new life in an eastern suburb of Seoul in 1945. A few days after moving into our new home, my parents enrolled me as a fourth grader at Jong-am Elementary School. My school was overflown by students from families who escaped from North Korea. The classes were held in two shifts, one group in the morning and another in the afternoon. There were four thousand students in the school, and we boasted that it had the largest number of students in Korea, if not in the World. (see photo 11)

One day my father brought two gifts for my brothers and me. One was a bugle, and the other was a basketball. I learned to play the bugle and later became good at it. In 1946, our local precinct office chartered a new Boy Scout troop in the district, which became Troop 11. I joined with my cousin Phillip Myong and attended troop meetings, which were held at a factory warehouse after school. I told the Scoutmaster about my bugle, and I became the troop bugler and played a few ceremonial bugle calls such as *to the color* or *assembly*.

But with my basketball, I had a problem. The manufacturer of the basketball made the inner tube with low-quality rubber. Rubber must be cured with sulfur at a proper temperature, but my inner tube must not have been adequately cured. It lost its elasticity, and the tube rubber got stuck to the inner leather lining of my basketball. I bought a second-hand inner tube, and I took it to a bicycle shop where they repaired it many times. The inner tube was not the only thing we repaired. We fixed and recycled almost everything.

Today, we have too much waste in America. We just throw everything away when it does not work, because it is too expensive to repair. I recall that in April 2013, during the Earth Day observance, MIT students opened the Fixit Clinic

on the campus to fix broken things like radios, vacuum cleaners, etc. The Fixit Clinic was a "do-it-together" hands-on project, a STEM-oriented activity, and a fix-n-learn community. The Fixit Clinic and ideas like that run against the grain of American consumerism and planned obsolescence. The lifespan of the product is made artificially short by design.

I graduated from the elementary school in 1948 as the class valedictorian and then entered Kyunggi High School (KHS). Since then, I have kept in touch with some of my classmates, one of whom was Sook-il Kwun. He and I went to the same elementary school, middle school, high school, and even college. He chose the SNU Liberal Arts and Sciences College, while I enrolled in the SNU Engineering College. We were lifelong friends. He too came to America for his graduate work, receiving his doctorate in Physics from the University of Utah in 1965. I went to MSU for my graduate work, receiving my doctorate in Electrical Engineering in 1962.

During the Christmas holidays in 1965, Sook-il came to visit us in Washington. As shown in the photograph (see photo 42), Sook-il enjoyed the visit. One month later, I received the following letter from him:

Chicago
Jan. 30, 1966

Dear John,

I hope this letter finds you and your beautiful bride in good health. During my visit to D.C. in December last year, you and your wife showed me heartwarming hospitality. I thank you and wish you a happy New Year. I am now back in the Windy City, and the weather in Chicago is living up to its reputation. It has been frigid, and the temperature is hovering around 15 degrees F at noon today.

Do you remember a poem we used to recite in high school which started with the phrase, "As the biting wintry wind

whips through tree branches……"?[27] I think it was a poem written by a 15th-century military leader, Jong-seo Kim, standing watch on a tower in a moonlit winter night in a far-away northeast province of Korea. Of course, I see no watchtower on the South Side of Chicago, but the pale wintry moon is all the same.

My commute on foot from my apartment to the laboratory is quite an effort every day on the snow- and ice-covered streets. John, do you remember the street vendors in Seoul on winter nights, peddling hot rice cakes? There are no peddlers here tonight. For my supper this evening, I will settle for a piece of pizza delivered to my lab.

Last weekend, in Chicago, we had a get-together of KHS classmates. There was the usual crowd of Suk-rai Cho, Jong-seong Kimm, me, and others. I told them how happy you both looked and how you were enjoying the blissful life of a newlywed couple.

By the way, Suk-rai may have already contacted you about a skiing trip. He wants the three of us, your wife and our girlfriends to go skiing this winter. I did not reply to him yet. But, John, what do you think about a skiing trip? Suk-rai is talking about going to a ski slope in Ohio.

All the best,
Sook-il Kwun
(Translated by John Kim)

Sook-il wrote to me in April 1966 to tell me about his plan to return to Korea. He had found a teaching position in the Physics Department at SNU. He also told me the news of Suk-rai returning to Seoul to take over his family business.[28]

Chicago
April 8, 1966

Dear John,

I trust all is well with you and your family. John, thank you for the photos you've sent me. They will be cherished memorabilia of my visit to D.C. in December last year. This morning, Suk-rai Cho left for Seoul. He will take over one of his family's businesses. I am also moving to Seoul at the end of the school year. I have been searching for a teaching position at Seoul National University and recently received an offer as an Assistant Professor in the Physics Department. I will leave the University of Chicago in June as soon as my obligation to the University here as Research Associate will be fulfilled. I will begin my teaching at SNU in September. It will not be as adventurous as coming to the States a few years ago, but there are many unknowns in my future.

I decided to return to Seoul with the two things in mind. One is the pressure from my parents to get married. The other is testing the waters and exploring a potential career at the alma mater. I really do not know what lies ahead. As they say, *un peu espoir, et un peu désespoire* (a little hope and a little despair.)

I want to find my niche at the University and in a broader sense in South Korea. I want to become someone who could make a difference in the field of science in South Korea. John, yes, I know, it is a big ambition and a tall order. If it does not work out, I could always return to a teaching position in America. I have bitten the bullet. SNU recently sent me a dozen papers to sign. The die was cast, and I have crossed the Rubicon. John, pray for me.

I will write you as soon as I settle down in Seoul. Thank you for everything.

All the best,
Sook-il Kwun
(Translated by John Kim)

❊ ❊ ❊

There was no news from Sook-il for about two years, but in January 1968, he sent me a letter with good tidings.

Seoul

Jan. 22, 1968

Dear John and Rahn,

I wish you a happy New Year. Also, I have heard joyful news about the birth of a baby girl in your family. Congratulations! I too have news to tell you. On October 21, 1966, I got married to Ke-ja Choe, who was three years junior to Rahn at Kyunggi Girl's High School. I apologize for not sending you an invitation card. We decided not to send invitations to you and all our friends in the States. We felt an invitation could be an imposition. By the way, my wife Ke-ja knows Rahn and her mother. A few days after our wedding ceremony, Rahn's mother telephoned and gave us her blessings. We really appreciated her thoughtfulness.

John, do you remember what I had told you about my two goals when I left Chicago and returned to Seoul? The first was marriage, and the second was making my career successful at SNU. Now, I am a happily married man. I am also pleased to tell you that I put my best foot forward at SNU. I have a good idea of what I must do to further my second goal. In coming

months, I plan on visiting America to procure more up-to-date laboratory equipment to expand my research activities in condensed matter physics. We would like to hear from you and what you folks have been doing lately.

With Warm Regards,
Sook-il Kwun

(Translated by John Kim)

❋ ❋ ❋

He and I exchanged correspondence from time to time about our families and careers. In 1982, he became the Dean of the Natural Sciences College at SNU. Then, in 1997, he became the Minister of Science and Technology, in the Kim Young-sam Administration. In 2014, he became President of the Korean National Academy of Sciences. In 2003, I received a letter from him congratulating me on the ONR press release announcing the development of the Rb CPT Atomic Clock.

Seoul
Dec. 20, 2003

Dear John,

I was pleasantly surprised to read a press release (Sep. 14, 2003) from the Office of Naval Research on your work in the development of an Ultra-Miniature Rb CPT Atomic Clock. I congratulate you on your accomplishment. I read the press release with keen interest. As you know, most of our contemporaries are no longer conducting research, as they are retired. You may claim yourself as one of the few remaining technologists actively engaged in scientific research.

My congratulations on your accomplishments again and with warm regards,

Sook-il Kwun
(Translated by John Kim)

KYUNGGI HIGH SCHOOL (KHS)

At the age of fifteen, I entered Kyunggi High School, a leading public high school in South Korea. (see photo 12)

Every ten years or so, I reflected on the following excerpt of the *Analects of Confucius,* which summed up six milestones of the life of the old Sage, Confucius.

"At fifteen, I set my mind and heart on learning,
"At thirty, through study, I found out where I stood in the World,
"At forty, learning history, philosophy, and spirituality, I had no more doubts about my judgment of human affairs,
"At fifty, I became a mandarin of my country, and I understood the mandate of Heaven,
"At sixty, as I struggled with my moral sense.
My ears were obedient organ for the reception of truth, and my ears heard no evil even if my adversary had uttered foul words.
"At seventy, whatever I do, I do as a human without violating moral codes."

From *the Analects of Confucius,* Book II (the Governance),[29]
Chapter IV

When I entered KHS, I found out that teachers taught us classic Chinese thoughts, equivalent to Greek and Latin classics in the Western World. The ancient text of the *Analect* above refers to the book written by Confucius in the 3rd century BC. We were probably the last class of the high school, which had classics in the regular curriculum. Our teacher told us Chinese classics being an essential part of the Korean civilization as the language of the learned. One cannot avoid learning classic Chinese as an educated person in Korea and Japan. In the East Asia, learned individuals have a yearning for knowledge about the rich Chinese civilization, which was developed over five millennia.

Poems of the Tang Dynasty were the culmination of many centuries of Chinese poetry, with refined forms, structures, and rhymes. I studied Tang poems and enjoyed reciting them. I read Wang Wei's famous poem *"Farewell to Won-I, who goes to An-Seo as Governor."* This poem was about sending off a friend of his to a frontier town, where the Silk Road originated in the western region of China during the Tang period. There were numerous battles and conflicts between the Tang Empire and the western kingdoms along the Silk Road. Following is the celebrated poem by Wang Wei,

"Farewell to Won-I, who goes to An-Seo as Governor."[30]
(Translated by John Kim)

The morning rain washes off the dust of the fortress
And the willow tree of the country inn becomes green.
I offer you, my dear friend, another glass of wine
Because you will find no friend when you leave the town.

Another favorite poem of mine was one of Du Fu's famous poem,[31]

"Looking forward to Coming of Spring."
(Translated by John Kim)

"The country is devastated by the war, but mountains stand, and the river flows.
In Chang-An, the spring awakened grasses and trees thick and green.

The flowers knew the coming season as they splashed with tears.

And my long sighs after many months of separation from the family, startled birds even.

All through March, the beacon fire was burning on the mountaintop.
But I am waiting for precious news from home.
My gray hair is thinning on the top,
But the hair is not thick enough to hold my hairpin."

He composed this poem during the devastating civil war of An-Lushan (755 A.D.-763 A.D.). He wrote this poem in the capital Chang-An, which was ruined during the war, but the fields and hills were green with the coming spring. As he was not able to escape the capital, he worried about his family's safety. The civil war made him tired and weary. In his poem, he wrote about the war being evil and the people yearning for peace.

Chinese classics influenced philosophy, politics, economy, and literature as much as Greek and Latin classics have shaped Western civilization. Interestingly, today in the Internet bulletin of my high school alumni club, I find my classmates posting essays about Chinese classics and Tang poems. Some of them became accomplished students of Chinese classics.

AMATEUR RADIO HOBBY

When I was in the seventh grade in KHS, I saw a bulletin in the corridor inviting new students to the Wireless Club. I had been interested in building a crystal radio, which consisted of a crystal, a coiled wire bobbin, a long wire antenna, and an earphone. I bought these parts from an Army surplus electronic store in East Gate Market. Also, I purchased a book on how to build electronic gadgets. When I joined the Wireless Club, the president of the club was Yo-han Cho, who had authored an introductory book on *Wireless Technology*. It was quite remarkable that he, as a high school senior, could have written such a book. These activities, no matter how simple they might have been, it

opened my window to technology.

A half-century later, in 2012, I got acquainted again with Yo-han Cho when he moved from Boston to Northern Virginia. One day, Yo-han Cho and his wife invited Rahn and me to dinner, and he showed us a dog-eared copy of his first-edition book, *Wireless Technology*, which I remembered well with the brown cover and the logo of a wireless antenna. I asked him what reference materials he had used for his book.

"I used *Radio Engineering*, authored by Professor Frederick E. Terman of Stanford University.

"I found it in the USIS Library in Seoul."

He sent me a photograph of the cover sheet of his books with the following letter.

Reston, Virginia
February 29, 2012

Dear Dr. Kim,

As you have asked a cover sheet of my old book, I am forwarding to you scanned cover pages as well as the table of contents of *Wireless Technology*, published in 1946. I appreciate your interest in my activities of the bygone time.

Regards,
Yo-han Cho

(p.s.) I am more than happy to show those Nikon accessories and cameras to your son. Please let me know. Y. Cho.

This club was the place where I got interested in wireless devices, electronics, and physics, and in a broad sense, technology and engineering. This was the beginning of my interest in STEM. Later, as a seventh grader, I built an amplitude modulation (AM) radio receiver with U.S. Army electronics surplus parts. An output transformer I used was an item salvaged from U.S. Army surplus electronic equipment. The current of the output transformer was 200 milli-Ampere, which was a much stronger current than the device required,

and I could see the output vacuum tube glowed in the darkness. A higher current tended to shorten the life of the vacuum tube. It also produced strong audio output power, which tore up the speaker cone. I enjoyed working with electronics, and it became my lifelong interest. In 1949, I knew nothing about amplifiers being classified as A or AB. I learned about these amplifiers at Trine University, when I took courses in radio engineering, using the Frederick Terman's textbook, *Electronic and Radio Engineering.*[32] By then, Terman added "Electronic" to the title of his book.

I also bought a second-hand turntable and long-playing (LP) vinyl records, including Chopin's *Etudes* and Liszt's *Liebesträume,* from a secondhand record shop. The stylus on my phonograph was also a second-hand needle, which tended to wear out vinyl records faster. My homemade turntable reproduced unnaturally high-pitched piano music, and the dull stylus made a scratchy sound resembling fingernails rubbing on a blackboard. But the sound coming out of the homemade audio equipment was "music to my ears." In my makeshift workshop, I had simple test instruments, one of which was a U.S. Navy surplus multimeter, which included an ammeter, a voltmeter, and an ohmmeter. The multimeter was in a Navy gray metal box, and I used it to measure the current, the voltage, and the resistance and checked the continuity of capacitors.

Much later in 2013, after I retired from ONR, I became an amateur ham radio licensee and a member of the Military Auxiliary Radio Station (MARS) in the Pentagon. My friend Eugene Kaiser was the club president. To be inducted into the station, I had to take an amateur technician class examination, which I did at the Landover Hill Amateur Radio Club in Maryland. I easily passed the technician class examination, and then the examiner recommended that I also take the next-level, general class examination on the same day.

Examiner: "John, congratulations. You passed the exam."

"Thank you very much."

"You got 33 out of 35 questions correctly answered. Based on the score of the technician class exam, the examination board recommends you to take the general class exam."

"Ya, but, I only needed the technician class license now and did not prepare for the general class examination. Besides, my wife is waiting in the parking lot."

After some discussion with Rahn, I took the general class examination and

also passed it. Then I received a license with the call sign of KM4HAQ from the Federal Communications Commission. In the summer of 2017, the Pentagon MARS station needed to move its relay station antenna from the Pentagon rooftop to elsewhere. The U.S. Navy offered us an antenna site at the Naval Facility (NAVFAC) Arlington, which was located on a hill near Fort Myer. On a hot summer day, Eugene Kaiser, Gary Sessums, and I climbed the ladders leading up to the rooftop of NAVFAC Arlington and conducted a site survey.

✻ ✻ ✻

I had an aptitude for things technological from early on in my life. When I was a youngster, I was like a "Curious George." I was interested in any mechanical or electrical gadgets. Once, my father bought me a second-hand wristwatch. A few weeks later, it stopped working, and the stopped watch became my challenge. I disassembled it with improvised tools and managed to fix it. I sometimes succeed in repairing things, and sometimes not. At the end of the day, I learned how the mechanisms worked, and sometimes I made matters worse. My father was quite skeptical about my efforts to repair clocks, radios, cameras, and even automobiles. I have been a car tinkerer, including engine overhauls. I have a collection of how-to-repair books for dishwashers, refrigerators, and other products.

WITNESSING IDEOLOGICAL STRUGGLES IN SOUTH KOREA

When I entered KHS in 1948, it was a turbulent time in South Korea with ideological and political conflicts. In the school, a few upper-class students were suspected of being members of the South Korean Communist Party. Struggles between left- and right-wing ideologies were pervasive in all walks of life in the South Korean society. One day, the entire student body gathered in the school parade ground for the daily morning assembly. During the assembly, we saw someone lowering the South Korean national flag from the flagpole. In its place, a strange flag went up. In the next moment, pandemonium broke out on the parade ground, and the principal immediately dismissed the assembly and closed the school for the remainder of the week altogether. This kind of

incidents happened frequently.

My sixth-grade homeroom teacher, Han-sul Jeong, was suspected to be a communist. He graduated from Taegu Normal College (TNC), which was a hotbed for Marxists in the 1940s in South Korea. South Korea's former President Park Chung-hi was also a 1936 graduate of TNC, and he was a leftist in his college years.[33] He was even suspected to be a Communist sympathizer, when he was a junior grade South Korean Army officer. In November 1948, the South Korean Army arrested Park on charges that he allegedly led a communist cell in the South Korean Army. The South Korean Military Tribunal court-martialed Park and sentenced him to death. They commuted his sentence at the urging of several high-ranking Korean military general officers when the Korean War broke out.[34] If he were not a leftist, he indeed was a revolutionary, and he eventually overturned the legitimate civilian government of the Second Republic of South Korea by coup d'état. My former South Korean Army General, Ung-soo Kim, told me:[35]

> "American military service academies select candidates for cadets and midshipmen by the process of recommendations from elected officials like senators and congressmen from their constituency.
>
> "This way, members of the American officer corps are assured to have not only academic aptitude and intelligence as future military leaders but also to have loyalty to the country."
>
> "For so many years from the late 1960s on, some cadets and midshipmen of the South Korean Military Service Academies were selected from economically depressed families. "Those members of the officer corps were more interested in politics than in their duty toward national defense.
>
> "Such officer corps brought about military dictatorships for three decades in the 1960s to 1980s in South Korea."

As a twelve-year-old youngster, I observed political and ideological turmoils in South Korea. In 1947, I heard about the tragic assassination of a prominent South Korean political leader of the conservative party, Deok-soo Jang. Two South Korean terrorists broke into Jang's house and assassinated him. His

home was two blocks away from the rear gate of my elementary school. The next day policemen blocked the road around our school. In 1938, he received his doctorate in Political Science from Columbia University and returned to South Korea as a political leader, whom the country could not afford to lose.

WINTER VACATION IN A MOUNTAINOUS PROVINCE

In the spring of 1948, my cousin Ki-song Kim came from a mountainous province to live with us to attend a high school in Seoul; he shared room with me for a year. During winter vacation of 1949, he planned to return to his home for a month and invited me to come along. My parents gave me permission to travel with him. His house was 50 miles east of Seoul. We rode train and then walked six hours to his house, as no public transportation was available. In the 1940s, traveling on foot for six hours was not uncommon in Korea. Nowadays, it takes 50 minutes by car on a superhighway to get to his village from Seoul. In the late afternoon, four other students joined us to climb up roads on foot. We went on foot about 10 miles carrying our backpacks. We climbed the Solchi pass and descended in the pitch-dark night. By the time we reached the foot of the mountain, it was nine o'clock in the evening. We saw a roadside farmhouse, where the six of us ate supper. Two hours later we arrived at my cousin's house.

During my stay, I enjoyed rural village life. In the evening, the family would gather in the great room. At one corner the adult menfolk huddled, and at the other corner the youngsters, and in the third corner, the womenfolk. We gathered around a brazier with burning charcoal on which we baked sweet potatoes and roasted chestnuts. My aunt served us sweet apples which were stored in large clay pottery in the cellar. There was no electricity, but a kerosene lamp provided the light.

I discovered for the first time an interesting rural event. It was a weekly market day in the village. The market day was held every Thursday in that village. In this old market system, peddlers would travel around to six different villages every week. Of course, at the end of each day the peddlers carried their merchandise and went to the next one, and on the seventh day, they rested. This market system had been maintained for several hundred years in

Korea. Nowadays, these rural areas are an integral part of the cities as they are connected by highways. Through these rural villages, four-lane highways now connect big cities on the East and West Coasts of Korea.

On the market day, the whole family walked about three miles to the village center. My aunt bought weekly supplies at the market. She also bought salted mackerel which became the *piece de resistance* at the dinner table.

People of the village also went ice fishing in the frozen river. Usually, there was a cardboard shelter with a charcoal brazier to keep them warm. We also ice skated on the frozen river wearing homemade skates. My cousin's house was large and had many rooms, which were heated by a hypocaust; firewood was burned under the floor, and between the ground and the stone floor of the room, the heat was circulated through stone channels. This was a traditional heating system. This type of heating system still exists in rural houses in Korea. I saw a similar heating system in Turkey near Antalya.

5

The Unforgettable Korean War

On June 25, 1950, the city of Seoul was quiet, with monsoon season approaching. On this Sunday morning, I was riding my bicycle in our neighborhood on an errand. On the radio, I heard about some trouble between North and South Korea along the border at the Thirty-eighth Parallel. As these conflicts happened frequently before, I paid no attention at first. By the afternoon, I heard public announcement speakers of the South Korean Army, broadcasting from their trucks that the military authority was ordering all soldiers to return immediately to their units. I then realized this was not one of usual border skirmishes. The North Korean Army had invaded South Korea in full force; the country began to be engulfed in war for the next three years.

The North Korean Army, which started the conflict, had slogans about liberating people from the tyranny and the so-called American Imperialism. I lived through several wars in my life, but the Korean War was the one in which I was in the middle of gunfire and artillery shelling. What was accomplished by the war? Nothing much. The peninsula remained divided, and no territory was gained by either side. There were millions of casualties and immense destruction. The Korean War caused the deaths of 5 million soldiers and civilians.[36] The direct cost of the war was about $390 billion, and the indirect loss was about $288 billion.[37] It destroyed the industry, commerce, housing, schools, and hospitals in both North and South Korea. We have been profoundly affected by the war.

INVASION OF NORTH KOREAN ARMY

On the afternoon of June 26, 1950, I saw for the first time North Korean propeller fighter aircraft flying above Seoul airspace. I later learned that they were Russian-made Ilyushin-10 and Yakovlev-9 planes, which dropped bombs on the air base in Kimpo near Seoul. The North Korean Army advanced swiftly to the south like a hot knife through butter. On June 28, 1950, three days after the outbreak of the war, my father decided to cross the Han River and go south to take refuge in one of the southern provinces. At daybreak, my family left our home and later arrived at a Han River ferry crossing. My father attempted to cross the Han River by ferry as he heard that the retreating the South Korean Army had blown up the main bridge over the Han River on the previous night. We walked about two hours and reached the ferry crossing. We were surprised that North Korean soldiers already controlled the ferry crossing. For the first time, I saw Russian-made T-34 tanks and Gaz-67 vehicles in the square. North Korean soldiers wore green Cossack cotton shirts. Each carried a rifle or a Russian-made PPD-40 submachine gun. The length of the infantryman's rifle was more than five feet, which the short North Korean soldiers were dragging along. These comic soldiers gave an air of deadliness all the same. Their Cossack shirts and baggy pants were bright green. I heard that soldiers could camouflage quickly in the Spring and the early Summer. Cotton shirts would become brown when dirt and sweat covered them, suitable for camouflage.

We were too late to cross the river, and North Korean soldiers ordered us to clear the boat launch area. The barrel of the machine guns mounted on the tank turret was aimed low to the crowd. I sensed imminent danger and my father whispered to us to turn back.

Our neighborhood was then controlled by the newly established district Commissar's office. A few weeks later the commissar of my high school notified us to attend school. At school, there were no classes, but a mass rally in the school auditorium. Communist apparatchiks and the commissar made speeches, urging us to enlist in the North Korean Army. The atmosphere was charged with tension. Upper-class students were forced to sign up as volunteer soldiers. I sneaked out of the auditorium and escaped the school grounds through a small gate at the rear of the campus, connected to the residential neighborhood. I never went back to school again during the Communist occupation.

The life under occupation by the North Korean Army was miserable; they snatched young people in the street and forced them to enlist. I was then 15 years old and too young to be recruited. As the North Korean Army needed the workforce, the District Commissar's office would draft citizens for forced labor to repair roads and bridges. Food supplies became short. Our neighbors would go off in the morning carrying their burlap sacks and would return in the evening bringing bags of potatoes, corns, and whatever food they could obtain from farmers.

During the summer of 1950, the citizens of Seoul had only a vague idea of where the front line was in the south. The North Korean newspapers reported distorted war information. The papers were full of propaganda telling readers that the North Korean Army was gaining ground, winning the "Liberation War" and expelling "the American Imperialist Army" and "Puppet South Korean Army" out of the peninsula. These were their slogans, which no one believed.

In August 1950, I saw steady streams of several types of American bombers (Martin B-26 Marauders and Boeing B-29 Super Fortresses) flying bombing sorties to North Korea. Silver aircraft, leaving behind white contrails, were flying at high altitudes. I knew they must be bombing someplace in North Korea because North Korean newspapers reported of air raids. Then one day I saw American jet fighter aircraft, Lockheed F-80 Shooting Stars, flying over Seoul. F-80 jet fighters were striking North Korean ground troops, trucks, trains, roads, and bridges. In the late summer of 1950, I began to hear rumors of American and South Korean forces approaching Seoul soon.

INCHON LANDING

In September 1950, American and South Korean forces landed at Inchon by amphibious landing operations. On September 20, I could hear the low but distinct rumbling artillery sounds. Sure enough, on September 25, massive artillery bombardments showered over the city center, not far from our house. The Inchon landing, masterminded by General Douglas McArthur, and the subsequent maneuvers by the South Korean and American forces, cut the North Korean Army supply lines to the south. Fighter aircraft, Vought

F4-U Corsair, bombed military targets in Seoul. For the first time in my life, I heard the sound of artillery shells flying over my head. Outgoing artillery shells whistled.

"If you can hear the artillery shell whistle, you will not get hit, it is the shell without the whistling sound, which is the one you should be concerned about," So remarked my uncle, who had combat experience in Manchuria in the World War II.

Throughout the afternoon and the evening of September 26, we were in the middle of shelling by American and South Korean artilleries. We moved to our basement shelter. On September 28, suddenly, the artillery shelling stopped. Instead, I heard heavy, rumbling tank sounds of American and South Korean Marine Corps. I ventured out to the main boulevard near the East Gate. I saw American and South Korean Marines near the barricade of the East Gate Police Station. Our neighbors came out of their houses and waved South Korean and American flags. The next day, on September 29, I found antitank barricades built by North Korean soldiers in the middle of Jongro Boulevard. I climbed to the top of the barricades. There I saw several dead civilians, mostly young men, shot by North Korean soldiers the night before. They were the detained political prisoners by the North Korean Army who had been held in the police station; they were executed before the North Koreans abandoned the city. For the first time in my life, I saw dead men who had been shot and killed. I lived under the North Korean rule for three months and survived the terrible war to tell this story.

Then, civil defense teams started clearing up of rubbles left by fighting. During the street battles, both sides destroyed buildings along the main Jongro Boulevard. I joined the civil defense team which assigned me to the Yongsan railroad depot. We found the warehouses and railroad yards were in disarray. We spent a day sweeping and clearing. Next day, my mother checked my work clothes and found acid sprayed on my jacket and pants with small holes.

In the fall of 1950, after the recapture of Seoul, my high school reopened classes in a temporary school building as the U.S. Army had requisitioned our high school buildings. Class attendance was thin, and school instruction

was marginal. Every day I heard news of bitter fights along the front line. A few weeks later, South Korean and American armies captured Pyongyang. On October 26, a contingent of the South Korean Army reached the southern bank of the Yalu River at the Korean-Chinese border. On the east coast, South Korean and American forces also advanced to the Tumen River, which bordered China and Russia. I heard that the war would end soon, perhaps before Christmas. However, the imminent collapse of North Korea made the mainland Chinese Communist regime quite nervous. Then in late November, we began to hear about the looming threats from the Chinese People's Liberation Army (PLA). The subsequent Chinese intervention prolonged the conflict for another two and one-half years.

Chinese PLA Crosses the Yalu River

In late December 1950, the PLA crossed the Yalu River and advanced southward. As soon as we heard about the news of the Chinese intervention, our family decided to leave Seoul and go south to avoid the misery we had experienced during the previous summer. We packed and carried knapsacks with essential items. My father arranged for us to go to the home of one of his acquaintances in Pusan. He remained in Seoul until the last day possible. We boarded a freight train packed with refugees like us. This retreat to the south was another displacement of the family against our wish, but such was the unpredictable political change which dictated our lives. However, unlike the evacuation chaos in June 1950, most of the two million citizens of Seoul evacuated in an orderly manner ahead of the advancing North Korean Army and Chinese PLA. We rode on a slow-moving, south-bound freight train without lights or even a window. Whenever the train passed through a tunnel, we coughed as smoke and dust filled the air. Our train frequently stopped and sidetracked to make a way for military priority trains. Although it was dismal situations, everyone in the train was in high spirits, knowing that we would return to Seoul sooner or later. After two days of train rides, we arrived at the Pusan railroad station and found the home of the father's friend. That evening, my mother borrowed pots and pans and cooked a hot meal for us in a makeshift kitchen. The next day my mother rented a one-room place for seven of

us. On January 4, 1951, Seoul fell to the enemy, and my father stayed one step ahead of the invading army. He came to Pusan and found us a few days later. Thus began our three-year-long refugee life in Pusan. This evacuation came just six years after our departure from the north after the World War II. But my family survived the Korean War unscathed.

My father's first order of business was to find a place to live. In 1951, as the population of Pusan exploded from a quarter of million inhabitants to one and one-half million overnight, it was impossible to find a house. Instead, he decided to build a temporary dwelling. He found a small empty lot not far from our rented room and leased it. He hired carpenters and laborers who built a clapboard house in a week with no building permit. The borough office simply threw building permit regulations out the window and let refugees build temporary houses. We had no electricity as the Pusan Power Company could not supply electricity to the exploding population on such short notice. Besides, my family had no devices which required electricity, other than lighting.

Soon, other people followed suit, building more houses in the area. A few weeks later, Rev. Seong-gon Choe and his wife built a two-story house next to ours. It was a temporary boarding house for students, all college girls. Rev. Choe was Chaplain-General of the South Korean Air Force with the rank of Colonel. He built the house with building materials donated by an American Air Force unit. Pastor Choe and my father became good friends. In 1960, the pastor officiated the marriage ceremony of my brother Phil and my sister-in-law Jeong-sook. Student boarders sang Christian hymns in the evening after supper and made the neighborhood atmosphere joyful. They sang many hymns, but the one I heard over and over was Eliza Hewitt's *Singing I Go Along*. I learned it and enjoyed humming the hymn to this day:

> "Singing I go along life's road, Praising the Lord, praising the Lord, Singing I go along life's road, For Jesus has lifted my load."

Indeed.

MY COUSIN PHILLIP MYONG AND I BECOME LONGSHOREMEN

In the winter of 1951, I was looking for something to do in Pusan, as there was no school. My cousin Phillip Myong and I heard about laborer jobs in the Port of Pusan, where American merchant ships were bringing supplies to the U.S. military in South Korea. Each evening, a staff sergeant of the U.S. Army Railroad Transportation Organization (RTO) and his Korean union fore-man hired night-shift longshoremen. Phillip and I were hired. Cargo cranes unloaded cargos from the ship to the pier. Longshoremen carried the cargo by hand trucks and dollies to the warehouse. The longshoremen's union fed us a hot meal at midnight, which we supplemented with American canned food and K-ration. We got paid in the morning when we finished our work. The longshoreman's job was hard, but the pay was good. Phillip and I worked as laborers for two months. We always had breakfast near the Pusan fish market, enjoying a bowl of spicy seafood chowder in the chilly wintry day on the Pusan waterfront. Phillip and I talked about the future, about returning to high school and college and about going to an American college. Then our high schools reopened in Pusan in March 1951, we returned to school.

In 1956, Phillip attended the University of Illinois for his undergraduate study. He then moved on to the Georgetown University-College of Dentistry. He prospered with a successful dental office in Fairfax. In the 1990s, he and his wife Susan lived a five-minute drive from my house in McLean. (see photo 57) What an enduring friendship and experience we shared together. Phillip Myong was a cousin, but he was like my elder brother. In Pyongyang, we lived in the same neighborhood and attended the same elementary school, we stud-ied at the same college in Seoul, and we both attended Sunday service at the East Gate Methodist Church in Seoul. Phillip and I both had a goal of getting an education. We managed to soldier on despite of incredible hardships in Pyongyang, Seoul, and Pusan.

ENGLISH AND FRENCH LANGUAGE STUDIES,

From 1951 through 1953, I studied foreign languages in after-school language institutes in addition to the regular high school curriculum. The one I attended was a French language institute, called "L'Etude Français." It was a private tutoring institute, taught by Professor Hui-yeong Lee of the SNU French Department. I attended Professor Lee's French lecture for two years in Pusan until I returned to Seoul. I still remember Professor Lee shrugged his shoulder like a Frenchman when he said, *"Mais Oui."* I read Paul Verlaine's *Chanson d'automne*[38] and *Clair de Lune* and others. I can still recite from memory several poems in French. I like Francois Coppée's, *A La Mort des Oiseaux.*[39]

> *"Le soir, au coin du feu, j'ai pensé bien des fois,*
> *A la mort d'un oiseau, quelque part, dans les bois."*

How sad the poem sounded.

The other language study was conversational English at the English Language Institute (ELI) in Pusan. We practiced English conversation with an American instructor to improve our spoken English. We also read articles on current affairs in *Time magazine.* These classes were more interesting than the regular classes at my high school where they emphasized grammar and composition. One day, the director of the Institute asked me if I were interested in helping him to tidy things up in the classroom at the end of the evening. In return, he offered to reduce my tuition in half, which was a good work-study arrangement, and I accepted his offer.

During my refugee days in Pusan, I broadened my horizon by learning foreign languages and reading literature in Japanese, English, and French. My mind was like a sponge, absorbing many subjects. I was like an intellectual butterfly, sucking nectar and pollinating my intellectual curiosity from many sources. My studies gave me bright and heady days in a dark war atmosphere.

6

Seoul National University, the South Korean Army, and the Korean Olympic Committee

═══════════════════════════════════

"Double-E" or Physics?

In 1951, Seoul was recaptured by South Korean and American forces, but it was not safe to return to Seoul so that we stayed in Pusan for two more years. The two sides continually exchanged artillery fires across the ever-changing border. Finally, in 1953, after three years of the refugee life in Pusan, we returned to our home in Seoul. We tried to get life back to normal amidst the rubbles left by the war.

When I finished my high school senior year in Seoul, I took the entrance examination at Seoul National University and passed it. My high school must have prepared me well. I narrowed down my major field of concentration to two areas, electrical engineering (double-E) or physics. The available career path for a double-E major was employment in the Korea Electric Power Corporation; the career path for physics major was as a high school science teacher. It was my good fortune that I chose double-E. That choice led me to my gainful employment, later in America.

In April 1954, I started my double-E coursework in electromagnetics, alternate current, power transmission, induction and synchrony motors, and hydro-electric and steam power generation. These courses were mostly about how electricity was generated, transmitted, distributed, and converted and applied in everyday life. The first college-level technical textbook I bought was Sezuzou Takeyama's *Theory of Electromagnetic Phenomena*,[40] an introductory book on

electromagnetic field theory first established by James Clerk Maxwell in 1862.

Our professors, who had returned from American universities as exchange professors, talked about the recent technological advances in America when I just entered SNU. Two noteworthy events were: (1) the development of the transistor by William Shockley of Bell Laboratories, and (2) the development of the Automatic Sequence Controlled Calculator (ASCC), the first-generation modern digital computer by Howard Aiken of the Harvard Computation Laboratory.

The buildings and facilities of our college were in disarray after three years of the war. The American military had commandeered the Engineering College buildings to use as a field hospital and had converted all heating systems from coal to oil. When the American Army returned the buildings to SNU, the university could not retrofit the system back to coal burning nor use the oil burners due to the high fuel cost. As a result, we had no heat in the buildings. I recall my chemistry laboratory, in which I heated a test specimen in a Bomex Florence flask. The only source of heat had been a charcoal brazier since the college could not provide methyl alcohol fuel for a Bunsen burner. It was hard to control the temperature, and my sample solvent in the flask boiled over. I lost the specimen, and I had to get another sample from a graduate assistant. Other laboratory classes were in poor condition, as laboratory equipment was not adequately maintained nor had been neglected for several years. Later, I found out I was ill-prepared for the laboratory work when I attended the engineering college of Trine University in America.

JOHN JAE-YOON YUH

In the summer of 1956, one of my high school classmates, John Jae-yoon Yuh (1935-2015), returned to Seoul from the Massachusetts Institute of Technology (MIT) during the summer recess. One day, John Yuh invited me to his house for lunch. His hairstyle was a flattop crew cut; he wore slim khaki pants, and a short-sleeve shirt with the sleeves rolled up. He sported the "Ivy-League" fashion, which I did not know at the time. He went to America in 1951 and enrolled in a prep school in Massachusetts. He then entered MIT, majoring in mechanical engineering. As I was planning to go to America, I was interested

in all the things he said about his educational experience as an undergraduate at MIT. During lunch, his mother served me a regular Korean meal but served him a bowl of rice with a chunk of corned beef from a tin can.

"John Kim: "Why are you eating canned foods?"

"John Yuh: "Oh, my diet changed. I stayed at an apartment hotel in Cambridge."

"What has that got to with corned beef lunch?"

"I had no time to cook any meals during school days."

"Didn't you stay with your sister in Cambridge?"

"No, I did not stay with her. The undergraduate school work at MIT was grueling. I worked eighteen hours a day. In my freshman year, I received one B, but that was in a sea of Cs. Later I managed to receive very few As. I thought I was a powerhouse in prep school, but MIT school work just overwhelmed me."

"John, let's eat this nice meal. You are scaring your Mom and you are spoiling my appetite."

I heard the disconcerting story about his experience in the top-notch engineering school in America. Before leaving for America, he had an American tutor, who had prepped him in English. His family was well-to-do, as his mother was a well-known obstetrician, and his father was a cabinet minister in the South Korea government. I found out his mother was a leader in the Jehovah's Witnesses, and I remember her handing me publications of the Watch Tower Society and telling me about her plan to attend the upcoming Jehovah's Witnesses Convention in Yankee Stadium in New York in 1958.

After John Yuh graduated from MIT, he worked in Engineering Magnetics Division of Gulton Industries, Inc., in Los Angeles. In 1962, I met him once in Hawthorne when I traveled to TRW Headquarters in Redondo Beach in Los Angeles.. His company was located about five miles away from Redondo Beach, and we had lunch together. That was the last time I saw him. He passed away in 2019.

TRAVEL TO THE YEONG-WOL POWER STATION

In my junior year, I began to think seriously about going to America for graduate studies. There was one obstacle. I needed a financial sponsor to obtain a student visa from the American consulate in Seoul. I knew no American who could provide me with an affidavit of support. Then, my mother told me about one of her cousins, Mi-sook Kim, who married an American, James O'Rourke, who was a representative of an American power equipment manufacturing company and stationed at Yeong-wol Steam Power Station. When I asked Mi-sook about her husband becoming my sponsor, she told me I must ask her husband, directly. During the winter recess, I traveled to Yeong-Wol, which was 120 miles southeast of Seoul. I asked Jim O'Rourke about becoming my sponsor. The next day, he told me he could not be my sponsor. It was a big disappointment.

But all was not lost. Before leaving for Yeong-wol, I had arranged for a tour of the steam generating station, as it was the biggest steam generating station in South Korea in 1956, with a capacity of 50 megawatts (MW). I had a letter of introduction to the managing director of the station from Professor Hyeong-ju Woo. Most of the engineers and the managing director of the plant were graduates of SNU Electrical Engineering Department, and I found the old school ties useful.

I have never seen so much dust in my life. The entire station and the town were covered with dust left from burnt anthracite coals. The station complex was three miles north of the city of Yeong-wol, and it was a busy place, crowded with coal hopper trains and a huge mound of coal repository. Conveyors delivered anthracite coals to the buildings, each of which housed a series of the furnaces, boilers, turbines, condensers, and generators. Steam generating turbines need plenty of water, and the station was connected to a lagoon, which in turn took in cooling water, and emptied it into the river.

Further north of the town, I could see transmission lines and distribution systems. The managing director boasted that his station was the largest in the country, and the plant employed 2,500 laborers, with 122 technicians and 15 engineers in the power station. In 1956, there was a shortage of energy in South Korea, and electrical power was at a premium. But not in the Jim O'Rourke's residence, and for that matter every house in the town. They were heated by

electricity in that mountain town. As I learned more about the steam power generation station, I became convinced that electric power engineering was not for me to pursue as a career.

Enlisting in the South Korean Army

Before I could apply for a South Korean passport for study abroad, I first had to complete military service. In December 1956, I enlisted at the Recruiting Office of the South Korean Army. A week later, I met a recruiting sergeant at Seoul Railroad Station, and we new recruits boarded our trains, which took us to the army boot camp in Nonsan. From the railroad station, we marched another three miles to the reception battalion. Thus I began my boot camp life. I got my boot camp haircut—shaved my head—and got vaccinated. Also, I received an M-1 rifle, which I carried day and night with me for the duration of my tour, along with personal gear including a winter uniform and a pair of recycled boots. My uniform was solid Army green fatigues, not a camouflaged uniform, as the contemporary military fashion goes.

Each company then was organized into three platoons of 30 recruits with a staff sergeant in charge of each platoon. On the first day, the company supply sergeant singled me out to ask if he could appoint me as his assistant. In my personal record, he discovered that I had received some military training in the Reserve Officer Training Corps (ROTC) in college. Moreover, he considered me to be a trustworthy trainee and figured out that I would not embezzle platoon supplies. He explained my duty would be keeping supply records and receiving and distributing supplies, uniforms, and equipment. However, the platoon master sergeant had a different idea. Since I had some ROTC training, he thought I should be the trainee platoon leader. I remembered my Uncle Heon's advice that, in the Army, one should avoid volunteering for anything as much as one could. I chose the assignment as an assistant quartermaster since it seemed the assistant quartermaster's duty took on less responsibility than that of the trainee platoon leader.

Each day, we marched several miles in close formation from our platoon barrack to various course sites. In the land navigation course, the instructor gave my battle buddy and me a map and a compass and told us to find our

destination using 14 waypoints. The technique involved dead reckoning by measuring our bearing on the compass and then estimating the distance traveled in the wooded area. By far the toughest course was the obstacle course, which was meant to simulate tactical movements in combat. This course included strenuous physical training in which recruits learned to climb over and crawl under obstacles and balance, hang, and jump over hurdles. Puddles of muddy water and ropes and nets were used to make the courses difficult. There was the chemical, biological, and radioactive (CBR) course to train us to protect ourselves from the chemical, biological, and radiological hazards. Many years later, in 2001 when I joined the Office of Naval Research, I received a gas mask and took a mandatory online course on CBNE. By then, the letter N for nuclear and the letter E for explosives have been added to the acronym and the course title. The military threats changed over the years.

Half-way through training, my mother came to the boot camp on one Sunday afternoon. She brought chicken casserole to the dining room of the boot camp visitor center. My mother asked the sergeant in charge of the visitor center to invite several of my fellow recruits to share food. We ate it all!

In our barrack, two mess cooks were on duty in our platoon. They brought from the battalion headquarters steamed rice in a large wooden box and soup and spicy cabbage. We ate food voraciously as we were hungry after a long day's training.

Our platoon leader was a second lieutenant, who asked me to lend him some money. I knew he would never pay me back. However, one week before I was to finish boot camp training, my platoon leader found out that I had received a Special Order to report to the South Korean Army Headquarters in Seoul. This Special Order made him worried about what might happen if he did not pay back the small loan. The next day, I was surprised that he produced the money and paid me back. Thanks to the Special Order from the headquarters!

A week later, a staff sergeant came to escort me to my new post, the Army Headquarters in Seoul. All new recruits were escorted to their assigned unit by a non-commissioned officer. It could be a company of 30 recruits or just one recruit as in my case. I returned to Seoul after nine weeks of boot camp training. The sergeant handed me over to the duty officer of the Headquarters Battalion in Yongsan. The duty officer processed my order and gave me my leave paper

for ten days. As it was almost noon, I ate lunch at the enlisted men's mess hall. The Headquarters chow was much better than that of the boot camp chow. After lunch, I boarded a streetcar from Yongsan to my home, which was about five miles away. My parents and the family were happy to see me back home safely after boot camp training. After a few days of rest, I bought a better-fitting uniform, along with ankle-high, leather jump boots out of my own pocket. I looked more like a soldier detailed in Army Headquarters. (see photo 15)

I Become a General's Orderly at the Headquarters of the South Korean Army

A week later I reported to the Administration Section, Logistics Bureau at the Army Headquarters. The chief of the Administration Section asked me if my uniform was an Army Government Issue (GI). I replied that I bought the outfit with my own funds. He made no comment and ordered me to report to the office of Deputy Chief of Staff for Logistics. It was the office of Major General Ung-soo Kim. I became General Kim's orderly and worked on the assignment for the next twelve months. In the bay, there were half-dozen officers, three of whom were flag officers. I settled down in a cubicle next to the general's office to handle my task of dealing with messages, visitors, telephone calls, and incoming and outgoing correspondence. I had the additional assignment of being a pharmacy orderly to tend to the general's sensitive stomach, caused by an ulcer. I carried several antacid tablets in my pocket and was ready to give him one with a cup of water whenever I saw a tell-tale sign of his discomfort. He avoided spicy food. For lunch, he preferred a chicken salad sandwich, made at a restaurant in downtown Seoul.

As an orderly, I was ready to jump at the beck and call of the general. When I heard him making sounds like dry coughs, I jumped to tell the driver to get the jeep ready at the portico. His jeep had a plate with two stars. I worked closely with general's special assistant Lieutenant Colonel Chang-hee Lee, who prepared briefing charts, and presented them to the American high command in Yongsan on behalf of General Kim. Colonel Lee spoke fluent English. During the Korean War, Colonel Lee was an instructor at the U.S. Army Foreign Language Center at the Presidio of Monterey, California where he taught the

Korean language to American military personnel scheduled to be deployed to Korea. I got to know Colonel Lee well, who from time to time reminisced about his life in Monterey.

One day, Colonel Lee ordered me to be an official courier to hand-deliver a document to the Second Military District Command in Pusan. He gave me my travel orders, and a brown envelope addressed to the Commanding General of the Second Military District. He instructed me to hand-carry the reply back to him. On my return trip, I had to wait until the next morning to catch a train to Seoul. I had time to visit my cousin in Pusan. I visited my cousin Soon-yo, who had become a flight instructor at the South Korean Air Force Base, K-1 Kimhae. He had just gotten married, and his wife prepared supper for us in their one-room apartment. They looked happy in their newly married life. The next morning, I boarded the train to Seoul and reported to Colonel Lee and handed over the sealed envelope.

I could hardly believe how quickly a year had passed and my time in the South Korean Army drew to a close. One day, General Kim asked me:

"When are you leaving for America?"

"Colonel Choe processed my discharge paper already and within a week or so I would receive it."

"I see. You were a very able orderly, and I really appreciate your diligent work. I wish you stay with us, but I guess you must go."

"John, now I'd like to ask you a question. What have you learned in your one-year-long Army life?"

"For the first time in my life, I entered into a society, which is more structured than school. I felt I became an adult, a member of society, with a position of private first class and a meager salary. I tasted the real world for the first time in my life."

Fate was not kind to him, however. Three years later, in 1961, when the South Korean military junta seized power by coup d'état, Park Chung-hi sentenced Ung-soo Kim to a jail term of ten years for his action to oppose the coup. General Kim was the South Korean VI Corps commanding general and was responsible for defending the capital from both external or internal attacks.

He pushed back the coup with force under his disposition, which had become a capital crime as far as the new military junta was concerned. Later in 1963, General Kim was released through the intervention of the U.S. Department of State; he then came to the University of Washington as a Fulbright scholar. A few months after his arrival in Seattle, he sent me a letter in which he mused on the irony of becoming a "private first class" in American society and attempting to restart his life anew.[41] Four years later, Ung-soo Kim came to study at the Catholic University of America, Washington, D.C. and received his Ph.D. in economics.[42]

On the other hand, Col. Lee's fortunes turned for better. After the coup in 1961, Colonel Lee became Special Assistant to Foreign Minister Hong-il Kim (1898-1980) in the military junta. Much later in 1974, I traveled to the Naval Electronics Laboratory, San Diego. As I was leaving the terminal at Lindbergh Field, I saw several Koreans entering the airport lobby. There, in the middle of the Korean entourage, was Colonel Lee, who was then the South Korean Ambassador to Mexico. When I bumped into Colonel Lee, both of us stopped momentarily, surprised, and looked at each other in disbelief. It had been seven years since we shared an office bay at the Army Headquarters. Both of us were delighted to meet with each other and were surprised by changes in our lives over the intervening years. One of us was in the diplomatic service of South Korea, and the other was an engineer in the American industry.

In the ensuing fifty years, General Ung-soo Kim and I became close friends until he passed away in March 2018 in Suwon, South Korea. I wrote the following short eulogy for him to memorialize in my small way.

> I am deeply saddened by the loss of Major General Ung-soo Kim, ROKA (ret.). He will be truly missed, and I will include him in my prayers. In 1957-1958, I was General Kim's orderly (personal secretary) for twelve months, when he was the Deputy Chief of Staff for Logistics, ROK Army HQ. In return, I became a lifetime friend and received advice both big and small from him.

Indeed, he was a man for all seasons. He was a patriot, a military leader, a scholar, an educator, a Christian spiritual leader, and family man.

A patriot who grew up in Harbin, China, in the 1940s, as a son of the resistant fighter against Japan in Manchuria.

A military leader, as he commanded an Army division during the Korea War, ROK Sixth Corps commanding general, Deputy Chief of Staff for Logistics and the builder of the South Korean military logistics system.

A scholar, as he received his Ph.D. in Economics from the Catholic University of America in his thirties,

An educator, as he was Professor of Economics at the Catholic University of American for three decades.

A true Christian, as he served as an Elder of his Church, to which he left a legacy of Ung-soo Senior Academy for the Korean community.

A family man as he was a devout husband to his late wife, Sil-mo Park, father of Mee-young, Yong-won, Yong-he, and Yong-kyun.

Brother to Tae-soo, Hwan-soo, and Hyo-hee, General Young-hoon Kang, and Yohanes.

I pray may God provide strength to his family members and may his soul rest in peace.

John C. Kim

I Become a Staff Assistant in the Korean Olympic Committee

A week before my honorable discharge from the South Korean Army, General Kim asked me if I would be interested in a temporary position until my departure to go abroad in June 1958. I was interested in his proposition, and he arranged a job interview for me at the Korean Olympic Committee (KOC), which had been looking for temporary staff. Two persons, Mr. Tong-jae Cho, a board member of KOC and the Director of the Asia Foundation in South Korea, and Mr. Myeong-gon Kim, the Secretary General of KOC, interviewed me. They hired me as a temporary paid staff person at KOC. (see photo 16)

The staff position required English language ability. My duties included handling the paperwork of the Third Tokyo Asian Games, scheduled for the summer of 1958, and submitting South Korean team entries to the 1958 Tokyo Asian Olympic Committee. I also attended the KOC board meetings, where the board members oversaw the activities of KOC. I got acquainted with Professor Sang-baek Lee (1904-1966), who was the Chairman of the Board, and Head of the South Korean Delegation to the International Olympic Committee (IOC).

I also got acquainted with a Hawaii-born Korean American Board member, Mr. Walter Seong-bok Jhung (1904-1986), who was one of the few international attorneys in Seoul in 1958. I acted as Walter's interpreter in the board meetings. He had limited Korean language ability as he was a second-generation Korean-American, born in Pahala, Hawaii. He was mostly silent during KOC board meetings, and when asked a question on some legal issue, Walter would turn to me for English translation. He would say: "I will give you my response through John." I worked for four months as a staff member and got paid handsome stipends. I appreciated General Kim's indirect but kind consideration.

More importantly, this job gave me a rare opportunity to observe how the amateur sports governing bodies and the national Olympic committee worked in South Korea. I saw how some influential politicians and businessmen made their individual fiefdoms through sponsorship. For example, Mr. Il-hwan Kim (then Minister of Commerce and Industry) was the president of the Korean Swimming Federation. The federation was sponsored by Minister Kim's private funds. But then, in Korea and Japan, it is a time-old tradition for most

professional sports teams sponsored by private corporations and the government agencies. Examples are the Samsung Lions and the LG Twins, which are the better-known professional baseball teams in South Korea today. These professional teams are sponsored by the Samsung Group and the LG Group respectively; coaches and players are all employees of the corporations.

There have been politics and dramas in the Olympic Games. In 1960, the South Korean team fielded two speed track skaters at the Winter Olympic Games held in Squaw Valley, California. I must declare that South Korean winter sports have come a long way since then. In 2018, I saw the fantastic opening ceremonies and the sports facilities for the Winter Games held in Pyeong Chang, South Korea, on TV.

In 2018, we also saw politics in Pyeong Chang. The South Korean President Moon Jae-in, the U.S. Vice President Mike Pence, Kim Yong-nam, the President of the North Korean Presidium, and Kim Yo-jung, the sister of Kim Jong-un, stood at the center stage during the opening ceremony on primetime TV. Vice President Pence stood when the U.S. team marched in. He remained seated and did not recognize the North Korean delegation. The North Korean and South Korean teams marched together under one improvised flag which printed the outline of the Korean Peninsula.

In 1960, at the VIII Winter Olympics in Squaw Valley, there were also political issues. It was inevitable. The issue was what to do with the entries from communist countries like the People's Republic of China (PRC), North Korea, and East Germany. The International Olympic Committee (IOC) allowed China (PRC), North Korea, and East Germany to participate in the Games.

Remember, it was the height of the Cold War. The U.S. Government refused to issue a visa to athletes from the three communist countries. But the IOC threatened to cancel the Squaw Valley Winter Olympic Games. The U.S. Government finally conceded to the IOC and issued the entry visas to athletes from those Communist countries.

Then and now, politics and the Olympics have been intertwined. I am sure there will be more political dramas in the coming years.

PART TWO

AMERICAN EDUCATION AND EMPLOYMENT IN AMERICAN INDUSTRY

(1958-1969)

7

Trine University, Indiana

I mentioned earlier in Chapter 2 that many of my high school classmates came to America during and right after the Korean War. Had there been no war, I most likely would have gone to Japan just as most Koreans did during Japanese colonial years. I did not know what fate might have had in store for me in going to America, and my continuing education took a different tack in America.

The first step in my travel to America was to apply for a student visa at the U.S. Consular Office in Seoul. I needed to submit a financial document called an affidavit of support from an American sponsor. Then, and now, it was a hurdle for a foreign student to get a visa from the consular office. For about a year, I struggled to find an American sponsor. Finally, my cousin Phillip Myong came to my rescue. Phillip had gone to America two years earlier, and he was then a student at the University of Illinois. He found me a sponsor, Dr. Woodrow Terrell, a physician in the Illinois farming town of Maroa. The town is about 30 miles west of Champaign-Urbana. Phillip told me that he had asked Mrs. Lois Schenck, who was a nurse at Dr. Terrell's office, for help finding a sponsor.

Woodrow Terrell (1913-1998) was born in Kentucky and served in the U.S. Army as a medical officer during the World War II. He then settled in Maroa after the war to practice medicine. He also served as Mayor of Maroa for 20 years. There was a newspaper article on Woodrow Terrell in the Decatur newspaper, *the Herald & Review*[1]. When he had retired from his medical practice in 1995, the Decatur newspaper wrote the following article.

> *"Dr. Woodrow Terrell never once turned away any patient who*
> *needed medical care during the 49 years he practiced medicine*

*in Maroa. Woodrow Terrell remembered how one patient fretted
because she had no cash.*

*She told me, 'Doc, I don't want you to take care of me for noth-
ing.' So, she brought me a chicken.*

*I can't remember what I did with the chicken, but I treated
the woman.*

*This sort of medical practice is the type of memory the 82-year-old
Dr. Terrell will take with him when he moves to Texas, where
he plans to fish and play golf."*

I appreciated this story, as I was also a beneficiary of his kind heart.

To America on Northwest Airlines

When I finally received my South Korean passport at the South Korean
Foreign Ministry and my U.S. F1 student visa at the Consular Office, my
parents bought me a ticket on Northwest Airlines flights. I was ready to leave
for America. The one-way airfare from Seoul to Ft. Wayne, Indiana, was $980
then. This was equivalent to $8,000 in 2019 dollar. At that time, air travel was
quite civilized, with a three-course meal, a generous amount of baggage allowance, and personal services provided by friendly flight attendants.

On the morning of my departure, my parents were emotional, since I was
leaving for America across the Pacific Ocean. My father expressed his emotion
by quarreling with me about something, which I do not remember. I boarded
my Northwest Airlines flights to Tokyo Haneda Airport and had an overnight
layover in a Tokyo hotel courtesy of the airline. (see photo 17)

Our flights arrived in Anchorage for refueling and continued to Seattle.
In those days, all Korean students traveling to America needed proof that
they were free of tuberculosis bacteria. I hand-carried an X-ray film of my
lungs and duly presented it to an immigration officer. I was glad to get rid of
it. I then changed my flights to United Airlines to Chicago Midway Airport.
One thing I planned to do during the layover at Midway was to call a friend
of mine, Benjamin Whi-so Lee (1935-1977), who was a graduate student at
the University of Pittsburgh. His mother, Dr. Soon-hi Park, was our family

doctor at Ja-ae Clinic in our neighborhood. A few days earlier when I bid my farewell to Dr. Park, she asked me to contact Ben and send her love to him. In the Midway terminal, I placed a long-distance call at a public phone booth to Ben, who answered my call and welcomed me to America. Ben was then a rising star in theoretical physics.[2] In 1977, a tragic automobile accident took his life prematurely.[3] Many of his contemporary physicists considered him as an eventual candidate for the Nobel Prize in physics.

After the telephone conversation, I decided to go sightseeing in downtown Chicago, as I had about five hours to spare. I took a Chicago city bus to the Loop. At the Midway bus stop, I rode a white and green Chicago Transit Authority (CTA) bus, which was beaten up, with graffiti all over the interior walls of the bus. This excursion was my first adventure in a big American city. Half an hour later, I arrived at the Chicago Loop. I window shopped along Michigan Avenue, where I found a Chinese restaurant and ordered noodle soup. I was calculating the exchange rate in my head. The price of the noodle soup was steep, compared to that of Seoul restaurants. It was the first time I paid for anything at all in dollars. I did bilingual arithmetic in dollars and Hwan (the Korean currency) and had my first cultural shock, as the meal price hit in my pocket.

I had to return to Midway Airport by five o'clock to catch 5:30 p.m. United flights. So I backtracked to Midway Airport. When I entered the Midway terminal, the public announcement speaker was blasting, "Mr. Kim, Mr. Kim, the final call!" It was a close call, and I nearly missed my flights. But in those days the airport was a small one-lobby terminal. There were neither concourses nor mega-terminals. I quickly jumped onto the ramp and boarded my flights to Fort Wayne.

In Fort Wayne, I stayed overnight at the YMCA, as suggested by the travel agent in Seoul. The next morning I took a Greyhound bus to Angola, my final destination. When the bus arrived in Angola, the driver announced, "Angola, Angola."

He gave me my baggage from the cargo bay and said, "Mister, the college is five blocks from here, and good luck with your study."

The first thing I had done was to find the administration building; I went to the office of Jean McCarthy, the Dean of Admission. She examined my passport and processed my registration on the spot; she then telephoned a fellow

Korean student, Seong-cheol Kim. He and I went to the housing office to find me a place to live. They recommended a rooming house at 308 South Superior St., three blocks from the college. The landlady asked me to pay the weekly rent of $5 in advance and every Friday from then on. She provided clean linens and a pillowcase every week, but I had to supply my own blanket. In the afternoon, Seong-cheol and I went to J.C. Penney store in downtown Angola. I bought a light green blanket, which I ended up keeping for over 50 years.

It may be of interest to readers what school expenses such as tuition and room and board were in 1958. For a year at Trine University, I managed to attend college on a total budget of $2,400, from which I paid tuition and fees ($1,200) and room and board ($750). In 2017 a Trine University student paid tuition and fees of $32,950 and room and board of $9,350. My parents provided all of my expenses for that first year. I was ever thankful for them, as I had an adequate amount of money to start my studies in America. That didn't mean that I had an abundance of money. My parents also taught their children frugality.

In my second year in America, my parents sent me a total of $1,200, since my tuition and fees at Michigan State University were only $200, plus I received a stipend of $960 and free room and board as a dormitory resident assistant. By my third year in America, I had become a full-time instructor at Trine University and was financially self-supporting. How fortunate I was.

THE UNDERGRADUATE DOUBLE-E EDUCATION AT TRINE UNIVERSITY

As the school started, I had met a friend, Larry Anderson, in my double-E classes. He was attending the university courtesy of the GI Bill. He once asked me to loan him ten dollars until his next monthly stipend would arrive. I received my monthly checks from my parents via the First National Bank of Chicago. We understood our predicaments and joined the club. That was how I began my American undergraduate studies at Trine University.

When I entered Trine University, I found the core courses of the double-E department were different from those of SNU. The curriculum of SNU had not transitioned yet from electrical power engineering to electrical engineering with an emphasis on electronics. In 1956, Professor Norbert Wiener[4] of MIT

wrote an article on the traditional electrical engineering curriculum:

"Electrical Engineering was divided into two more or less clearly separable fields, known as power engineering and communications engineering."

Power engineering, in which I did most of my undergraduate studies in SNU, was the traditional academic field. Communications engineering began as the study of scientific aspects of the telephone and telegraph, and later electronics and solid-state physics. This curriculum became the backbone of present-day high technology.

A few days before the class started, my academic advisor Professor Clyde Shaw interviewed me:

"John, I reviewed your academic report from SNU. Everything is fine except for two issues."

"What are they?"

"The first is too much emphasis on power engineering, and the other is the lack of laboratory work. The SNU double-E curriculum was behind that of American universities in electronics. It was the curriculum of American universities in the pre-World War II years, concentrating in power engineering.

"That was what I did when I studied double-E at Texas A&M University. Our goal at Trine University is to produce practicing engineers who can work in electronics industries after graduation."

"Yes, I know, and I would like to shift my emphasis to electronics."

"A large part of our core curriculum emphasizes communications engineering like VHF/UHF engineering. We offer the transistor course, which used to be in the physics department. It became part of the double-E department because of the application of transistors to communications engineering.

"The other issue is your lack of laboratory courses. You must take more junior- and senior-level laboratory courses. You have an adequate mathematics and physics background. We teach courses with the right balance between classroom theory and laboratory techniques."

Even though I started out behind, my SNU education helped me to catch up with the new curriculum in double-E. I repeated my studies of James Clerk Maxwell's electromagnetic equations and how they governed the theory of

radiation, which was a form of energy traveling through space without the need for supporting medium. In 1865, Maxwell predicted that high-frequency (from 3 MHz to 30 MHz) radio waves could travel a long distance in space. This became the theory behind developing radar, wireless radios, and modern electronic equipment. Maxwell developed the theory which unified electric and magnetic forces. His theory predicted radio waves and X-ray radiation , even though no one had discovered electromagnetic waves. In 1887, Heinrich Hertz built an apparatus to generate sparks that transformed into electromagnetic waves. A receiving loop across the laboratory observed sparks, which provided evidence of electromagnetic waves.

A few years ago, I visited Cambridge University and Berlin Technical University and paid my homage to physicists James Maxwell and Heinrich Hertz. These two pioneers helped point the way for modern technologies, from satellite communications to radar, and you name it, just about all of the modern technology.

SLIDE RULE CALCULATION

Do you know how one calculated and solved a mathematical formula in the classroom in the 1950s? One did not use a computer or an electronic pocket calculator. One used a pencil, paper, and the CRC Standard Mathematical Table[5] which was a book of 300 pages of mathematical tables of trigonometric and other transcendental functions. Or, one used a slide rule. At Trine University, I calculate values for complicated trigonometric, logarithmic, transcendental functions, etc., in my double-E classes by using a slide rule. I bought my K&E 68-1100 slide rule at the campus bookstore, and I still own it. When I used the slide rule, I felt I knew the theory more intimately than just punching function keys into a scientific electronic calculator. Just remember bridges, ships, and other complicated machinery were designed and built by using the slide rule before the advent of electronic computers.

My Stomach Aches

At the end of the summer session of 1958, I felt uncomfortable with my stomach, so I went to see a doctor at Cameron Memorial Hospital in Angola. After the doctor heard my complaint, without further ado, he put me under sedation, emptied my stomach, and took an X-ray image with a barium tracer. I found out about the procedure after the fact. When this procedure was completed, he could not find anything wrong with my stomach. My stomach-ache disappeared after a few days of fasting in the hospital. Fifteen years later, another doctor determined why I had stomach aches. My primary care doctor Dr. Leo LaRow in Fairfax diagnosed it as the lactose intolerance symptom. When I came to America, my stomach was shocked by my new diet, which consisted of a bowl of cornflakes and milk for breakfast. It was the cause of my stomach aches. My stomach was fine and settled when I stayed away from dairy products.

I had suffered from stomach aches when I was a young child, which my mother thought were caused by the damp weather and the inadequate heating system in our house in Tokyo. She would wrap me with a wool belly wrap. Looking back with 20-20 hindsight, I do not recall having any stomach problems from about 1945 to 1958 because the Korean food I ate did not include dairy products. Even after I learned of my lactose intolerance, I occasionally succumb to my taste for ice cream or cheese, and suffer a day or so with an unsettled stomach.

Visiting Dr. Woodrow Terrell, My Sponsor

After the summer session, I took a Greyhound bus to Champaign, Illinois, to visit my cousin Phillip and then my sponsor, Woodrow Terrell. Several days earlier, I had telephoned Phillip and told him about my homesickness, which he understood as we were more or less in the same boat. He invited me to come to Champaign, and I was on my way. My first stop was at an apartment in Chicago where a half-dozen fellow high school alumni roomed together in a large, rented apartment. They had come to Chicago to earn money during the summer recess. In the morning, all of them left the apartment, heading for their

workplaces. Some worked as busboys in restaurants, and others in factories. In the evening, we gathered in the living room and swapped stories of our lives in America as foreign students. After two days of freeloading in the apartment, I did not wish to outstay my welcome, so I continued my travels on Greyhound to Champaign. I was glad to see Phillip. The next day he and I drove in a friend's car to Maroa to pay a visit to Woodrow Terrell. I expressed my gratitude to him and Lois Schenck for their help. The good doctor was all smiles and welcomed me to Maroa. Lois Schenck fed us a picnic lunch of hamburgers, hot dogs, corn, potato salad, and coleslaw at her house. I remember the return drive to Champaign in the summer night on an Illinois state highway. We listened to a major league baseball game on the Chicago Cubs radio network. On both sides of the road were corn fields, which made a rustling sound in the summer breeze. I miss the farming communities of the Midwest.

I Receive a B.S. Degree from Trine University

At Trine University, I took an academic load of 18 quarter credit hours and accumulated 70 quarter credit hours in 12 months. Since Trine University accepted my credits from SNU, in June 1959, I had enough credit hours to receive a Bachelor of Science degree in Electrical Engineering at the end of my first full year in America. One of the fellow graduates was Lieutenant Tessema Abaderash of the Royal Ethiopian Air Force. (see photo 18) Tessema Abaderash was always a serious student. The Ethiopian Government supported his Trine University education with a scholarship. In 1974, Tessema Abaderash became Colonel in the Royal Ethiopian Air Force. He joined the coup d'etas of 1974, led by Mengistu[6]. In the spring of 1976, I met Tessema at an Ethiopian restaurant in Northwest Washington when he came for an official visit. He was then the Minister of Electric Power in Ethiopia.

Most of my fellow double-E classmates were several years older than usual undergraduates. Most of my classmates received one or two job offers and became gainfully employed in industry as electrical engineers. A few, including myself, decided to continue our education by attending graduate school. Many of my classmates had served in the Korean War and paid their tuition and the room and board with their GI Bill scholarship. Some of them came

well-prepared with electronics skill, as they had been enlisted technicians in the Air Force, the Army, or the Navy in areas such as electronics, radio, sonar, and radar. They understood laboratory work and received job offers as entry-level engineers in aircraft, armament, radio, automotive, and steel companies in the industrial states of the Midwest such as Indiana, Michigan, Ohio, Illinois, and Pennsylvania. Now in 2019, these once-prosperous industrial states became rust belts. This region must adapt to the technological realities of today.

Homecoming to Trine University in 2011

A half-century later, in 2011, Rahn and I visited the campus of Trine University. It had expanded not only its classroom buildings but also other buildings and facilities like the library, the gymnasium, the auditorium, and dormitories. In my undergraduate days, the campus occupied three city blocks, but, in 2011, it covered more than 20 city blocks. I had a meeting in Ann Arbor, Michigan, at Michigan Aerospace Company and wanted to visit Trine University. When I called Bob Keller from McLean, the Director of Development, he answered.

"John. What a pleasant surprise.

"Where are you?

"Are you in Angola?"

"No, Bob, I am in Virginia.

"But I have a meeting in Ann Arbor.

"I am wondering if we could meet at the University on Friday."

"Yes, I am free around noon. I will see you, then."

Bob introduced us to University President Earl Brooks, Dean of the Engineering College V.K. Sharma, and Professor Sean Carrol of the Electrical Engineering Department. They gave us a warm welcome. My alma mater was and is still a warm place. Rahn and I sat on a sofa in President Brooks' office and had a pleasant conversation for about half an hour.

From my undergraduate days, I remembered a spruce tree next to the Old Administration Building. There was a stone block in front of the tree, on which an excerpt of Joyce Kilmer's poem, "*Trees*," was engraved. I remembered the snow-covered spruce in the winter and the excerpt:

"Poems are made by fools like me, but only God can make a tree.[7]

During our visit, I searched for the spruce tree and the stone block. There was no trace of them. Oh, well, that is the price one must pay for progress. When I was a senior at the university, I used to pass in front of the tree every day; it comforted me in my busy walks from a classroom to the next. Its loss saddened me.

MICHIGAN STATE UNIVERSITY IN EAST LANSING

After graduation from Trine University, I went to Michigan State University (MSU) in East Lansing for graduate study. When I reported to the double-E department, Professor Lawrence von Tersch, the chairman of the department, interviewed me. He asked me about my preferred area of concentration so that he could assign my academic advisor.

"John, welcome to the university.

"What area would you like to study?"

"Professor von Tersch, I have no firm area in mind."

"That is alright.

"Do you have any interest in space technology?"

"I am not sure.

"What is space technology?"

"John, you know the Russians put an earth satellite, Sputnik, in orbit last year.

"Also, you heard about the American satellite Explorer."

"Yes, I did."

"The U.S. has created a new government agency called the National Aeronautics and Space Administration (NASA) to explore the space.

"Space technology is the study of space vehicles, boosters, satellites, computers, and telemetry.

"It is going to be a promising area."

"Why is it promising?"

"Space technology is where the hard science will be concentrated in the next decades."

I was hesitant about his suggested field of concentration as I had studied

electronics and communications engineering at Trine University. At the end of the interview, Von Tersch told me that Professor Herman Koenig would be my academic advisor. The next day, I met with Herman Koenig (1925-2010).[8]

"John, Larry told me that you are interested in communications engineering and electronics. As a starter, you could take two graduate courses during the summer session. One is Computability and Unsolvability, and the other is Information Theory."

"Why don't you take these two courses, and see if you like it. In the fall we will talk more about the area of concentration, and we will go from there."

It turned out that the first course was the theoretical foundation of computation using the electronic computer and the second was the fundamental theory of communication systems. Herman Koenig had not explained to me what these courses were about. These subjects were different from the classes I had taken at Trine University because what Trine University taught undergraduate double-E students was the current practice of radios, radar, microwave engineering, and transistors. What MSU offered to new double-E graduate students was the theoretical foundation of science and technology for the coming decades. The topics I studied and subsequent courses I took in both computer and communications engineering became the basic science of my professional career for more than a half-century. I was grateful for his recommendation.

THE TURING MACHINE AND SHANNON'S INFORMATION THEORY

So I enrolled in Computability and Unsolvability, taught by Professor Gerald Weeg, who was a mathematician and computer science professor, using the textbook, *Computability, and Unsolvability*[9] by Martin Davis, which dealt with the solution of mathematical problems using the Turing Machine. You may have heard about Alan Turing, who cracked the code on a German military encryption-decryption device called the Enigma machine[10] during the World War II. Alan Turing made an electro-mechanical machine at Bletchley Park, a U.K. Signal Security Agency, and the British version of the National Security Agency in America.

By the way, I ended up buying and owning three copies of the same Davis book. The first copy I bought was the textbook of the course. Some years

later I misplaced the book, and I ordered another copy in 1978. I loaned the second copy, which I could not recover at the time. So, I bought a third copy in 2006. I always wanted to have this book in my library. A few years later I found the first copy buried in my library, and honest borrowers returned the loaned copies to me.

Computability and Unsolvability introduced a subject difficult to comprehend for me. The book introduced a hypothetical sequential computation machine called the Turing Machine. The Turing Machine assumed to perform an infinite length of instructions, but only allows four operations, that is, left shift, right shift, blank, and print. With these simple operations, one can decompose any mathematical formula. The more I studied the theory, the more I appreciated how the subject matter influenced the development of the digital computer. I often thought about Larry von Tersch, Herman Koenig, and Gerry Weeg and appreciated their academic mentoring to a beginner engineer like me.

I enrolled in the other course, *Information Theory*, lectured by Dr. Richard Filipowsky, who was then on the research staff at the Westinghouse Electric Company Research Center in Pittsburgh. The class used the textbook, *Foundation of Information Theory*, by Amiel Feinstein[11]. Information theory was the theoretical foundation of digital communication and introduced Shannon's theorem on reliable communication in a noisy channel by applying error correcting codes. When I studied information theory, I was surprised that it contained much probability theory and the concept of entropy. Entropy was a measure of the degree of randomness in thermodynamics of molecules. I understood the degree of randomness in the noise of digital transmission was similar to entropy.

The concept of information theory became the foundation for reliable communication of digital signals and an important part of electrical engineering. At the beginning of Richard Filipowsky's course, I struggled to understand the theory, and I was skeptical about its practical applications, but I worked hard to grasp them. When I took the final exam, Prof. Filipowsky gave me a grade of B-minus. I did not like that, so I went to his office and had a talk with him:

"Professor Filipowsky, you gave me a grade of B-minus.

"I worked hard on this course, and deserve a grade better than that.

Could you give me another exam?" He was surprised, but after some

thought, he said,

"O.K., John. I will give you another chance. Rather than giving you a set of questions, you tell me what you have learned in my course this summer."

I was glad to have another shot at a better grade. I thought long and hard about my response to Professor's question, and I answered:

"O.K. Thank you, Professor Filipowski. What I am going to write on the blackboard is what I have learned from your challenging course."

Then, on the small blackboard in his office, I started to write several essential theorems and their proofs as I memorized them a few days ago. When the blackboard was half filled, Prof. Filipowsky stopped me.

"O.K. John, you've made your point. If you can memorize the proof the way you have covered my blackboard, you deserve a grade of A-minus."

"Thank you, Professor."

"If you are satisfied, I have to go. I have a luncheon appointment."

"Sure, of course. Thank you, Professor Filipowsky."

From this coursework, I began to understand how important information theory was for the modulation theory of communications system and the coding theory for error detection and correction.

By the way, Richard Filipowsky was an Austrian engineer from Vienna. I knew another friend from Vienna, Dr. Eugen Muehldorf. Eugen and Richard first met at Vienna Technical University in the 1940s. In 1965, Filipowsky had co-authored two books with Eugene Muehldorf, *Space Communications System,*[12] and *Space Communications Techniques*, both published by Prentice-Hall Publishing Company[13] when they worked together at Westinghouse Electric Company. Much later, Eugen and I coauthored *Naval Shipboard Communication Systems*, also published by Prentice-Hall Publishing Co. What a small world it was! I told my story about getting the A-minus to Eugen, who chuckled by saying, "That is a classic Richard."

Campus Life at Michigan State University

By the end of summer session in 1959, I had finished two graduate courses at MSU and liked the campus life in East Lansing. In the fall, my friends and I went to Spartan Stadium to watch football games. During the winter months, we attended basketball games at Jenison Field House. I enjoyed walking on the tree-lined campus in the summer. (see photo 22)

During the summer session, I met fellow Korean students including my high school classmate, Man-hyung Yoo. We walked the campus together in the summer evenings. I put together a hi-fi system using surplus electronic parts from the laboratory in the Electrical Engineering Department. The frequency response of my homemade hi-fi was poor, and one could not hear the bass sound. When I played my homemade audio system, a friend of mine commented:

"John, what happened to your woofer?"

"Oh, it's there."

"But my amplifier and audio speakers cannot filter out the low pitch."

"You mean it was a bad design."

"No, it was not a bad design."

"Blame it on cheap surplus components I've used."

General Douglas McArthur as Commencement Speaker

I attended the 1961 Commencement Ceremony at Spartan Stadium. At the head of the academic procession, next to MSU President John Hannah, we found General Douglas MacArthur, who was the commencement speaker that year. A year earlier when I received my MS degree, President John Hannah had managed to bring General McArthur's erstwhile adversary, former President Harry Truman, as the commencement speaker. President John Hannah was Chairman of the U.S. Commission on Civil Rights and had many political connections. Before the academic procession started, my roommate Charles Kimm and I approached General MacArthur. Charles told him,

"General, I am Charles Kimm, a retired ROK Naval officer. I want to tell you that I participated in the Inchon landing in September 1950."

"Charles, I am delighted to meet you. What subject are you studying at the college?"

"Sir, my specialization is the seaway transportation."

"Wonderful, I am glad to hear that."

MacArthur shook Charles's hand and congratulated him. He was eighty-one years old then, and there he stood still, and his steely eyes focused far. Then, the old soldier returned to his pensive mood. (see photo 23)

Dormitory Resident Assistant

In 2009, I had visited Armstrong Hall, which was my old dormitory while I was a graduate student at MSU in East Lansing. When I walked into the lobby, I found the same music room well enclosed in the corner to quiet down the piano music when someone played the keyboard. Opposite to the music room was an office with mailboxes for 240 students. The area was much faded, and the carpet had seen better days. When I saw a student in the office reading a book, he reminded me of myself in that office a half-century ago. (see photo 20) I was in charge of sorting the mail, selling meal tickets, and operating the switchboard for Armstrong Hall. I considered the office as my fiefdom. I was also in charge of the fourth-floor B-wing as a resident assistant (RA). This job brought me my first paycheck, which was a monthly stipend of $80, along with free room and board. The paycheck was important for me because, for the first time, I paid my Federal Insurance Contributions Act (FICA) tax to be credited in the Social Security program. The only financial support I needed from my parents in 1961 was $450 for tuition, as I had made in-state student status since I was paying the income tax to the State of Michigan. When I had received my first stipend at the end of the month, I went to Kosticheck's haberdasher in East Lansing and bought myself a dark gray sports jacket for $35. As an RA, I provided counseling to 30 undergraduate students. During the winter and spring recesses, I stayed and took care of the dormitory.

When the school was in session, I walked two miles from Armstrong Hall to the double-E building every day, following the Red Cedar River. My classroom was on the ground floor of the double-E building, where Professor Meryl Reed lectured on filter design, and Herman Koenig had his office. Meryl Reed wore

a bolo tie, as a proper Texan would do. When Rahn and I visited the MSU campus in 2012, we found the number of the building had increased from about 50 to 300 on the campus. I failed to locate the double-E building. What an embarrassment it was!

DAVIDSON HEPBURN

During the time I stayed in Armstrong Hall in my first year as a graduate student, Davidson Hepburn from Nassau, Bahamas, was a fellow RA. Davidson studied Miguel de Unamuno, a Spanish philosopher, who fought against the Franco regime, and Davidson introduced me to Unamuno's tragic sense of life. Davidson earned his doctorate from the University of Madrid in 1965. Later, he became Ambassador of the Bahamas to the United Nations. In 2011-2015, he became President of the United Nations Educational, Social, and Cultural Organization (UNESCO) (see photo 21). Recently, I had a chance to talk to him over the phone about good old days in East Lansing. One episode we shared was about his teaching me how to drive my newly bought car, a 1954 Pontiac Chieftain (see photo 19). I told him I received two tickets from the Lansing police for poor driving. I said his teaching was flawless, but I must have been a poor student to have gotten traffic violations. We both chuckled.

Both Davidson and I became friends with an American family, the Atkinsons, in Okemos, Michigan. Woody Atkinson and his wife Dee Dee were always gracious hosts at their home to us foreign students, especially during the holidays like Thanksgiving and Christmas. I got to experience a typical middle-class, Midwest family life when I visited the Atkinson home and their summer cottage near the town of Alpena, Michigan. The Atkinsons had a boat with outboard motor, and Davidson and I learned to water ski in Lake Huron. We became quite good at it.

Map 1

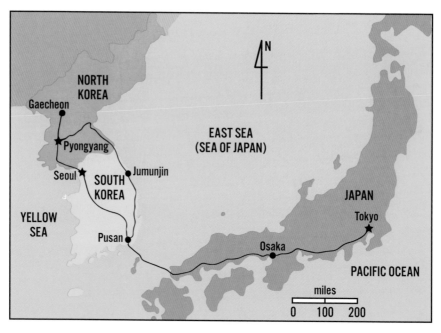

Map of Korea and Japan; in 1929, my father moved from Pyongyang to Tokyo; In 1934, my parents were married in Tokyo; in 1935, I was born in Tokyo; in 1941, the family moved to Jumunjin; we moved to Pyongyang in 1941; we moved to Gae-cheon in 1944; we lived in Seoul (1945-1950); in Pusan in 1951-1954; in Seoul in 1954-1958.

Map 2

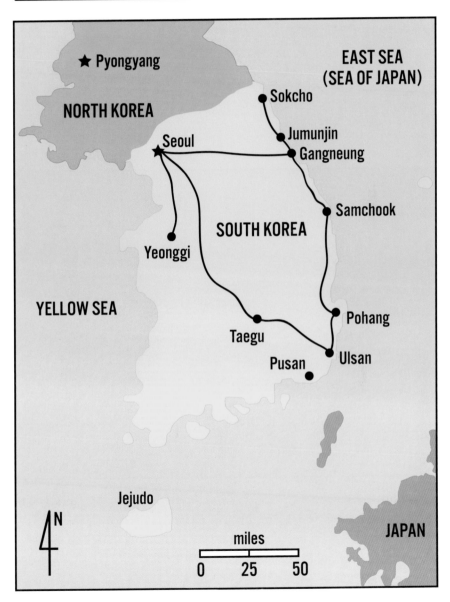

Map of the site survey tour of Korean Counter Infiltration System (KCIS) Project in South Korea in February-March, 1972. We visited Taegu, Ulsan, Pohang, Samcheok, Gangneung, Jumunjin, and Sokcho. I also visited the Kim clan tomb in Yeon-gi, South Korea.

1

I am holding the physics package of the Ultra-Miniature Rubidium CPT atomic clock, which my children called "Dad's electronic mustache."

2

My mother in Jumunjin, Korea, c. 1933. She was tall and beautiful in a Korean skirt and top.

3

My parents in Tokyo, Japan, c. 1937. My father wore his Sunday best three-piece suit while my mother sported a Kimono.

4

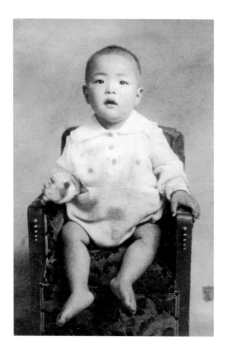

My earliest portrait, taken in Tokyo, Japan, c. 1937. My family called me by my baby name, Humijang.

5

Sitting on the lap of my maternal grandmother in Jumunjin, Korea, c. 1941. I wore a pair of gaiters, a sailor suit, and a military cap—the fashion of those days. I remember my legs itching from the coarse, home-knit woolen socks.

6

My blue sailor suit with the petty officer third class (PO3) insignia, worn through Tokyo, Pyongyang, Seoul, and Washington, D.C.

7

Holding my younger brother Phil's, hand in Tokyo, Japan, c. 1940. We wore sweaters knitted by my mother, who knitted the five-ring Olympic mark on the sweater. The 1940 Tokyo Olympic Games were canceled due to the impending winds of WWII.

Families of Governor Luther Park, my great-uncle, and an American missionary doctor, Marian Hall, vacationing at Mount Little Diamond, Korea, c. 1928. (From left to right): Susan Noh; Moon-Hyeok Park; Geol-Jeong Hong Park, wife of Governor Luther Park; Dr. Sherwood Hall, Marian Hall's son; Dr. Marian Hall; Moon-Ok Park.

My uncle Ke-Ju's estate and farmhouse in Gaechon County, North Korea, c. 1945. The estate and farmhouse were nestled in the foothills of Mt. Gae-Ma. The estate was surrounded by rice paddies and cornfields.

The narrow-gauge train carried coals of Mutsui Mining Company from Gaechon, North Korea, to the Naval Base Chinnampo, the Japanese Naval homeport in the Yellow Sea. The railroad was a half-mile away from our estate. The Mitsui Mining Company ran a telegraph line along the track, which was the only piece of the modernity in the rural village.

My class photo, taken at Jong-am Elementary School, c. 1948. I was the class president. I am standing in the pond (front-left), and beside me is Je-Soo Park, the class vice-president.

*My senior-class portrait, taken in Seoul, South Korea, c. 1954.
I wore my school uniform with a stand-up collar.*

13

Posing with two classmates in the Physics laboratory of SNU, c. 1954.

14

Posing with my cousin Soon-Yo Lee, who was a South Korean Air Force Lieutenant at the time. We were in a downtown Soeul department store "Metropolitan", c. 1958.

15

I am posing with Jeong-Soo Park, the Public Information Office photographer. I served as an orderly of Major General Ung-Soo Kim, the Deputy Chief of Staff-Logistics., South Korean Army Headquarters from 1957 to January 1958.

16

Working as a staff member in the office of the Korean Olympic Committee in Seoul, South Korea, from January to May 1958.

My friends and I in front of the Northwest Airlines office the day I left for America in June 1958. Out of the nine friends who saw me off at the airport, six would come to the U.S. for college. (Back row, from left): Soon-Yo Lee, Peter Choe, Sang-Soo Sul, Jong-Ho Park, Sung-Ho Nam, and Byung-Gi Park. (Front row, from left): Ki-song Kim, me, and Young-Deok Kwon.

I received my Bachelor of Science in Electrical Engineering at the commencement ceremony of Trine University, in Angola, Indiana, c. 1959. (From left): Seong-Cheol Kim, me, Raymond Dong, and Tessema Abaderash (Lieutenant of the Royal Ethiopian Air Force). Abaderash was always a serious student.

My first car, a 1954 Pontiac Chieftain. It had a two-tone, green-and-yellow color, and a V-8 engine (316.6 cubic-inch displacement and 202 horsepower). It was a gas guzzler, although the word was not a part of anyone's lexicon yet. I bought it c. 1961 for $350 (my monthly salary was $500).

20

I was on duty at the reception room at Armstrong Hall at Michigan State University, c. 1961. I was the switchboard operator, and took care of guest meals, tickets, and mail.

21

Friends at the MSU Armstrong Hall dormitory, c. 1961. (From left): I posed with Davidson Hepburn (2nd), a fellow resident assistant. Davidson later became the Bahamian Ambassador to the UN (1978-1988), and the President of the UNESCO (2013-2016). He always called me "Chan Kyu" in perfect Queen's English.

Professor Lawrence von Tersch

Larry von Tersch (1923-2010) introduced me to the field of computer engineering. One of the early computer inventors John Vincent Atanasoff (1903-1995) was Larry von Tersch's mentor at Iowa State University. In 1953, Von Tersch became a visiting researcher at the University of Illinois (UI) and participated in the construction of the first-generation computer, ILLIAC.[14] In 1956, Dean John Ryder invited Von Tersch to construct the Michigan State Instructional Computer (MISTIC), which was the second generation computer of ILLIAC.

In 1973, there was a court case on the ownership of the patent right on electronic digital computers. Judge Earl R. Larson of the District Court of Minnesota presided over this court case. Coincidentally, Rahn was a boarder at Judge Larson's house when she was a graduate student at the University of Minnesota. Judge Larson ruled that Sperry Rand Corporation did not own the Atanasoff-Berry's digital electronic computer patent. In this judgment, Judge Larson ruled John Atanasoff as the legal inventor. Sperry Rand would not collect any royalties derived from the patent. Unfortunately, John Atanasoff never made a dime from his invention of the digital computer. How unfair it was to him.

Professor Gerald Weeg

Gerry Weeg (1927-1977) helped me with my minor field, mathematics. He was the lead mathematician in the MSU Computer Laboratory and was a pioneer in the field of computer science. I took courses from him in the numerical analysis using the digital computer. His lectures included numerical analysis for solving mathematical problems like ordinary differential equations and Fourier analysis. For example, I can solve an ordinary differential equation by a method known as the Runge-Kutta method.[15] Each numerical analysis topic in Weeg's lecture included a mathematical discussion, a flowchart, a sample problem, computer memory requirements, and an estimation of the program run time. I had to pay careful attention to the memory requirement as the random access memory was small and I also had to carefully estimate the runtime so as not to

exceed the time limit. I still own one of the earliest, comb-bound programming manuals of MSU MISTIC, published in 1958. The instruction set has ten operations, i.e., ADD, SUBTRACT, MULTIPLY, DIVIDE, LOAD, STORE, etc. This expanded set of instructions was an improvement as the instruction set of the Turing Machine had only four operations. One may consider these operations as the irreducible set of instructions. We have come a long way in computer programming. Several years later the course became a formal academic discipline, called computer science.

I BECOME AN INSTRUCTOR AT TRINE UNIVERSITY

When I was a graduate student at MSU, quite a few graduate students worked as graduate teaching or research assistants. These students had to limit their academic loads to half-time to devote the other half of their time to teaching an undergraduate class or assisting a professor's research project. Since I was not a graduate assistant, I was able to take the full-time load of 15 credit hours. By the end of summer 1961, two years after I started my graduate study, I completed not only my academic coursework for my doctorate but also passed the comprehensive examination. The exam was a specific type of test for graduate students in their major and minor coursework, along with a demonstration of reading knowledge in two foreign languages.

Then an opportunity came my way. Professor Ralph Gilchrist, the newly appointed Chairman of the EE Department of Trine University, came to East Lansing to attend faculty seminars occasionally, where I met him. After the seminar was over, he wanted to see me. He was looking for a faculty in Trine University, and he offered me a full-time instructorship at Trine University. I sought Herman Koenig's advice about pursuing a full-time teaching position while working on my dissertation. It turned out that Professor Koenig recommended me to Ralph Gilchrist when he asked Prof. Koenig for a candidate of the instructor. I accepted the teaching job offer at Trine University. The salary was much better than what MSU could provide to a graduate student, as my annual salary at Trine University would be $6,050, which was three times that of a graduate assistant. Ralph Gilchrist himself was Herman Koenig's former student. Koenig told me that I should see him at East Lansing campus once

a week to complete my doctoral dissertation. Angola was 45 miles south of East Lansing, and it was a reasonable commuting distance. So I moved on to become a full-time instructor at Trine University. The university also agreed to submit my application to change my visa status to a permanent resident, which would put me on a path to naturalization to become a U.S. citizen.

As Ralph Gilchrist was revamping the curriculum of the double-E Department at Trine University at the time, he asked me to teach two senior-level core courses and one freshman laboratory courses on motors and generators. The first core course was on electromagnetic theory and the second was on servomechanisms. These two classes were not easy subjects for seniors at Trine University as students had to have a good background in vector analysis and ordinary differential equations to understand Maxwell's electromagnetic theory. I told the class that I had taken the subject course twice, once in my freshman year at SNU, and the second time in my first-year graduate study at MSU. They did not believe me. I told them that the memorization would be the best way to tackle this coursework. I told them if they can memorize a derivation of the electric field with a point charge, for example, they will understand the theory later. My students were at first reluctant to follow my teaching method, but most of them prevailed.

I taught lab course on motors and generators. Only three years earlier, I had taken the same course taught by Professor Clyde Shaw. I repeated his method of teaching laboratory work. For example, we observed the velocity and torque of a DC motor as a function of voltage. In the middle of the laboratory, there still was a prominent notice posted, which said,

> "On this motor, several students were injured. Be careful when you handle these machines."

The lab work was easy enough, but it was structured to hone student's report-writing skills. They had to write a report to demonstrate their understanding of the theory, the list of apparatus used including the model number, the observed data, and the conclusion.

I Become a Permanent U.S. Resident and a Naturalized Citizen

After I joined the faculty, Trine University filed a petition for me to become a permanent U.S. resident. Two months later I received a letter from the Immigration and Naturalization Office notifying me to appear at the office in Chicago in person to swear and sign the immigration paper. A year later I became a permanent resident and a U.S. person. In 1965, I became a naturalized U.S. citizen at the U.S. District Court for the Eastern District of Virginia, in Alexandria. I remembered a Bible verse of Matthew 25:35, "I was a stranger, and you took me in." Fate smiled on me with random kindness. When I received my student visa at the American Consular Office in Seoul, it never crossed my mind that, one day, I would become a U.S. citizen through naturalization. I had no idea that fate would guide me to cross the threshold of the U.S. District Court and would become an American citizen in seven years after I came to America. Naturalization and then U.S. citizenship were necessary qualifications for employment in the defense industry and the U.S. Department of Defense and the requirements needed for a security clearance.

I already mentioned that I have had four legal names and three citizenships. I was a Japanese citizen by birth; a Korean citizen by blood when Korea became an independent nation in 1945; and a U.S. citizen by naturalization in 1965.

8

Systems Research Laboratories, Inc., Dayton, Ohio, and Minneapolis-Honeywell Company

From 1962 to 1969, I changed jobs four times in seven years. It may appear to be excessive job-hopping, but I was merely taking advantage of employment market forces. American companies were expanding, especially in the defense sector, and creating substantial employment opportunities for those who had studied in science, technology, engineering, or mathematics (STEM) disciplines. I advanced my career by surfing on the crest of the wave.

In the spring of 1961, I was winding down my first year as an instructor at Trine University. One day, an elderly gentleman came to Trine University to recruit "June graduates" on campus. He was Dr. Clarence Ross, Director of the Applied Mathematics and Science Department of Systems Research Laboratories (SRL), Inc., a small R&D company in Dayton, Ohio. I don't know how he got my name, but in the evening I found myself dining with him at a restaurant in Angola. He was not only interested in recruiting June graduates but also faculty members like me. He apparently had done some background checks on me before the dinner meeting. At the end of dinner, to my surprise, he offered me a job with an annual salary of $8,500, which was a significant pay raise for me.

The following week, I met him again at SRL in Dayton. He would initially assign me on two computer-related projects, sponsored by the U.S. Air Force. Once more, I sought the advice of my academic advisor, Herman Koenig. I went to see him in East Lansing, and we had the following conversation:

"Dr. Koenig, as I told you on the telephone I have a job offer from a small R&D company in Dayton, Ohio."

"So you have another job offer. But to give you advice I must know more about this company. Do you know if it is a stable company? You know Trine University has been there for over 100 years and is very stable."

"An engineer named Fritz Russ established the company in 1955. This year the total number of employees is 100."

"John, what did this director, Clarence Ross, say about your job and your assignment?"

"Apparently, they just won two contracts from the U.S. Air Force. The principal investigator is Professor Howard Aiken of the Harvard Computation Laboratory."

"Wait a minute. Did you say, Howard Aiken?"

"Yes, he is Chairman of the Board of the company. He retired from Harvard."

"John, I knew him. I had met him when I was at MIT. I think it was 1955 when he was developing a drum memory device for his Mark IV computer for the U.S. Navy. He needed help from the MIT Laboratory for Electronics on the servo-mechanism for a drum spinning gadget. That is very interesting. So, what is your job going to be?"

"Dr. Clarence Ross and others, including me, will be working on two Air Force contracts which Howard Aiken brought into SRL. Professor Aiken became an industrial entrepreneur and came to SRL as the Chairman. He works a few days per month."

"The first contract was awarded by Wright-Patterson Air Force Base to develop a new computer device based on the non-binary number system. The other contract was awarded by Griffiss Air Force Base to develop software, called the system administration software, for general purpose computers."

"John, that sounds like real state-of-the-art stuff. I think you should grab the opportunity. Trine University would not be able to provide you the exposure to the kind of quality

projects like the ones you've described. Of course, Howard Aiken has a reputation for being a tough taskmaster. But you will survive. I recommend you accept the offer. Did you talk to Ralph about the new job offer?"

"No. I wanted to speak to you first. Now I've got to get myself released from Trine University. I know Ralph will not like my leaving his department."

When I returned to Angola, I broke the news to Ralph Gilchrist, who was not pleased with the news as I thought. But he knew he could not match the salary nor provide the same kind of research opportunities at Trine University. However, I ran into another roadblock from Dr. Leslie A. Willig, Vice-President for Academic Affairs, who was displeased with SRL, which offered jobs to three faculty members. However, Trine University did release me from the following year's teaching obligation. This employment change was another step in building my career. For the first time, I would work on projects funded by the Department of Defense. I certainly did not plan my career path the way it was unfolding, but I took the opportunity when it came to my way.

HOWARD AIKEN AND HIS AIR FORCE CONTRACTS

When Professor Howard H. Aiken retired from Harvard University in 1960, he became an industrial entrepreneur. He was invited to become Chairman of the Board of Directors of SRL. In that capacity, he brought in two Air Force contracts on *the residue number computer* and *the computer command structures*. These two projects were managed by Clarence Ross, who in turn recruited several engineers and applied mathematicians to carry out research.

The first contract was research on the residue number computer.[16] In the residue number system, a number was represented by a system developed by the Chinese remainder theorem.[17] In 1963, three organizations were conducting DOD contracts on the residue number system computer. They were Dr. Richard Tanaka of Lockheed Missile Systems Division, Professor H. L. Garner of the University of Michigan, and Howard Aiken of SRL. There were several exchanges of R&D results among the three organizations. Critical issues of the

residue number system computer were the elimination of carry-propagation in the addition operation, magnitude determination, sign determination, overflow, scaling, and division operation.

The second contract was research on computer meta-language and computer command structure. What is meta-language? A computer operator communicates with a machine using meta-language, which is known today as the operating system.[18.] Howard Aiken conceived of this idea ahead of his time. Larry Irwin, a mathematician, and I worked together on this computer command structures language.[19.] This was a precursor to the Disk Operating System (DOS) meta-language developed by IBM.

I knew that Howard Aiken was an early pioneer in computer technology. In the SRL's library, I found the multivolume *Annals of the Computation Laboratory of Harvard University* in which many of his accomplishments were recorded. Clarence Ross knew about Aiken's work and told me the following story.

"When Howard Aiken was working at the graduate school of Harvard University, he drew up a plan for a programmable electromechanical machine that could perform complex calculations. But he had no luck in convincing anyone in the university to give him the resources to build it until 1939 when the President of IBM, Thomas Watson, Sr., agreed to fund the Howard Aiken's project. The result was the IBM Mark I ASCC (Automatic Sequence Controlled Calculator), which was considered the first automatic electromechanical digital computer. Howard Aiken and his team became the scientists, who ushered in the computer age."

"Howard Aiken completed the construction of IBM ASCC (Mark I) in 1943 and made it fully operational in 1944; it operated at a speed of three arithmetic operations per second. The speed of computation was slow, but it was a revolutionary machine in the sense that it was the first electromechanical computer to perform routine automatic sequence calculations. By the way, contemporary computers could perform 500 million operations per second."

Howard Aiken came to town from New York City and Florida to take care of his business as the Chairman of the Board, SRL. Howard Aiken and Clarence Ross reviewed our two Air Force projects on the residue number system computer, and meta-language for computer–to-peripheral communication.

As I explained, the residue number computer was a revolutionary approach to designing a computer. Note that the existing computers were based on the binary system. The SRL team tried, but no tangible result was found. The meta-language for computer-to-peripheral communication represented another innovative idea. The meta-language became a reality after 30-some years as the language for operating systems such as DOS, UNIX, and Windows.

Besides his residue number system computer and meta-language, Aiken discussed an idea of building a smaller version of his Mark IV for home use. In retrospect, Howard Aiken was thinking about a personal computer (or PC) as we call it today.

DR. CLARENCE ROSS

I was fortunate to have Clarence Ross (1906-1981) as my mentor at the start of my career. He had more than 40 years of government and industrial experiences. He became the first user of Howard Aiken's Mark III computer at the Naval Surface Warfare Center, Dahlgren, Virginia, where he was Chief of the Computer Laboratory. Then, he introduced the Mark IV computer to the National Security Agency at Fort Meade, when he became the Assistant Deputy Director of the Agency.

Ross introduced me to several friends and colleagues of his, Colonel Jack Steele of the Air Force Aerospace Medical Research Laboratory, Dr. Wolfgang Braun of the Air Force Aerospace Research Laboratory, and Lieutenant Colonel Leonard Butch of the Air Force Avionics Laboratory. I was grateful for him to share his friendship and his wisdom in our private and corporate lives, an experience that I could not have duplicated anyplace else.

Pay Scales in Industry and Government

I received my Ph.D. from MSU, in December 1962. One day, Clarence Ross offered me a pay raise of $3,000 to bring my salary up to $11,500. Why did he do that? At Defense Department agencies in 1963, the pay scale for a new employee with a Ph.D. was at General Schedule (GS)-12 (and it still is at the level in the 2010s). And what was the annual salary of GS-12, step 5 in 1963? It was $11,590. It seems to me that Clarence wanted to make sure he was paying me a competitive salary so he wouldn't lose me. (see photo 24)

Here is a table showing my annual salaries from 1962 to 2013. Some readers may be interested in my pay progression during the last 50 years.

TABLE OF THE SALARY ANALYSIS				
EMPLOYER (YEAR)	MY ANNUAL SALARY	INDEX OF THE ANNUAL SALARY	CPI	GS SCALE
Trine University (1962)	$6,050	100.0	100.0	GS-11, Step 5
SRL, Inc. (1963)	$8,500	140.5	101.3	GS-12 Step 5
Honeywell (1964)	$14,634	241.9	102.6	GS-13 Step 1
Raytheon (Melpar) (1969)	$19,108	315.8	121.5	GS-13 Step 5
Northrop Grumman (TRW) (1975)	$32,872	543.3	178.1	GS-14 Step 1
Northrop Grumman (TRW) (1985)	$61,021	1,008.6	356.3	GS-14 Step 5
Northrop Grumman (TRW) (2001)	$123,920	2,048.3	586.4	GS-15 Step 1
ONR (2013)	$158,500	2,619.8	771.4	GS-15 Step 10

The above table shows my salary rose 26 times in 51 years (from 1962 to 2013), while the Consumer Price Index (CPI)[20] rose only eight times over the CPI (1962) during the same period. Why were there such significant differ-

ences? The differences are due to professional's years of experience and increasing productivity. That curve is known as the maturity curve, which measures salaries based on years of directly-related work experience since the first educational degree of an entry-level engineer. As a professional's career advances, so does his salary curve. One's pay scale rises on a higher maturity curve than on the previous maturity curve. For example, the salary curve of a senior engineer is higher than that of a junior engineer. The rightmost column of the table shows comparable General Service (GS) levels for the positions I held. The GS pay schedule is important as the American industry often anchors its pay scale to the GS pay schedule of the federal government. The pay scale for a GS-15, Step 10, was $158,500 in 2013.[21] Note that the table shows the equivalent GS Scale as the reference point.

Dr. Wolfgang Braun, USAF Plasma Physics Laboratory

In October 1963, Clarence Ross and I visited the laboratory of Dr. Wolfgang Braun, Chief, Plasma Laboratory, at WPAFB. Dr. Braun gave us a tour of the plasma arc facility. He was working on the basic science of plasma physics and studying the properties of the arc and the underlying phenomena of the arc plasma. An apparatus he was working with generated a plasma arc up to 36 inches long. His research would ultimately be applied in plasma jet propulsion of future space vehicles. His laboratory performed theoretical and experimental studies of emission absorption of radiation from the fully ionized plasma in the presence of a magnetic field. The magnetic field pushes hot plasma away from the rocket wall, and the plasma rocket overcomes the limitation of chemical fuel rocket.

Wolfgang Braun gave us a mini-lecture on the plasma. Plasma is an electrically neutral gas in which all positive and negative charges—from neutral atoms, negatively charged electrons, and positively charged ions—add up to zero. Plasma exists everywhere in nature; it is designated as the fourth state of matter (the others are solid, liquid, and gas). It has similar properties to gas but is affected by electric and magnetic fields and is an excellent conductor of electricity. Plasma is the building block for all types of electric propulsion, where electrical and/or magnetic fields are used to push on the electrically charged

ions and electrons to provide thrust. An example of this plasma effect can be found in fluorescent light bulbs.

Plasma ion system is the propulsion of choice for scientists and engineers in the U.S. Air Force and the NASA and science fiction writers. It involves the efficient use of fuel and electrical power, enabling spacecraft to travel faster and cheaper than any other propulsion technology currently available. Ion thrusters are today used for station-keeping on communication satellites and for the main propulsion on deep space probes. Ion thrusters expel ions to create thrust and can provide higher top speeds for spacecraft than any other rocket system currently available.

STATISTICAL ANALYSIS OF SMOKING AND HEART DISEASE

Richard Talbot, a physician in Dayton, solicited SRL to assist him in analyzing data he had collected on the effects of tobacco smoking on the cardiovascular disease. Clarence Ross assigned me to this project to model the design of experiments using factor analysis, which is a tool for investigating relationships of designated variables into interpretable factors. I designed an experiment and attempt to find the connection between the cardiovascular factors (cholesterol, lipid, etc.) and tobacco use characteristics (the amount of the nicotine intake, the frequency, the length of use, etc.).

Richard and I presented our results at the 1964 American Heart Association (AHA) convention held in Los Angeles. We gave our findings that nicotine may increase one's metabolic rate. This result meant that smokers burned more calories than nonsmokers. However, losing weight by smoking would not provide the overall health benefits. At the convention, we were interviewed by the news media on the topic.

GREAT-UNCLE CHIRL HYUN, AN EARLY
KOREAN IMMIGRANT TO AMERICA

During the American Heart Association (AHA) convention, I stayed at the Beverly Hilton Hotel in Los Angeles. I wanted to meet with my father's uncle, Chirl Hyun (1895-1992), who had come to America in 1917. I had exchanged letters with him in the past but had never met him. I invited Great-uncle Chirl to the Hilton for dinner. After dinner, I listened to his recollection, especially that of racial prejudice in America over past three-quarters of a century. He could not have imagined in the 1920s that a young Korean like me could participate in a research project and present its result at a professional conference. Uncle Chirl told me the following story in the lobby of the hotel that evening.

"John, tell me what you are doing in L.A."

"I am attending the AHA convention, held in this hotel. I helped a physician in Dayton who had done research on the relationship between tobacco and heart disease. We presented our research results this morning."

"You and young people from Korea today are the lucky ones.

"Back in 1925, when I graduated from college, I could not have imagined that an Asian could participate in a professional meeting like the AHA convention."

"Yes, I heard about that."

"John, you only heard about it, but I experienced it painfully."

"Great-uncle, tell me when and why you came to America?"

"I came to America to study in 1918 during the World War I.

"As you know, our family lived in Yongbyon in North Korea. I attended Soong-deok Mission School in Yongbyon. When I graduated from the mission school, I wanted to go to America. My family gave me ¥300 for my travel to America. I studied several routes I could take to America. They told me that it would be difficult to board an America-bound ship in one of the Japanese ports. I learned that Shanghai was the better port to get started.

"It was not easy to get passage. I went to Shanghai, where I met several America-bound students.

"After three or four weeks, I met a Seventh Day Adventist Church pastor in Shanghai. He helped me find a passage on the SS Columbia, which was headed to San Francisco via Kobe and Yokohama. In those ports in Japan, Japanese

Maritime Police would not allow Koreans to go to America. My fellow Koreans and I stayed in the cargo bay for several days, until the ship was in the open sea.

"After fifteen days, when we finally docked in San Francisco, our real ordeal had started. The U.S. Immigration Office in San Francisco would not let us disembark at the Emarcadero, as we had no passports nor visas. During the summer of 1917, we were detained on Angel Island in the San Francisco Bay for forty days. The Consular Office of the Provisional Korean Exile Government, represented by Mr. Jin-ha Choe, helped us by petitioning that we students were allowed to disembark in San Francisco and go to college. There were altogether sixteen Koreans detained on Angel Island.

"Finally, the Immigration Bureau in Washington decided to allow us to go to college, but first we had to take an examination to verify that we were real students. Some of the questions the immigration officer asked were:

"What is the capital of England?"
"Who was the famous Emperor of France in the 19th century?"
"Who was the American President during the Civil War?'"
"Out of sixteen would-be students who took this test, only eight of them, including I, passed.
"We finally set our feet on the Embarcadero, where Mr. Jin-ha Choe welcomed us to America.
"The Provisional Korean Consular Office in San Francisco asked me to which college I wanted to go. I told the consulate office that I wanted to go to the Lowell Textile Institute."
"Why did you choose Lowell?"
"I often had heard about Boston from Pastor Charles Morris at Soong-deok Missionary School in Yongbyon. In 1917, one of the viable industries in Korea was the textile industry. I thought it would be a good career for me."
"O.K. What happened when you got there?"
"Well, in the spring of 1918, I finally arrived at Lowell Textile Institute in Boston and enrolled at the institute.
"The college now became the University of Massachusetts-Lowell."

"How did you pay for college?"

"When I arrived in Boston, America entered the Great War in Europe. Young men were conscripted into military service. There were many job opportunities.

"The Institute gave me financial aids for tuition and free room and board, arranged me to a work-study program, doing table waiting and dishwashing. It took me five years to graduate from the Institute.

"After graduation, I could not find a job in the textile industry. Instead, I got a job as a sales agent for the Ford Motor Company in Riverside, California. Many Asians were living there. Many of them became my customers. With their help, I established an excellent sales record. For the next dozen years, I worked hard and became branch manager of the Ford Motor Company in Riverside."

"After Pearl Harbor, I joined the U.S. Army, and was commissioned as a Second Lieutenant."

"That's wonderful."

"During the war, I was an instructor in the Army Foreign Language Institute at the Presidio of Monterey. I retired as a Captain in the U.S. Army, and I was proud to wear the American uniform and contribute to the war effort."

"That's great."

"By the end of the World War II, more Americans were coming in contact with other races. They became more enlightened on the race relations in America. After the Korean War, I witnessed a transformation in the attitude of Americans toward Asians. Young Koreans like you are the lucky ones who can get professional positions in America."

"I think your generation laid the groundwork for us young Korean immigrants."

"During successive wars, they send young Americans overseas, and those returning GIs and sailors brought home more open-minded and positive attitudes toward people of other races. These wars were terrible things for all of us, but they

also had redeeming value."

"Great-uncle, Thank you for telling me your fantastic experience."

I could not but see wrinkles on the old gentleman's face, which told me his many years of struggle for racial equality in America. I was ever thankful for him to share his life experience with me.

Colonel Jack Steele, an Aerospace Flight Surgeon

In the 1950s, an Air Force flight surgeon, Colonel Jack Steele, MD (1924-2009) coined the word "bionics" while he was working on the electronics aspect of biology, Later he became known as "the father of bionics." In the 1970s there was a TV series called *Bionic Woman* in which the heroine almost died while skydiving, but later they rebuilt her body "bionically." This TV series popularized the term bionics but misrepresented from Jack Steele's original idea. Jack Steele explained to me Bionics:

"John, my idea of Bionics was not referring to the concept of bionics as it has been popularized in the TV series.

"My idea of bionics was to the study of biological systems and organisms to find solutions to problems in electronic engineering.

"We analyze biological systems, which we find in nature every day.

"For example, the function of a human ear could be analyzed by the examination of elements or structure of auditory systems, which transfer sound from the ear and to the brain.

"Using this biological system, we could synthesize an electronic system by combining ideas observed in the analysis to form a new biological electronic system.

"For example, the function of an artificial acoustic system by modeling an electronic signal passes through the acoustic system.

"John, that was my idea of bionics."

"Jack, it is unfortunate that the popular TV show *Bionic Woman* depicted a superwoman by adding electronic gadgets to her body."

That was the time when scientists of the Air Force Aerospace Medical Research Laboratory (AMRL) had been working on aerospace and medical technology to support future space flights.

SRL assigned me to work with Jack Steele in his bionics research. He had received his B.S. degree in electrical engineering and his MD degree from Northwestern University. Our first study topic was the human auditory system. He modeled how the human auditory system transmits and receives signals from the ear to the brain, and how the human auditory system uses frequency modulation. I helped him to model the function of a cochlea as a frequency analyzer.

Jack was an active pilot. He flew his Cessna 150B airplane, maintained his flight surgeon status by logging the required hours, and flew to Washington National Airport and other places from Dayton Municipal Airport. For his daily commuting in and around Dayton, he drove his beat-up Ford sedan for his ground transportation. In 1963, Jack asked me to represent him at a Bionics Conference in Arlington Hall Station, in Virginia. At the conference, a dozen researchers compiled a thesaurus of bionics for the first time and which was later published by Defense Technical Information Center (DTIC). During my visit to Washington, D.C., Clarence Ross arranged a faculty seminar for me to present at George Washington University (GWU), hosted by Professor Solomon Kullback. Kullback became Professor of Statistics at GWU after his retirement from the National Security Agency. The topic for my seminar was the *Residue Number Computer*, for which GWU gave me an honorarium of $75.

ARTIFICIAL INTELLIGENCE

In the 1960s, interests in artificial intelligence (AI) grew in academia, along with pattern recognition. Dr. Tom Curry of Melpar, Inc. established the Washington Section of the IEEE Man, Systems, and Cybernetics (MSC) Society. In 1967, he became the founding chairman. I was the secretary, and later became the chairman of the Washington Section of MSC. I also served on the technical program committee of the First International Joint Conference on Artificial Intelligence (IJCAI) held in Washington, on May 7-9, 1969. I was elected as a session chair by the conference committee of the IJCAI-69 at the meeting held in Las Vegas, Nevada, in August, 1969. My session was on "Self-organizing system." I had one paper from Eastern Europe, by Fridrich Sloboda and Jaroslav Fogel of Institute for Engineering Cybernetics, Slovak Academy of Science, Czechoslovakia.

From 1956 to the 1980s, AI was on the fringe of philosophy and mathematics. Before the IJCAI-69 Conference, there was the first AI conference in Dartmouth College, in 1956, where the word AI was coined. During this early phase, AI was pursued in the academia only. An occasional highlight of chess games made the news. The chess match between IBM Deep Blue and the World chess champion Garry Kasparov was resulted in IBM Deep Blue defeating Kasparov.

In the 1970's, Government research funding in AI was drastically cut. But the AI field gradually becomes more useful and found practical applications in pattern recognition (PR). Today PR is used in various everyday tasks like fingerprint minutiae reading, check processing, voice recognition, and other applications.

However, from the 1990's on, machine learning (ML) gradually began to make inroads into technology. Today, ML is everywhere. For example, Virtual Personal Assistants can find data and information when asked questions like:

"Where is the nearest watch repair shop?"
"What is the shortest route from New York to Chicago?"

Another application of AI is the battlefield management with C4ISR, known as persistent intelligence surveillance reconnaissance (ISR). The rapid

advance of military technology brought great evolution and revolution in the concept of persistent ISR. When I was in ONR, I worked in the C4ISR Department. We developed various AI systems, using UAV and GPS to expand maritime ISR. One could consider it as the fruit of AI technology.

Dr. Yoon-soo Park, Physicist

I frequently visited Wright-Patterson AFB when I was at SRL in 1962. In the Aerospace Research Laboratory (ARL), I met Yoon-soo Park, who had become a government employee at ARL, after receiving his doctorate in solid-state physics from the University of Cincinnati. His wife, Dju, had lived for several years in Gaecheon, where my family lived as evacuees in 1945. Often, Dju and I would reminisce on life in the village. Yoon-Soo Park made a six-year excursion to the U.S. Embassy in Tokyo as Science Attaché. Upon his return to the states, he joined ONR as the Program Officer in Electro-optics Technology. My office was three doors down the corridor on the same floor.

I attended his ONR retirement party in 2003. I made a 20-minute slide show. During the party, his boss, Dr. Max Yoder, the Director of Electronics Division, told us that Yoon-soo and his colleagues in his division had an ongoing contest about who traveled to the most exotic places. Max declared that Yoon-soo was the winner by popular acclaim.

Office Politics at Systems Research Laboratory

All was not well in the Applied Mathematics Department of SRL. For the first time in my career, I inadvertently got mired in office politics. There was discontent among some members of the department. Two fellow scientists, David Brandt and William Fahle, seemed unhappy with the favorable attention I have received from Clarence Ross. There was a rumor that Clarence would retire soon, and these two fellows must have thought that Clarence was grooming me for the next head of the department. David Brandt was a graduate of Ohio State University in mathematics and had been in the laboratory for more than three years. As I sensed his hostile attitude toward me, I thought some-

thing had to be done to clear the poisonous atmosphere in the department. One evening, I invited Clarence to dinner. Even before I broached the subject, he told me that he knew what was going on in the department. He said that I would not become the new department head. I certainly was not looking for the position, and I was much relieved to hear him saying that. We then had one more glass of beer, which did not solve the problem, but it cut the problem down to a manageable size.

A month later, Fritz Russ, President of SRL, announced Clarence's retirement. He would go to his country home on Vashon Island in Puget Sound, Washington. Fritz Russ appointed Dave Brandt as the new head of the department. When he became the new head of the Department, he became friendly towards me. His primary concern then became how to continue the two ongoing Air Force contracts. He had to satisfy our Air Force customers, but more immediately, he also must prove so that Aiken would be convinced about Dave Brandt leading the projects. (see photo 25)

This unpleasant episode was my first baptism to office politics. There were undoubtedly more episodes of office politics down the road. I lost track of Dave Brandt's career. SRL was acquired by CALSPAN. Fritz Russ donated from his proceeds, $124 million to his alma mater, Ohio University, Athens, in 1994. In 2009, when I visited the campus to review Professor Frank van Grass's GPS AJ project sponsored by the Office of Naval Research (ONR), I saw a modern building on which "Fritz Russ College of Engineering" was inscribed. I explained to Rahn how the name of the building came to be, and we saluted Fritz, his wife Dolores, and their well-spent gift to Ohio University.

FLUTE LESSONS

One of my fellow workers in SRL, Bob Marble, and his wife Ashley invited me to dinner at their home in Vandalia, Ohio. Bob was a graduate of Tulane University, and he played flute in college. Bob encouraged me to take flute lessons, so I bought a Selmar-Bundy student model flute at Hauer Music Company in Dayton, Ohio. I took private lessons. When our daughter Janet entered Langley High School, she learned to play the flute with my old Selmar. Eventually, we bought her an Armstrong flute. Later, she took private lessons from Mr. Tom Perazzoli, Assistant Principal Flutist of the National Symphony Orchestra. My friend Eugene Kaiser introduced her to Tom Perazzoli. After the first audition, Tom told us that he gave lessons only to college students. But we persisted, and he accepted Janet as his student, and she received solid music lessons from him. In college, Janet joined the Northwestern University Marching Band (NUMB), playing the flute and the piccolo. She traveled with the band to participate in many Saturday performances at football games.

MOVE TO MINNEAPOLIS-HONEYWELL COMPANY

In 1964, I made another career move. This time I moved to Minneapolis-Honeywell Co. How did I get a position at Honeywell? I attended a meeting of the Association for Computing Machinery (ACM) to participate in a panel discussion on the Residue Number System Computer. At the ACM meeting, I met Hugo Schuck, the Director of Honeywell's Military Product Group (MPG) Research Laboratory. Hugo Schuck was interested in what I had been doing on the residue number system computer with Howard Aiken and offered me a job at Honeywell. I liked Honeywell, a Fortune 500 company, which had its own research and manufacturing divisions in various product lines in aerospace, materials, and building control systems. After two years at SRL, I left the Laboratory and joined the Honeywell MPG Research Laboratory.

One month after I joined the company, the Honeywell security department notified me that the DoD had approved my security clearance. This allowed me to access sensitive information on a "need-to-know" basis. I had submitted my clearance application when I was working at SRL. This approval marked

a significant milestone in my career since most of my employment from then on involved defense-related programs, which required the security clearance.

When I joined the Honeywell MPG Research Laboratory, which had 200 professional staffs in a dozen engineering disciplines, the company had been a center of excellence in control systems such as the aircraft autopilot system, the gyroscope, and the inertial navigation system. In the 1960s, Honeywell reorganized its defense-related business into the Military Products Group, which included the Aero, Ordinance, and Gyro Divisions. My task, as a senior research engineer, was to work with several departments in the Aero Division. The continuing flow of government contracts helped fund several R&D projects for the group. Until 1960, Honeywell developed gyros as stand-alone products. However, the group began to move away from manufacturing components like gyros and autopilots to building systems like automatic flight control systems.

The Honeywell Gyro Division had its gyro manufacturing facilities at Stinson Boulevard. The division was housed in rows of factory-like structures, which had flat-top roofs with glass panes. The division designed and built Ring Laser Gyroscopes (RLG's) for ship and submarine navigation. During my tenure at ONR in the 2000s, Honeywell became one of the contractors that provided state-of-the-art gyroscopes and inertial navigation systems to my INS projects using the Hollow-core Fiber Optic RLG.

Another newly initiated product line was mainframe computers. Honeywell developed the H-200 general purpose computer, and later the H-6000 computer for the World-Wide Military Command Control Systems (WWMCCS), which were installed at command centers at the Pentagon, the Pacific Command, the Atlantic Command, and the European Command. During the Cold War, the WWMCCS supported operations of American global military activities in intelligence, communications, data collection and processing, executive decision-making tools, and supporting facilities.

While Honeywell succeeded in integrating digital technologies in the traditional control system markets, it failed to capture meaningful market shares in general-purpose computers. After struggling in the computer market, the company made the painful decision to discontinue its computer business. Honeywell then had devoted all its defense sector resources to the production of aeronautical and ordnance systems.

I Meet Rahn in Minneapolis

Pursuing my career in Minneapolis was the best move I ever made; it was Minneapolis, where I met my future wife. I first met Rahn at my cousin's wedding in September 1964. I was the best man for my cousin Dr. Won-chang Park; she was the maid of honor. I must say I fell in love with her at first sight. In December 1964, I invited her and my friends to a Christmas gathering at my apartment in Minneapolis. At the end of the party, it began to snow heavily. At the time, Rahn was staying at her sister's home in Northfield, Minnesota, about 40 miles south of Minneapolis. It was snowing heavily, but my cousin Soon-yo and I drove her in the snow to Northfield. Minnesotans certainly knew how to deal with driving in the heavy snow. When we arrived after midnight at her sister's house, her sister served us hot coffee; then, Soon-yo and I returned home to Minneapolis in the snow. About our courtship, my cousin Soon-yo wrote his observation in his memoir about Rahn and me.[22]

> "I remember the courtship of my cousin John and his future wife, Rahn in Minneapolis in 1964. I visited John from Chicago once in a while, when I was a graduate student at the University of Chicago. I felt that she would become the very helpful wife and the partner to John. My expectation proved to be right. Two years ago Rahn and John celebrated their 40th wedding anniversary. They have built a happy family. I am forever thankful for God's blessings upon them."

Rahn was born in Seoul in 1940 and graduated from Yonsei University-College of Law and Political Science. She came to America to attend graduate school at the University of Minnesota. Those were days when her family was going through hard times. On May 16, 1961, a military coup d'etat led by Major General Chung-hi Park toppled the South Korean Government. The military junta placed her father under house arrest. Her father was the Minister of Commerce and Industry in the Chang Myeon government and a leading member of the Democratic Party in South Korea.

Rahn completed her courses for MS degree and found a job at the Voice of America in the U.S. Information Agency in Washington. Over Christmas

holiday, I traveled to Washington on company business. I arranged for a date, and we had dinner. After dinner, we walked around Georgetown in the snow, looking in quaint shops, which lined on Wisconsin Avenue.

HONORABLE JUDGE EARL LARSON

When Rahn was a second-year graduate student at the University of Minnesota, she boarded at the house of Judge Earl Richard Larson and his wife, Cecill. The house was on Lake of the Isles, in Minneapolis. Rahn told me about her experience during her stay in the Larson home and her graduate studies at the University of Minnesota.

"Rahn, how did you find the Larson's home?"

"The judge's two children were attending college, and their rooms were available for needy foreign students like me and Ashnedal Hilmi, a high school girl from Egypt to live in and go to school.

"I paid $46 per month for room and board.

"It was a nominal amount, but it made me feel better living in the house with interesting people coming and going all the time.

"There were a lot more benefits.

"It was certainly not quantifiable beyond the cash value that I paid.

"On frigid mornings, the judge would give me a ride to the university en route to his chambers in St. Paul.

"He was impressed with my scholastic aptitude and even had offered me his financial support to complete my graduate work.

"Almost at the same time, I was informed by the Financial Branch of the Foreign Students Office that I was to receive two scholarships.

"One was awarded from the Kappa Kappa Gamma (International Society of Key Women Educators).

"The other was awarded from the Bernice Gestie Fellowship for Foreign Women Educators, which covered my school expenses.

"I finished all the coursework and headed for the Library of Congress, Washington, to write my master's degree dissertation."

In 1978, when Judge Larson and his wife visited Washington, Rahn and I had invited them for dinner at the Yenching Palace, a Chinese Restaurant. We

ordered some appetizers and main dishes. The judge mistook the big tray of appetizers as the main course and only ate a small portion of it. I happened to mention that it was an appetizer. Then, he realized more food was coming, and he ate the appetizers. (see photo 66)

In 1961, President John F. Kennedy appointed Earl Larson as a federal judge for the District of Minnesota. Rahn told me her observation of the Larson's home as a political gathering place in Minneapolis:

> "John, the house was like a train station.
>
> "It indeed was a hub of the Minnesota Democratic-Farmer-Labor Party.
>
> "I ran into several notables of the party who frequented the house, like Hubert Humphrey, Walter Mondale, and Orville Freeman.
>
> "One day Orville Freeman, a former Governor of Minnesota and a former Secretary of Agriculture in the Kennedy Administration, drop by the house.
>
> "I saw Cecill Larson served him a dish of cold spaghetti and a cup of coffee.
>
> "When you were a kingmaker, you could serve a simple cold dish to a former Governor and a Cabinet Secretary.

JUDGE LARSON AND THE EARLY YEARS OF COMPUTER INDUSTRY

Among the many court cases decided by Judge Larson, the most important one were his landmark judgment on the patent rights of the general purpose electronic digital computer.[23] The other notable case was his judgment that the NFL's "Rozelle Rule" violated antitrust laws.

The court case for the computer patent rights was centered on a conflict between Honeywell Co. and Sperry Rand Corp. on the Electronic Numerical Integrator and Computer (ENIAC). Sperry Rand asserted its patent rights on the invention of ENIAC, which was the first general-purpose electronic digital computer. Judge Larson's verdict invalidated the Sperry Rand patent rights and put the invention of the computer into the public domain.

The question of who invented the digital computer had more than one answer. Professor Larry von Tersch of MSU was a student of the computer pioneer, John Atanasoff, who built a prototype digital computer at Iowa State University. In 1946, Sperry Rand's UNIVAC computer was conceived and designed by two electrical engineers, John Mauchly and Presper Eckert of the University of Pennsylvania, who filed and disclosed a patent on their all-electronic computer. Judge Larson deliberated on the Sperry Rand case, which had potentially substantial financial implications. Larson's verdict on the Sperry Rand versus Honeywell case resulted in Sperry Rand Corp. not collecting any royalties; neither did the original inventor, John Atanasoff. Indeed, it was "the legal battle that changed computing history.[24]

9

Moving to Fairfax, Virginia, and our Wedding

In the winter of 1964, I decided to leave Minneapolis for Washington so that I could be near Rahn. I looked for a job in the Washington area and applied for a position at Raytheon (Melpar Division) in Falls Church, Virginia. Bill Fuhr, the Melar Computer Laboratory Manager, invited me for an interview. He gave me a tour of the company's main building and the Computer Laboratory in Falls Church. The four-lane capital beltway had just opened, and cherry trees were in bloom. He offered me a position at the Computer Laboratory as a Senior Staff Engineer. That was how I found myself settling down for many years in the Washington area. It was a good move.

In April 1965, movers came to my Minneapolis apartment, and packed and loaded furniture, boxes of books, and belongings. I had accumulated more stuff since last year when I moved from Dayton to Minneapolis. After my belongings were loaded, I hopped in my Rambler and drove to Northern Virginia.

After two days of travel, I arrived in Falls Church. I rented a one-bedroom apartment on Persimmon Drive in Fairfax City. When I met Rahn that evening, she greeted me, "It is so nice to see you again," with tenderness in her voice. At that moment I realized that, for the last seven years, I had been wandering around places like Angola, East Lansing, Evanston, Dayton, and Minneapolis, where I had no one to greet me as Rahn did that evening. I felt as though I had come to the homeport after a long voyage. As Analects of Confucius says,

> "Indeed, at 30, with my study, I found out where I stood in the worldly affairs."

I found where I stood in my personal life and professional career.

A week later, I pinned her with my American Institute of Electrical Engineers (AIEE) badge, which was in the shape of a kite; it represents Benjamin Franklin's kite. This pinning was a symbolic step before becoming engaged. I was happy that Rahn understood the meaning of wearing my pin. (see photo 32)

Almost every evening after work, I would drive to the house where Rahn lived, the Young Women's Christian House (YWCH), located two blocks from the U.S. Capitol building.

Rahn and I shared a similar Korean heritage. Although we met for the first time in Minneapolis, we grew up in Seoul. Except for her illustrious father, she was just like a girl next door for me. She was then writing her dissertation to submit to Professor Charles McLaughlin of the University of Minnesota. In the evening, I helped her type the dissertation paper in the lobby of the YWCH under the watchful eyes of the house mother. The house mother was a little surprised when she saw me with a typewriter in the lobby of the all-female YWCH but was soon delighted to see love blossoming in her house. A few blocks away there was a café where we could grab a cup of coffee and a sandwich. I remember a small theater in Georgetown where Rahn and I saw the Rogers and Hammerstein musical *Oklahoma*; we held hands and enjoyed each other's company.

On Rahn's twenty-fifth birthday, we went to a show at Arena Stage, where I gave her a Mikimoto pearl necklace. She liked the pearl necklace as it was her birthstone. I grew up in a family in which I had no sister of the similar age group. I had seldom seen any public expressions of affection between my parents. I appreciated her feminine approach to life. She grew up in a family in which her mother treated her father with love, deference and honor. I became the recipient of the love and affection nurtured by the upbringing she had received in her family.

In the late spring, Rahn went to Minneapolis to complete her MA degree. During her time in Minneapolis, I spoke with her on a long distance call nearly every night according to telephone bills which she kept in her scrapbook. When she came back from Minneapolis, I asked her to marry me, and she accepted my marriage proposal. I slipped on her finger a diamond engagement ring with the word "love" engraved on it. She kissed me with tender love.

By telephone, we announced our engagement to Rahn's and my parents in Seoul. Rahn's parents sent their blessings to us, while my parents welcomed Rahn to the family.

Shortly after our engagement, Cecill Larson came to Washington and invited Rahn, me, her son Dick, and daughter Jane, to a Lebanese restaurant, the Golden Parrot, which was at the corner of Connecticut Avenue and R Street, NW. Cecill did not miss the engagement ring and the AIEE pin Rahn was wearing, and she asked:

"Rahn, is the ring you are wearing an engagement ring?"

"Yes, John gave it to me three weeks ago."

"It is beautiful."

"Thank you."

"John, what do you do for a living?

"Where did you go to school?

"Where are your parents?

"How long have you known Rahn?"

"Mrs. Larson, hold the phone. I will answer all of your questions.

"I am an electrical engineer at Raytheon (Melpar).

"I went to Michigan State University.

"My parents live in Seoul.

"I met Rahn ten months ago at my cousin's wedding."

"Oh, Mom, please stop your inquisition and let's eat."

Dick Larson interrupted and said,

"John, Congratulations."

Our Wedding

In September 1965, we got married at Fairfax Presbyterian Church; the ceremony was officiated by Pastor Henry Bauman. Dr. Chan-mo Park was my best man, and the matron of honor was Rahn's sister, Dr. Tong-he Koh. Rahn walked down the aisle with her brother, Dr. Bill Chu. After the ceremony, we had a wedding dinner at Yenching Restaurant in Washington (see photos 33, 34, and 35). Seven thousand miles away in Seoul, the Kim and the Chu families held a small family wedding party, celebrating the marriage, hosted by the Rahn's parents at the Diplomat's Club. (see photo 36) Rahn and I honeymooned in Colonial Williamsburg and made a circular tour around the shores of the Chesapeake Bay. (see photo 37)

Looking back on our lives together for over a half-century, I can say that Rahn was my conscience and provided me moral standards and kept me on an even keel on occasional changes of life I took. She came from a family which tacitly assumed Christian ethics. Her grandfather, Gong-sam Chu, was one of the earliest Christian ministers in Korea. She was naturally a caring person. Rahn was the third daughter and the sixth child out of eight siblings of the Chu family. As such, Rahn had learned to survive and thrive in a large family with three sisters and four brothers. She had a good head on her shoulders, and was the class president of her high school and later top drawer academically in her college. I was a lucky man to have her as my life's companion, and to provide peace and harmony in our home.

Putting Down Our Roots

So Rahn and I started our family and put down our roots in Northern Virginia. In 1967, we bought our first house in the Greenbriar subdivision in Fairfax; it was a two-story, newly constructed, four-bedroom house. We lived there until 1978. The price of the house was $33,000, and we took out a mortgage amount of $30,000 to purchase it. It was a good investment as we sold it for $89,000, thanks to the real estate boom in Northern Virginia.

I have lived in the Washington area for over half a century, and I like the area. I have traveled to many cities around the world, but Washington is

indeed a world-class city. For several years, I had my Northrop Grumman (TRW) office at a premier location in the city, two blocks from the Washington National Mall and three blocks from the Capitol. At lunchtime, I often walked to the National Gallery of Art. The mall has pedestrian-friendly walkways criss-crossing between a half-dozen museums. I liked the National Gallery of Art's special exhibitions, which came from all over the world.

Washington is in the Potomac basin, which makes the city hot and humid in the summer, but I like the Washington weather because it has four distinct seasons. The Washington winter is mild, and in the spring we enjoy cherry blossoms around the Tidal Basin. The autumn offers fall colors along the Skyline Drive in Shenandoah National Park, which is an hour's drive from the city. In 1962, I visited Washington for the first time, which was a sleepy southern town. Its broad boulevards and diagonal streets laid out by Pierre L'Enfant were lined with trees in leafy neighborhoods. Whenever I approached Reagan National Airport or Dulles International Airport, flying low over the treetops, I saw many green trees spotting school playgrounds and open meadows.

Another view of Washington that I appreciate is on the water, downstream from the confluence of the Potomac and the Anacostia Rivers. On my 19-foot Winner boat, I used to approach Haines Point, from where I could see the handsome-looking red brick National Defense University building in Fort McNair and the Jefferson Memorial on the small point just above the water-line. I could see the gray-white buildings of the mighty federal government, some of which were built with marble and others with sandstone, glaring in the sun. From time to time, I took my boat upstream, and I passed the Key Bridge and the Three Sisters Islands in the Potomac River. I approached the Little Falls near Fletcher's Boat House and saw both banks of the Potomac River Palisades covered with trees. I could hear the sound of cars passing by on the George Washington Parkway, but I often had illusions that I might be in the wilderness.

MY FATHER-IN-LAW YO-HAN CHU

My father-in-law, Yo-han Chu (1900-1979), was born in Pyongyang. He was a poet, a chemist by education, a journalist, a statesman, and a politician.[25.] Indeed, he was a man for all seasons. In 1912, the Korean Presbyterian Synod in Pyongyang sent his father, Rev. Gong-sam Chu to a Korean Christian church mission in Tokyo. Yo-han Chu accompanied his father to Tokyo.

In 1919, Korean poets and writers in Tokyo published the first Korean literary magazine called *Creation*, in which Yo-han Chu published his celebrated poem, *The Firework*. He also published *The Sound of Rain* in the literary magazine *Ruins* published in Tokyo. *The Sound of Rain* was the first of two modern freestyle poems ever written in Korean.[26.] These poems are in most of the high school textbooks in South Korea today.

He participated in the March First (1919) Independence Movement, for which Japanese police tried to arrest him for the subversive activities. He decided to leave Tokyo and traveled on the Nippon Yusen liner from Nagasaki to Shanghai.[27] Shanghai was then the hotbed of Korean revolutionaries. A year later, he entered Hujiang College (now the University of Shanghai for Science and Technology), where he majored in chemistry. He graduated from Hujiang College in 1925 and returned to Seoul. He later became the Editor-in-Chief of Dong-a Ilbo in Seoul. After the independence of South Korea, he was elected to the National Assembly. He served as the Minister of Commerce and Industry in the Chang Myeon government.

For many years, Yo-han Chu had an interest in building a Korean (Hangul) typewriter. In 1948, Byeong-wu Kong, an ophthalmologist, and Yo-han Chu collaborated on inventing a Korean typewriter. Kong filed a patent disclosure of a Korean typewriter with the U.S. Patent Office.[28.] Their approach was to use an existing typewriter manufactured by the Underwood Typewriter Co., which was then largest typewriter manufacturer in America. They modified the keys by replacing English characters with Korean Hangul consonants and vowels.

The Hangul character is a two-by-two matrix construction.[29.] Yo-han Chu continued research on Hangul mechanical typewriters.[30.] His research led to a prototype of the three-stroke keyboard Korean typewriter. This model was popular for its speed of typing. The South Korean government developed the second-generation standard Korean typewriter, which became the forerunner

of modern standard two-stroke Korean computer keyboards. The Kong Byung-woo Korean typewriters were reliable since the only part modified was keys from the proven Underwood typewriter.[31]

Much later, in 1973, Dr. Heon-seo Park of Northrop Grumman (TRW) developed the Hangul computer input device. This device was named the Micro Hangul Processor, and it typed Korean Hangul characters, which were more pleasing to the eye than those of the Kong Hangul typewriter. For example, the character 가 was produced by inserting ㄱ ㅏ ㄱ serially in single-line construction. The Micro Hangul Processor automatically arranges two consonants and one vowel to produce a balanced character 각. The newly developed Micro Hangul processor keyboards could readily interface with the output of computers or teletypewriters.

I received the following letter from my father-in-law in which he commented on the Micro Hangul Processor, which was developed by Dr. Heon-seo Park, a fellow employee at TRW.

KOREAN SHIPPING CORPORATION

Seoul

March 12, 1973

Dear John,

Please find enclosed a newspaper clipping about a "Micro-minicomputer for Typing Korean Alphabet." According to the article, Mr. Heon-seo Park of TRW invented the Korean electronic typewriter. I have been watching very closely for the development of a Hangul typewriter using electronic circuits, which will print the Korean character only with the elementary alphabets, which numbers 28 letters only. Recently, in Korea, they have developed an electronic typewriter, specifically for the "Teletypewriter" machine.

The problem with such a scheme is that the total number of "strokes" required to form a word increase up to some 40%, compared to a similar machine having 40 plus "keys."

That is, if you use 40 keys and the strokes number 100, the 28-key typewriter requires 140 strokes. Consequently, efficiency of the device is reduced by 40%. These additional strokes mean a considerable loss of efficiency.

The problem arises because, in the case of 받침 (for instance if you want to print 김, the consonants ㄱ and ㅁ are entirely different forms and position), you have to use two strokes instead of one stroke. In 1936, Professor Ki-joo Song had invented a device to form a 모아쓰기 글자 by single strokes; that is, 김 may be formed by only three strokes instead of 4. This process accumulates and holds the input until the next combination is started, which releases the output section.

(For instance, to print 한국, the input for ㅎ ㅏ ㄴ is held until ㄱ of 국 is touched. Then the input will see that there is no combination of ㄴ and ㄱ in 한글 writing, and ㅎ ㅏ ㄴ is released to the output). Could you obtain a brief summary of Mr. Hyeon-seo Park's invention and send it to me?

We are all well. I am sending my love to Janet, William, and Rahn.

Dad

(p.s.) What I am interested in is an electronic typewriter that prints 한 in 3 strokes, not in 4 strokes.

Another innovation of Yo-han Chu's was his experiment with writing the Korean language, Hangul, in a linear spelling as English and European languages were written. Photograph 41 is a facsimile of his handwriting in Korean, written with a calligraphy brush in a linear spelling. He attempted to rearrange characters. His linear writing proposal did not succeed, although it appeared to be a good idea at the time.

Mother's Day Hymnal

In the Korean Protestant hymnal, there is a song which we sing every Mother's Day, titled *Mother's Love*[32]. My father-in-law, Yo-han Chu, wrote the lyrics in Korean, which were translated by John Thomas Underwood, who was a member of a third-generation American missionary family.

Precious Love, the Love of Mother[33]

Precious love, the love of mother,
Broad and deep beyond all praise!
Precious love, it stirs my spirit.
Gives me gladness all my days.
Mother pray'd when I was weeping,
Made my sorrows all her own;
And when I was glad and smiling,
Sang her praises at the Throne.

Precious Book, mother's Bible,
Which she read me morn and night?
Still, I see her read, and pausing,
Call some treasure to my sight:
"Whosoever but believeth
Shall receive eternal life."
Precious words of her reciting,
Still my strength in mortal strife!

When I lie alone and troubled,
Restless with exhausting fears,
Mother's voice, in hymns she sang me,
Echoes living in my ears;
"From the rock flow springs of water;
In the desert flowers grow,"
"Those who walk the way with Jesus
Need fear nothing here below."

Mother's life was sweet and humble,
Strong and firm in doing right
I can make my life worth living
With her ever in my sight.
Mother, in a world of tempests,
Fought the good fight all her days,
Soon, by streams of living water,
I shall live with her always.

Rahn as a VOA Announcer

After our wedding, Rahn continued to work at the Voice of America (VOA). She was a scriptwriter and an announcer. She translated English news pieces into Korean, interviewed visiting guests, and broadcasted live the "Current Affairs" program and the "U.S. Campus" series.

After Rahn graduated from the University of Minnesota, she entered the American University-School of International Service, where she pursued her doctorate program. Janet was born in 1967. I took care of Janet while Rahn attended evening classes. After William and Doug were born, her priority shifted from attending American University to raising the family. When our children grew up, she enrolled at George Mason University while she was working in the Fairfax County government. Rahn received her Bachelor's degree in Business Administration in 1992 from George Mason University. She was an evening class student, a county government employee, and mother of three children and the wife of an engineer. Rahn did well in all her roles. At Fairfax County Government, her first position was in the Equipment Management and Transportation Agency; her next position was in the Park Authority; and her third position was in the Public Works Department, where she became a financial analyst for several large capital projects. In April 1995, Rahn was commended by the county for her outstanding performance for closing an EPA grant, which saved the county $1.7 million. (see photo 115)

10

Raytheon (Melpar) Division in Falls Church, Virginia

In 1965, I started my job at Melpar as a Senior Staff Engineer in the Computer Laboratory, reporting to Bill Fuhr. The laboratory performed Department of Defense contract projects on sonar and signal intelligence (SIGINT).

> "What is SIGINT?
> "Military units send and receive electronic signals.
> "The enemy units gather electronic intelligence."
> "These collection activities and analyses of them are SIGINT. Some sensitive messages are encrypted, and enemy units perform analysis of the encrypted signal."
> "SIGINT performs traffic analysis, by performing statistical analysis on 'who talks to whom' and 'how often.'
> "For example, a sudden increase in the overall volume of messages could indicate an impending commencement of military operations."

In the 1950s, Melpar claimed to be one of the largest defense electronics companies in Washington and attracted a wide variety of technical people in many STEM disciplines. I once read a local newspaper article featuring the company headlined,

> "Melpar to Interview Engineers, Physicists, and Mathematicians.
> "Representative of South's Largest Electronic R&D Firm on Campus Soon."

The government awarded contracts to the company to solve scientific, military, and technological problems, and it became one of the firms that came to be called "beltway bandits."

"What is a "beltway bandit?

"It used to be a semi-derogatory name for a company located near, and around the Capital Beltway, which performs consulting services, and technical and financial support works to various agencies of the federal government.

"The word 'beltway bandit' was not in anyone's lexicon yet."

In 1965, Falls Church was a quiet suburb on the western edge of Washington. Unlike other large American metropolitan areas, Washington lacked preeminent science and technology universities. During this period, the company filled this void by playing the role of leading technical societies, organizing symposia, and hosting high-level professional meetings with top government officials.

The Computer Laboratory used an SDS 910 to perform much of the analysis using machine programming language and FORTRAN. Punch cards were used for program input. I remember carrying metal boxes of these punch cards, which contained algorithms.

Sonar Projects

In 1969, Melpar performed several sonar projects for the Navy Bureau of Ships (BuShips), which were managed by Ken Fawcette. Fawcette and I met with Mr. Pat Pitt of BuShips at the Main Navy and Munitions Buildings. BuShips was looking for a way to archive the voluminous acoustic intelligence data, which was collected on magnetic tapes by the AN/SQS-23 sonar system[34]

"What is a sonar system?"

"Dolphins use sound to communicate with each other and to detect underwater objects of interest like fish.

"Navy submarines likewise use a sonar device to detect and track underwater objects and vessels.

Let us review a brief history of sonar technology as of 1966.

"After the World War II, the U.S. Navy continued to use older sonar equipment like AN/SQS-4."

"The detection range of the AN/SQS-4 sonar equipment was three nautical miles, and sonar acoustic signals were thought to travel only in a straight line, known as the Direct Path (DP).

"The AN/SQS-23 sonar equipment was built to deliver higher output power, twice the power of AN/SQS-4."

"The AN/SQS-23 sonar device was a low-frequency sonar, operating at a frequency of 5 kHz."

"AN/SQS-23 was the state-of-the-art active sonar system deployed in 1965[35]

"Submarines routinely collected acoustic intelligence data of various classes of friendly and adversary submarines on a magnetic tape recorder."

Volumes of recorded magnetic tapes could fill the already crowded submarine space. BuShips wanted to know if we could reduce the volume.

Then, acoustic researchers developed a more sophisticated method to extend the detection range. They found out that one can increase the detection range of sonar signals by using the Bottom Bounce (BB) and the convergence zone (CZ) propagation paths.

"What are BB and CZ propagation paths?"

"O.K. Sonar signals would travel in a straight line if the temperature of the sea water were constant at all depths.

"But, the temperature of the ocean tends to be cooler in the deeper ocean and warmer in the shallow ocean.

"Maurice Ewing of the Woods Hole Oceanographic Institution, Massachusetts, discovered that sound signals do not

travel straight but bend, with the varying water temperature.

"After traveling on a curved trajectory, the sound signals will hit the bottom of the ocean floor and will bounce upward.

"Such a propagation became known as the BB propagation path, which could extend the detection range.

"There is another acoustic path, known as the CZ path in the deep sound channel.

"The AN/SQS-23 active sonar device could extend the detection range to 30 nautical miles on the CZ path, although the signal strength is attenuated."

Later, I worked on the SOund SUrveillance System (SOSUS) in Northrop Grumman (TRW). Using the SOSUS system, the U.S. Navy detected Soviet submarines in the Pacific and Atlantic Oceans, and the Mediterranean Sea by the sound traveling on the acoustic CZ path.

Returning to the question asked by BuShips on recording sonar signals, the existing recorder-reproducer set in the 1970s was a two-track device with reel-to-reel magnetic tapes, like the Ampex 631. Ken Fawcette discussed a recording device using frequency modulation (FM) pulse compression. He had an experience of working on the FM pulse compression method employed in a radar SIGINT project. He offered this technique as a solution to the problem. These discussions with BuShips helped me to understand the problems encountered by the operational fleet. This meeting was also my first exposure to marketing meetings with the Navy engineers.

My Sonar System Study

At the beginning of my participation in the sonar signal processing project, I struggled with my assignment, because I only had basic knowledge of sonar in my formal education. The pace of science and technology advanced so fast that I had to learn new subjects continuously. I considered myself a technologist with adequate training in mathematics, physics, and electrical engineering. With this basic science background, I had learned and tackled new subjects as they came along my way. Four years of electrical engineering education could only cover

so much. Preparing for many fields in real-world jobs would be impossible. My advice to beginner technologists who want to pursue electrical engineering and physics is to build a strong basic science background in the STEM discipline.

Ken Fawcette was my mentor for the sonar project. The first time I reported to Ken to work on the sonar project, he asked me several questions about acoustics and signal processing. He then suggested that I read and study two books on sonar: Robert Urick's *Principles of Underwater Sound for Engineer*[36] and Tolstoy and Clay's *Ocean Acoustic*[37] He told me that I had a good grasp of the sonar detection and classification theory, but I needed more practical knowledge of underwater acoustics.

ROME AIR DEVELOPMENT CENTER (RADC) HF COMMUNICATION CHANNEL SIMULATOR

The federal government publishes its contract opportunities in a *Commerce Business Daily (CBD)* (later replaced by *FedBizOpps*[38] which was the official gazette for posting all federal procurement opportunities with a value of $25,000 or more. The RADC Communications Division announced in the Research and Development Sources Sought a forthcoming contract for developing a *12-KHz Bandwidth HF communication channel simulator.* Melpar management sent three engineers, Hal Caldine, Eugene Kaiser, and I, to the Communication Division of RADC, Griffiss Air Force Base, New York, to gather market intelligence. We met with H. Crowley, Captain Richard Sandefur, and Captain Richard Northrop.

RADC was looking for a company that could build an HF communication channel simulator, with which they would evaluate the performance of HF radios. This HF simulator would be a device capable of simulating and evaluating digital communications networks by using both the wireline and HF links and had to interact with HF signals as if simulated signals were propagated through the real ionosphere. The HF simulator had to behave like the signal being transmitted via HF media as specified in the procurement document[39] and would become part of a Digital Communications System Evaluator (DICOSE) system.[40]

We reported our findings to Milton Fivel, the Manager of Applied Elec-

tronics Center, about the opportunity to bid on a new project. Why had the company sent us to RADC? The company continuously sought research and development procurement opportunities. Whether the company would bid on this HF Simulation procurement or not was up to the profit center[41] manager. In the competitive defense industry, if a prospective bidder found the contracting opportunity in a *CBD/FedBizOpps* for the first time on the day of the announcement, it would be too late for putting together a winning proposal.

"Then, tell me how Milt Fivel made the bid decision?

"He made it based on the result of the win-loss analysis."

"Wait, you lost me.

"What is the win-loss analysis?

"O.K. For each profit center, the company allocated an annual budget for bids and proposals (B&P) effort.

"The decision maker, in this case, Milt Fivel, would ask the technical manager a series of questions.

"For example, what would be the potential contract value?

"The technical manager may not know the contract value if he had not done a prior market analysis.

"The Defense Department and the Congress publish the RDT&E Budget Item Justification (R2 Exhibit) for all DoD programs. R2 described the funding profiles by fiscal years for all programs."

"But, R2 does not spell out the detailed budgetary data for each project within the program element in the R2 Exhibit.

"He just had to tell the profit center manager his best estimate. Let us assume that the contract value was $250,000.

"The next question would usually be the probability of winning the competition.

"Now that would be a tough one.

"The probability was dependent on many factors such as the number of competitors, and the strength of one's technical and cost proposals.

"Often he as the bidder may not have the full knowledge about these factors. Without the concrete knowledge of the competition, he would have to guess the probability."

"Let's assume that the probability would be 10%. The expected value of the proposal would be $25,000.

"From the profit center manager's point of view, if he spends $25,000 of the B&P fund, he breaks even for this business venture.

"Also, he was not the only one who wanted to use the profit center manager's B&P fund. Milt Fivel usually had in his inbox several requests from other prospective bidders besides him.

Let me tell you another theory related business strategy, which Igor Ansoff of Carnegie Melon University developed in 1957. He created a matrix involving strategy and products, which was published in an article in the Harvard Business Review.[42] He built a model of the four ways one's business could grow.

"The first was selling existing products in the existing market.

"The second was selling existing products in the new market.

"The third was selling new products in the current market.

"The fourth was selling new products in the new market.

"The first was known as market penetration, which would have the least risk.

"The second was market development, which would have moderate risk. These were not related to technology but concerned with the market penetration or market development.

"The third situation was product development, which would have involved technology and would have a higher risk than the first two.

"Finally, selling a new product in a new market was diversification, and it exposed the company to the highest risk."

"That was how a bid decision was made."

Returning to the bid decision of the RADC procurement on the development of an HF communication channel simulator, this project fell into the fourth case in the matrix selling a new product in a new market. Due to the high risk, the profit center manager decided not to bid the procurement. The three of us, marketing team members, were disappointed as we were ready to

shoot anything that moved to work on a project. But Milt Fivel and Bill Fuhr made the right decision on this particular marketing effort. Was it a waste of time? I think not as we learned the importance of HF communication channels in the emerging digital signal transmission system.

On-the-Job-Training (OJT) on Business Management

As a senior staff engineer, I not only dealt with technology but also assisted the laboratory manager with business management. Our company could not win a contract by simply proposing a good technical approach. The cost proposal often determined a contract award. Often the labor cost was one of the determining factors in the cost proposal. What was the cost part of a proposal? There were three factors: the labor cost, the overhead rates, and the profit fee. For example, the labor categories in a research and development proposal could be as follows:

Labor - Exempt Category:

Code	Positions
01	Department Manager, Laboratory Manager, Head of Technical Staff
11	Professional Engineer, Principal Engineer, Branch Chief
21	Senior Engineer, Senior Mathematician
31	Senior Design Engineer
41	Senior Engineering Assistant

Labor - Non-exempt Category:

Code	Positions
51	Junior Electrical Engineer
61	Senior Technician
71	Technician
81	Junior Technician

Also, the company expected the government to reimburse the costs incurred in doing business in two categories, the overhead and general and the administrative (G&A) costs.

Profit Centers	Overhead Rate	G&A Rate
Engineering Division	128 %	25%
Manufacturing Division	150 %	25%
Research Division	115 %	25%

As shown in the table above, the manufacturing division overhead rate is higher than that of the engineering or research divisions. The overhead is the cost incurred by the buildings, facilities, capital equipment, and operations such as proposal preparation, and in-house research and development efforts. The G&A rate usually was about 25%. Also, there were other direct charges such as travel expenses, and the profit fee for the stockholders, which could be typically 8%.

For example, let's say the Computer Laboratory planned to spend B&P funds of $64,000 from the total overhead budgets of $130,000. Each year the company allocated the annual overhead budgets for the operating unit, and following was an example of discretionary funds:

Items	Amount
Bids and Proposal	$64,000
IR&D	$50,000
Misc	$8,000
Travel	$6,000
Consulting fees	$6,000
Total	$130,000

By the way, the non-exempt category was defined by the Fair Labor Standards Act as particular categories of employees, such as technicians and clerical workers, who got paid by the hour, not by the annual salary. The exempt category included professional employees in engineering and management, who were paid by the annual salary. The nonexempt category employees receive overtime pay. Thus, an employer is obligated to pay them 1.5 times their regu-

lar pay for hours worked over 40 hours per week.

Bill Fuhr, my laboratory manager, asked me to work with the business staff member, Ed Balchunas, who prepared cost proposals.

"O.K. Ed, let's get started with the cost proposal."

"From the technical manager, we received the man-hours required by technical personnel, classified by the labor categories of professional staff.

"He gave us following man-loading and salary data: laboratory manager (5% of his time at his salary of $35,000), senior design engineer (60% at $22,000), and technician (70% at $19,500).

"Then, the direct labor cost of the proposed project is $28,600."

"Yes, I agree. Next, the overhead burden rate is 128%, and the overhead cost is $36,608."

"The sum of the direct labor and overhead is $65,208."

"Very well, John, but now we have to add G&A burden at the rate of 25%."

"The G&A cost is $16,103.

"The sum of burdened labor and G&A cost is $81,510."

"John, wait a minute, we must not forget the profit fee for the company's stockholders. "Bill Fuhr told us to use the profit fee of 8%. Or the fee is $6,520.80.

"Also, the technical manager estimated $950 for travel, which is a direct cost.

"The total price of the proposal becomes $88,980.80."

"O.K. we have the price for this proposal."

I became the Program Officer in ONR with the yearly budget of $10 million in my program. To carry on my job, the DoD required me to receive formal training in business management. After one year of off-class and in-class lectures on defense acquisition, I received my Certificate of Defense Acquisition Level III, as required for senior grade employees. My share of OJTs on the budgetary and financial matters in Raytheon (Melpar), Northrop Grumman (TRW), and ONR helped me to understand the defense acquisition process.

DR. THOMAS F. CURRY

Tom Curry (1924-2004) came to Raytheon (Melpar) from Syracuse University Research Corporation (SURC), where he was the founding director. He became the Chief Engineer of the Applied Electronics Department in Melpar. The primary business of the department was sonar, communication equipment, and electronic warfare (EW). Bill Fuhr gave him a briefing to review the laboratory business. Fuhr asked me to prepare a presentation on the ongoing program development efforts, which covered sonar signal processing and military radio improvement. Fuhr and I recommended that the company invest more IR&D funds in these areas. One year later, I became Tom Curry's Technical Assistant and continued to pursue these technologies in the Applied Electronics Department.

One day Tom was mowing the lawn in his home, and he injured his toe. As he used the wheelchair temporarily, I also became his "wheelchair assistant" as well. During his recovery, Tom Curry was feeling "fair to middlin" most of the time, but "who don't," he would say.

One summer evening, we invited Tom Curry and his wife Mary for an informal dinner at our apartment. Tom and Mary rang our apartment doorbell, and to my surprise, he came to dinner, wearing a tuxedo and Mary wearing a flowing evening dress. I did not know where Tom got the idea that the party was a black-tie event. I said nothing about the dress code. That was my mistake. Tom always sported a chin goatee and claimed that he was one of the "original hippies" who sported long hair and beards as flower children and demonstrated against the Viet Nam War. Of course, Tom was a proper gentleman of the old guard from Georgia.

Tom Curry departed Melpar without any prior warning. He became a corporate officer of Ling-Temco-Vought (LTV) Company's Electro-Systems (E-Systems) Division. Two months after he had left the company, Melpar was acquired by LTV E-System, and Tom Curry returned as the Vice-President of the Melpar Division. In 1980, President Ronald Reagan appointed him as the Deputy Assistant Secretary of the Navy for Command, Control, and Communication.[43]

Dr. Eugene Kaiser

In my life, I could count my real friends on the fingers of one hand. Gene Kaiser has been one of those friends. I first met him at Melpar when he came from the University of Pennsylvania, where he was working on his doctoral program at the Moore School of Electrical Engineering. He prepared his dissertation on an advanced coding theory. Later I got to know him and his family well. He was a caring person as he took care of his handicapped wife Rita for many years.

Gene Kaiser left the company and went to the Defense Information Systems Agency (DISA), where he managed the National Military Command System (NMCS) program including the renovation of NMCC at the Pentagon. One day he and I finished a meeting at an office of the Pentagon and headed for the visitor parking lot. After he surveyed the area, he first found a staircase, which led us to the ground floor, and passed two swinging doors and found the parking lot where we parked our cars. I was impressed. He supervised the renovation of that particular section of the Pentagon. That section of the Pentagon was destroyed during the 9-11 terrorist attack. He then managed the renovation of that section all over again.

Besides being an excellent engineer, he also was an accomplished flutist and played flute semi-professionally with the Fairfax Symphony Orchestra. He even played the flute at our daughter Janet's wedding. In the 2010s, he and I were active in the Pentagon Military Auxiliary Radio Station for Contingency Communications.

Ringling Brothers and Barnum and Bailey Circus, and the Melpar Facility

Melpar moved its computer facility from Bailey's Crossroads to its main building in Falls Church. The Bailey's Crossroads facility was a sprawling industrial high-bay facility for manufacturing, and we welcomed the move to the main building for research and offices.

Bailey's Crossroads is at the intersection of Old Leesburg Pike and Columbia Pike, which had the interesting history. The historical marker described the site as the winter home of the Ringling Brothers and Barnum and Bailey Circus. Next to our computer laboratory, there were an outdoor drive-in movie, the Sunset Drive-in Theater, and the old Washington-Virginia Airport (WVA), which served general aviation and a flight school. The drive-in movie theater had a huge 45x65-foot-high screen, located near an approach for the airport runway. One time, a small plane almost ran into the screen during nighttime landing. The runway was also very close to Leesburg Pike. Often an aircraft approaching for landing passed close to the top of moving cars. The large bright screen of the drive-in theater and its nearness to the runway made exciting nighttime approaches.

As the city grew and developers built high-rise apartments and condominiums and commercial shopping centers closer to the airport, it made no sense to keep operating the airport. It was closed and demolished. The Skyline high-rise buildings now occupy much of the old airport site.

11

Personal Miscellany I

When Rahn completed the graduate school at the University of Minnesota, we drove to Minneapolis to attend her commencement. Along the way, we picked up Bill Chu and his family, In-soo, Joan, and Jean, who lived in Columbus, Ohio. Our destination was Faribault, Minnesota, about 30 miles south of the Twin Cities, where my sister-in-law, Dr. Tong-he Koh and her husband, Dr. Soon-deok Koh, lived.

During Rahn's commencement ceremony, the security was very tight because Vice-President Herbert Humphrey was the commencement speaker at the Northrop Memorial Auditorium. It was the time of frequent student demonstrations against the Viet Nam War. My brother-in-law, Soon-deok, and I were standing near the steps of the auditorium; we were sporting our Panama hats. A police officer approached and asked us to show him our press passes as he mistook us for members of the foreign press corps. When he discovered our identity, the policeman quickly escorted us behind the yellow police lines.

On the way back to Washington after the commencement ceremony, as we were driving to Chicago, Rahn wanted to eat sushi. She was expecting and craved for sushi. I knew there were Japanese sushi places on North Clark Street in downtown Chicago. We drove into downtown Chicago and bought sushi and drove to Lincoln Park on the shore of Lake Michigan for picnic lunch. When we got there around noon, the sky was overcast, and soon it started to drizzle. By the time I placed sushi on a picnic table, she had lost her appetite. A police officer patrolling his beat was curious about us, sitting in the rain eating sushi. We continued our travels on the Skyway Expressway. In the afternoon Rahn wanted to eat Chinese dumplings. Again, we made another detour, this

time into downtown South Bend, Indiana, where I found a Chinese restaurant. Janet was born in February the next year; she weighed nine pounds and six ounces. I wonder if dumplings contributed to her healthy weight.

JA-HEON LEE, MY CLASSMATE

Ja-heon Lee was my KHS high school classmate and lived in the same neighborhood in Seoul in 1948. He became a reporter for *The Seoul Daily Newspaper* after graduating from SNU, entered into South Korean politics, and was elected to the National Assembly. He became Minister of Post and Telecommunications in the Chun Du-hwan Government.

When Ja-heon was a reporter at *The Seoul Daily Newspaper*, he asked me to contribute an article to the newspaper. I wrote a short article titled "A Letter from an Overseas Korean Scientist."

Tremendous Growth of the Electronics Industry
in the United States[44]

By John Kim, Senior Staff Engineer, the Computer
Laboratory, Melpar, Inc., Falls Church, VA.
(Translated by John Kim).

On March 28, 1967, The Seoul Daily Newspaper – Harbingers of spring are here again along the Potomac River. The spring haze rises on the water surface, and new buds are sprouting on old branches, covering them with fresh green color. It has been over a decade since I left the homeland, South Korea. I still miss the aroma of the earth especially in the springtime along the banks of the Han River. Washington has a sizeable Korean community, which includes many immigrants, students, and diplomats. We share news from homeland at gatherings of Koreans, sometimes through churches, and at gatherings on Korean national holidays. I have been working in the American electronics and computer industry for the

last six years. There has been tremendous growth in the computer industry since the 1960's. The computer industry has grown with the annual output of one and a half billion dollars. There are some thirty-five computer manufacturers such as IBM, UNIVAC, Honeywell, Control Data Corporation, GE, and Philco. Universities, governments, the military, and industries use electronic computers for various applications. Their applications were for processing a significant amount of information and data. I worked on several projects related to the defense applications such as the automatic control of weapons, command, and control of military systems, and ballistic missiles. In April 1967, I presented my recent work on "Degradation Analysis of Digital Signal Transmission," at the 1967 Spring Joint Computer Conference of the American Federation of Information Processing Societies (AFIPS), in Atlantic City, New Jersey.

I quote this article not because it is news today, but because it shows how much the electronics industry has grown in 50 years. When I wrote this newspaper article, the computer was just about to touch some parts of our lives. Now, it is at the center of almost everything we do. The data transfer rate has grown from 32 kilobits per second (in 1967) using wirelines to 400 gigabits per second (in 2017) using fiber optic cables. The speed of transmission increased 12.5 million times. The annual revenue from computer hardware sales has grown from $1.5 billion (in 1967) to $400 billion (in 2017), that is, an increase of 266 times. A question I would ask here is:

"What would future technology look like in the next year, in five years, or in ten years from now?

"But I will pass on making such forecasts because I simply do not know, and it is a foolish business to look into crystal ball about the progress.

"Thomas Watson, President of IBM, once allegedly had said, "I think there is a world market for maybe five computers.[45]

My Father-in-law's Visit

My father-in-law visited our home on his way to Seoul from Athens, Greece. He was the head of the South Korean delegation to the United Nations Conference on Trade and Development (UNCTAD)[46] held in Athens (see photo 39). In 1962, he was the Minister of Commerce and Industry in the Chang Myeon government of the Second South Korean Republic. He was one of the architects of building South Korean industry and the trade-based economy after the Korean War. He developed the policies for building primary industry as well as promoting the international trade when he was the Chairman of the Policy Committee of the Chang Myeon government. He was twice elected to the National Assembly from the central district in Seoul. After the military coup-d'etat of Park Chung-hee had toppled the Chang Myeon government, the military junta prohibited him from playing any role in South Korean politics. However, in the mid-1960s, the South Korean government sought his counsel on economic policy, and he was appointed as a member of the Science and Technology Review Board.

During his stay at our home, we gave a party in his honor. My father-in-law met with several old friends, including one guest, Cheol-seung Lee, who was a one-time rising politician. When I invited him to dinner, Cheol-seung Lee wished to avoid any publicity on meeting my father-in-law and asked me to pick him up, not at his house, but at a nearby restaurant in the Kalorama area in Washington. These two politicians met at our home. They had a long conversation as it had been their first meeting since the 1961 coup d'état. I listened to their conversation:

> "I regret my failure to stop Park's military coup.
> "Seok-ho Hyun (Minister of National Defense in the Chang Myeon government) and I heard about unusual activities of Major General Park Chung-hi and his cohort a few weeks before the coup d'état.
> "We asked Park to meet us at my office.
> "We misjudged and failed to assess the situation, and it was the gravest mistake of my life.
> "I could have arrested Park for treason.

"The arrest surely could have aborted the coup d'état."

After the military takeover in 1961, we saw South Korea go through vicious cycles of military-led governments for three decades, led by Park Chung-hi, Chun Du-hwan, and Roh Tae-woo. Since 1993, we have seen South Korea peacefully elect presidents every five years. I salute these early statesmen like Chang Myeon, Yo-han Chu, Young-sam Kim, and Dae-joong Kim, who laid the foundation of democracy.

MY BROTHER MOON-KYU

After my brother, Moon-kyu, received his B.A degree in economics from Seoul National University, he came to America for graduate studies. In the fall of 1969, he started his graduate studies at the University of Illinois. After he finished his first year of graduate school, he came to stay with us during for the summer recess. My elder son William was born when Moon-kyu arrived. I asked my brother to babysit two-year-old Janet at the house while I visited Rahn at the Fairfax Hospital maternity ward. When I came home from the hospital and knocked on the door, no one answered. Moon-kyu was sound asleep after his long bus ride from Champaign, Illinois. I finally climbed the wall and knocked on the window of his room. He woke up and opened the curtain to see my angry face as I waved my fist and yelled at him to open the door.

After four years of graduate study, Moon-kyu received his doctorate from UI. His doctoral dissertation was "A Two-Stage Financing Approach to Long-Range Financial Planning under Uncertainty: A Dynamic Programming Model.[47] When he was an undergraduate at SNU, I had suggested to him to study mathematics and statistics. I had a friend who majored in economics at MSU and had been doing research on a new branch of economics using mathematics and statistics. What is dynamic programming? It was a branch of operations research which had been widely used in control theory when Richard Bellman[48] of the Rand Corporation used the theory for missile control. After Moon-kyu had received his doctorate, he was appointed Professor of Finance at the Whitman School of Management, Syracuse University, and later became the head of the Finance Department. He had a distinguished career until he retired in

2007. He published over one hundred research articles and papers on finance and investment. Besides his teaching and research activities, he also served as the member of the Doctoral Boards, Promotion and Tenure Committee, Consultancies with Governments and Industry. (see photo 113)

MY BROTHER DONG-KYU

Following Moon-kyu, my next younger brother Dong-kyu came to America for graduate studies. He had graduated from Hanyang University-School of Architecture; he enrolled at the School of Architecture, Ohio State University in the fall term of 1971. The next year, he became an employee at Thomas, Mall, and Klose (TMK) Associates, an architectural firm in Dayton, Ohio. Al Klose, a friend of mine, was a partner of the architectural firm. After one year at TMK, Dong-kyu returned to Columbus and completed his master's degree in architecture in 1974. He then started an architectural firm, D.D. Kim Associates in Washington, which became a very successful business. He designed the East Falls Church Metro Station and several churches in Montgomery County, Maryland. I liked one of his churches, the Ichthus Korean Mission Church.

He was a man of many hobbies and interests, one of which was rock climbing. One summer day in 2009, he asked Rahn and me to meet him at Great Falls Park in Virginia, where he climbed rocks in the Potomac Mather Gorge. When we got there, there was no sign of him, but we discovered his dog, Tito, guarding his master's belongings at the top of the rock. I found out that he would first hike down the cliff to the Potomac River, and then returned to the top by climbing up. His ropes were hanging down 60 feet of a rock cliff. He was a brave man to scale the cliff. Usually, a two-person team would climb the cliff, but to our dismay he climbed alone. I called to him, and I heard his answer way down the cliff. I saw two ropes hanging down the cliff; he had attached two anchors, one to the left and the other to the right of the rock cliff. Two ropes were attached to his harness. I wouldn't even dream of climbing a ten-foot cliff. During his college days in Korea, he scaled many climbing courses. When he was climbing rock cliffs, he carried many carabiners around his harness belt and over his shoulders. He needed them for fall protection as he was climbing without a partner.

Dong-kyu's son Alex became a professional tennis player after he won the National Collegiate Athletic Association (NCAA) singles championship in his junior year in 2000, playing for the Stanford University team. Later in 2000, he made his debut Grand Slam appearance at the U.S. Open. His best year was 2002 when he was ranked 106th in the world (in June 2002). For his first tournament appearance, the family went to Flushing Meadows, New York. In the Open, he played none other than Andre Agassi, who was top-seeded and the defending U.S Open champion. The Open placed Alex as a wildcard in the main draw that year as he was the 2000 NCAA men's singles champion. Each year, the Open reserved a spot for an upcoming American tennis player. Alex played Agassi in the main stadium in Flushing Meadows, losing to him in straight sets. In Andre Agassi's autobiography *Open*.[49] Agassi described that he was the number one seed at the 2000 U.S. Open, and the favorite to win it. In the first round, Agassi described Alex as sick with anxiety. In the first set, Alex played well against Agassi and went up 3 to 2 in the first set. John McEnroe, who was a Stanford alumnus, commented in the broadcast booth that this could be an upset in the making. Not so. Agassi recovered and won the match over Alex by 6-4, 6-2, and 6-0.

Dr. Arthur McTaggart

When Rahn had worked at the Voice of American (VOA), Dr. Arthur McTaggart (1915-2003) was in the Korea Section also.[50] Arthur was a foreign service officer, stationed for many years in South Korea. He was the Director of American Cultural Center in Taegu, Korea, and spoke fluent Korean with a mixture of the thick American missionary accent and the Taegu dialect.[51] One spring evening, Art invited Rahn and me to his recently purchased townhome in the Capitol Hill neighborhood in Washington.

"Art, this is a lovely townhome.

"When did you move in?"

"Two months ago."

"I like your backyard.

"How many blocks is it from the Capitol?"

"Oh, two and a half blocks.

"It is a quiet neighborhood in the evening after the government people empty the Hill."

"Make yourselves comfortable."

"We brought a bottle of Cointreau."

"Oh, John, thank you. I ran out of my aperitif."

"I am going to save it in my cellar.

"I will serve you rum instead.

"Rahn and John, I made a special dish for you, chicken with chocolate sauce."

"You made a chicken dish with chocolate sauce?

"I've never had it before."

"Today is Cinco de Mayo, and Mexicans serve it at the festival."

"I warn you it's hot with jalapeno and sweet with chocolate."

"Uum, it sounds delicious. . . . . . ."

"As a dessert, I made a rum baba.

"I hope I did not douse the cake with rum too much."

We changed our conversation from chocolate chicken dish to Art McTaggart's earlier years.

"Now, Art, you are from Indiana."

"I wanted to know how you wound up in South Korea from Indiana."

"John, I grew up in the farmland of Indiana, in the town called Logansport on the bank of the Wabash River.

"You have been in West Lafayette when you were at Trine University, haven't you?"

"Yes, I have been at Purdue campus two or three times.

"I know Logansport.

"From Angola, I drove on U.S. Route 24 to Ft. Wayne, Logansport, Wabash, and West Lafayette.

"Also, Trine University had a satellite campus in Logansport."

"John, you are right. There once was a college called Smithson College on

College Hill in Logansport.

"Trine University bought Smithson College.

"John, it all started with the Great Depression.

"When I was attending the high school, I had been looking for work.

"Our town was slowly recovering from the Depression.

"I found out that I could be trained as a mechanics apprentice at Logan Machinery Company. "Although I knew nothing about the machinery, they paid me $2.64 per week through federal subsidies.

"The town was a blue color community, mostly farmers.

"John, so I became an original American proletariat."

"So what happened as a proletariat?

"You did not join the Communist Party, did you?"

"Certainly not.

"I enrolled at Purdue University in 1937.

"In my freshman year, Professor Herbert Muller found me a scholarship at Cornell University. I received a Telluride Scholarship and enrolled at Cornell University.

"The recipient of the Telluride Scholarship was required to study fundamentals of machinery.

"It was not an engineering curriculum like what Purdue or Trine Universities offered but a vocational training curriculum.

"Cornell, an Ivy League school, did their share of war efforts by offering vocational training on machinery during the World War II."

"They taught us machine shop operation, sheet metal work, and aircraft machine shop work, which were in demand during the war.

"Also, I joined ROTC at Cornell as the country was on a war footing. When I received my Cornell BS degree in 1942, I was also commissioned as a Second Lieutenant in the Army.

"I became an auto-mechanics instructor in the U.S. Army Artillery School, Ft. Sill, Oklahoma.

"After the war, I pursued my graduate work at Stanford University and received my doctorate in education.

"Then I became a Foreign Service officer and posted in the Vatican and Taegu, South Korea.

"After the tour of duty in Taegu, I became the Director of USIA in Hue,

Vietnam, until the North Vietnam Army overran South Vietnam in the spring of 1975.

I have known just one American who claimed that he had never owned an automobile in his life. That person was Arthur McTaggart. One day, Rahn and I invited Arthur to our home in Fairfax City.

"John, I accept your invitation. I'm looking forward to. But I'll travel by bus from DC."

"Rahn told me you do not own a car."

"I have no car, and I don't drive."

"How do you get along without a car in DC."

"I lived more than a half of my life outside of the States.

"When I returned to the US, I made sure that I lived in DC because the city had a good public transportation system.

"I buy my daily groceries on my way home.

"With some planning, I can live without a car."

"O.K. I am very proud of you.

"This Saturday afternoon I will meet you at the Annandale bus stop."

"See you then."

KOREAN ART COLLECTION OF ARTHUR MCTAGGART

During his stay in South Korea as a foreign service officer, Art McTaggart collected Korean arts of antiquities. His collection included pottery, paintings, and calligraphy of the Shilla (57 BC-937 AD) and Gaya (42AD-532AD) periods. His collection became known as the Arthur McTaggart Collection.

In 1966, my former general, Ung-soo Kim, and I met in Washington again. General and his wife moved from Seattle to Washington. They stayed in Arthur McTaggert's house near the Catholic University of America in Washington.[52] When Rahn and I visited Arthur's home, we saw a couple of the calligraphy scrolls, hung on the wall.

"These calligraphies are beautiful."

"Yes, I like live brush strokes."

"Arthur, do you understand the poems?"

"No, I do not understand what these calligraphies say."

"But, I like the beauty of these flowing cursive scripts and brush strokes."

McTaggart shipped his collection to America and kept it at the Asian Art Museum of San Francisco with the help of the curator of the Korean Art section, Ms. K. J. Baek. He agreed to return his collection to South Korea eventually. He kept his word. In March 2000, 478 items were returned to South Korea and found a home at the National Museum of Korea, Seoul.[53] The repatriated items included 380 items from the Gaya and the Shilla periods, including 8 blue vases and 21 white vases. Earthenware in McTaggart's collection was Fifth and Sixth-century treasures from Kyeong-sang Province. His collection provides valuable clues of an ancient way of life in Korea.

KOREAN ART COLLECTION OF MARCUS SCHERBACHER

I knew another cultural attaché in the American Embassy in South Korea. He was Marcus W. Scherbacher (1913-1997). I first met him in 1958, when I was working for the South Korean Olympic Committee (KOC). He maintained a good relationship with cultural and sports communities of South Korea. Just like Arthur McTaggart, Scherbacher also collected ancient art objects including ceramics, paintings, screens, and calligraphy scrolls. He also collected contemporary paintings from Korean painters. He brought his collection to America, and it became known as the Korean Art from the Estate of Marcus W. Scherbacher.

After his death, Sotheby's of New York auctioned the Scherbacher estate on Sept. 20-26, 1997.[54] Before the auction, Sotheby's published a catalog describing the collection and also held a traveling exhibition in Seoul, Tokyo, Los Angeles, and New York. I do not know who bought these artworks at the auction. I wished that they were bought by South Koreans and brought back to South Korea. The Sotheby's auction catalog listed an eight-panel folding screen in ink and color brocade created by an anonymous painter in 1901. This screen commanded the highest list price of $850,000. This screen depicted the 1901 royal banquet held to celebrate the 50th birthday of Emperor Gojong at the

Deoksu Palace, Seoul. The catalog also listed inlaid celadon vases and bowls and incised celadon bowls of the 12th century with a price of $150,000. The bowl was six and seven-eighths inches in diameter and three and three-eighths inches high. *The Spring Landscape* painting of Sang-beom Lee, circa 1980, was listed at a price of $2,000. (see photo 85)

During the World War II, Marcus Scherbacher served in the U.S. Navy and then became a foreign service officer, and was posted in South Korea. After the Korean War, he supported the war-devasted National Museum of Korea by providing grants from the American Embassy.

A DINNER PARTY FOR HWAN-SOO KIM AND GREGORY HENDERSON AT OUR HOME

Rahn and I invited Hwan-soo Kim to our home when he had visited Washington in 1984. Along came Gregory Henderson from Boston. Greg was another cultural attaché in South Korea from 1953 to 1962. When he was a political officer of the U.S. Embassy, he was a friend of my father-in-law, Yo-han Chu. South Korean politics was in turmoil during Greg's time in Korea. Throughout that period, he was more than a casual bystander; in 1968, he published a book, *Korea: The Politics of the Vortex*[55] describing unfavorably events in Korean politics during his stay in Seoul. This caused him to become persona non grata from the military junta.

Rahn told me that, during Thanksgiving 1959, in Seoul, Greg Henderson gave a live turkey as a Thanksgiving gift to the Chu family. But the turkey outgrew the makeshift chicken coop, and the family decided to donate it to the city zoo.

On the Easter Sunday, in 1960, Greg and Maria Henderson invited Yo-han Chu to Henderson's home in Seoul. Rahn accompanied her father, but they could not find Henderson's home. Finally, they found a wooden name block on which Chinese characters were inscribed, Han Dae Sun, which was Greg Henderson's Korean name. After dinner, Maria Henderson boiled and colored many Easter eggs and gave them to Rahn in a bronze bowl.

When Greg came to our home, he exchanged typical Korean style greetings with me in fluent Korean.

"John, to what clan do you belong?" Greg asked

"My family belongs to An-dong Kim clan and Jeong-sang sub-clan."

"My Korean name is Han Dae Sun, and I belong to Cheong-Ju Han clan."

He was not only a diplomat but also had in-depth knowledge of Korean cultures such as the surnames, clans, and Jokbo. Some American foreign service officers adopted their names in Korean-Chinese. Marcus Scherbacher took his name as Seol Baek.

Korean Art Collection of Gregory Henderson

Greg Henderson (1922-1988) received a BA degree from Harvard University and joined the foreign service and posted in South Korea and Germany. He was the third American collector of the Korean art whom I have known. While posted in South Korea, Greg collected 150 items of ancient Korean art objects. These collections dated back to the 1st century through the 19th century.[56] After Greg's untimely death in 1988, Mrs. Maria Henderson donated the entire Gregory Henderson collection to the Harvard University Arthur M. Sackler Museum. According to Robert D. Mowry, the Head of the Department of Asian Art at the Arthur M. Sackler Museum, the Gregory Henderson collection is one of the finest collections of the Korean ceramics and art objects of antiquities.

I have mixed feelings on these three American collectors of Korean art of antiquities, Art McTaggart, Marcus Scherbacher, and Greg Henderson. Indeed, they preserved these art treasures, but affluent Americans bought up art treasures in impoverished Korea on the cheap during and immediately after the Korean War. Once to Art McTaggart, I made a case for returning his collection. Arthur told me, "John, don't worry, there are enough pieces to go around." He did return them to rightful places in South Korea, and I salute Art for returning his collection.

Job Offers from RCA and the University of Pennsylvania

In 1968, an opportunity came my way for a new job at the Radio Corporation of America (RCA), Ground Radar Division, Moorestown, New Jersey, which built the Ballistic Missile Early Warning System (BMEWS) Ground-Based Radar. They offered me a department managership. Also, I met with Professor Aravind Joshi of the University of Pennsylvania, Moore School of Electrical Engineering, as I was associated with them as an Outside Reader in 1967. The University of Pennsylvania offered me an adjunct professorship. The University was located in West Philadelphia, and RCA was in Cherry Hill, New Jersey, across the Delaware River.

Rahn and I went to Cherry Hill and Burlington, New Jersey, to look at houses on sale in case I decided to accept the job. But the relocation and employment changes seemed like a daunting task. The whole thing never materialized. Oh, well, so much for a midlife crisis. Changing jobs and selling and buying houses are some of the most stressful events in life. I sent letters declining the RCA and UPenn positions and overcome a midlife crisis.

"At 40, with the study of history, philosophy, and spirituality, I have no more doubts about my judgment of the worldly affairs."

PART THREE
TRW YEARS
(1969–2001)

New Employment that Lasted More Than Three Decades

New Position at TRW

In 1969, I began to notice signs of Melpar's business drifting. Then, one day, my boss Tom Curry announced that he was leaving the company. About that time, Dr. Sidney Kissin of TRW, who was my former colleague in Raytheon (Melpar), offered me a position in his department. I accepted the position, and TRW became my employer for the next 32 years.

In its halcyon days, TRW (now part of Northrop Grumman) was a significant player in American industry, ranked 57th on the Fortune 500 list, with 122,000 employees. The company was one of the leaders in aerospace, electronics, automotive parts, and the consumer credit reporting business. It was a pioneer in electronic components, integrated circuits, and software engineering. The company built many spacecraft, including Pioneer 11, launched in 1973, which was the first satellite to encounter Saturn and Jupiter. The company also developed a space-based surveillance satellite, called the Defense Support Program (DSP).[1] During the Operation Desert Storm, I have seen on CNN news how the Patriot Missile Defense System in Israel intercepted Iraqi SCUD missiles. The DSP was a space surveillance system, which detected Iraqi SCUD missile launches and gave advance warning to the Israeli Patriot Missile Defense System.[2]

TRW built the warfighting Defense Satellite Communications System (DSCS) Phases II, and the Fleet Satellite System (FLTSAT) to connect and transfer information from ships in the ocean to shore stations, or from UAV operators in the middle of a desert to its base camp.

During those years, the company rose like a meteor, which burned and

glowed brightly in the American industries until the company fell and merged with Northrop Grumman Corp. It disappeared from the roster of the American industries by 2000.

When I started my career at TRW, I was a 34-year-old engineer. I began as a staff engineer and moved up the career ladder, later became a Technical Fellow, which was the highest honor a scientist or engineer at TRW could attain. For three decades, I worked on a dozen projects related to military and aviation. While these projects involved many technologies, I consistently dealt with communication technology projects.

HARRY WATSON AND ASW PROJECT

For my first assignment, Sidney Kissin, my department manager, sent me for an interview with Harry Watson. Harry was a former Rhodes Scholar, a retired Navy Commander, and a member of the Naval Academy class of 1946. During the interview, Harry asked me:

"John, how much do you know about ASW?

"Could you explain what a LOFAR system is?"

I was somewhat surprised by his no-nonsense questions. I replied hesitantly:

"In Melpar, I've been working on a NAVSEA ASW project for two years.

"My task was sonar signal processing, using the AN/SQS-23 high frequency active sonar.

"But I know nothing about the LOFAR system."

My SQS-23 sonar experience was good enough for him to take me under his wings. Then, I asked him several questions.

"Harry, what is the LOFAR system?"

"John, unlike SQS-23, the LOFAR system is a passive sonar equipment, which detects, classifies, and tracks enemy submarines.

"The system produces a LOFARgram, which is a plotter of sonar signal signatures.

"The U.S. Navy deployed passive sonar systems, called SOSUS (SOund SUrveillance System) in the Pacific and the Atlantic Oceans, and the Mediterranean Sea.

"SOSUS is the primary submarine listening network of the Navy."

"Harry, tell me more about SOSUS."

"After the sonar operator made contact, the first thing he examines is the primary frequency (60 Hz) of the submarine generator.

"He also looks for propeller cavitation noise.

"Using these data, the operator classifies the unknown submarine."

"Why is the 60 Hz signal the first thing the operator is looking for?"

"That is a good question.

"All submarines are powered by DC batteries.

"But most equipment like radios, computers, HVAC's, and etc., operate on AC.

"DC electricity must be converted to AC electricity by a motor-generator at 60 Hz.

"No electrical generator produces a pure tone waveform.

"Each generator produces an impure waveform.

"The impure waveform produces small but significant harmonics.

"These harmonic components are one of the key signatures of each submarine class.

"It is one of the important clues for the SOSUS operator to classify a Russian submarine in question when the sonar operator makes contact."

"What is the importance of propeller cavitation noise?"

"It tells the operator the change of speed and bearing of the submarine."

"Thank you, Harry.

"Very interesting."

I could not have foreseen the future, but it turned out that my work assignment with Harry Watson on the ASW project was the beginning of my five-decade-long association with various U.S. Navy projects. I am grateful for Harry Watson's mentoring. As fate would have it, by chance I stumbled into the fertile ground of naval science and technology. There indeed was a pattern to my job assignments, mostly in maritime subjects, but my Navy taskings were stochastic (or random) such that I could not predict what my next post would be. However, I always channeled my energy into staying abreast of latest technology.

Our office was in the K Street corridor of Washington, which was the home to dozens of think tanks and advocacy (lobbyist) groups. In the office, I remember the way Harry answered his telephone. He replied by pronouncing

"Watson" with the emphasis on the second syllable, "wat-SON." His speech sounded as though he was still at the University of Oxford as a Rhodes Scholar.

Once, Harry invited me to his farmhouse in Oakton, which was about two miles north of the Fairfax Courthouse. In the days before the real-estate development boom in Northern Virginia suburbs, he lived in a farmhouse on ten-acres of land. He used to ride a horse from the farm to the general store on Hunter Mill Road in Oakton and hitched his horse to a post in front of a country-style general store. There was roadside parking space for cars as well as a hitching post for horses. Harry would go to the store to buy groceries. Now, these rural scenes have all but disappeared, and high-tech corporate buildings and Flint Hill School fill this area.

Harry and I frequently attended meetings at the Main Navy and Munitions Buildings. Our discussions with Navy engineers were often about improving the data link between aircraft and the Tactical Support Center (TSC), which was the operations center for ASW patrol aircraft (a turbo-propeller Lockheed Orion P-3C). These aircraft were deployed in some naval air bases in the Pacific and Atlantic Oceans, and the Mediterranean Sea. Over the years, I had opportunities to visit several TSCs at Bermuda, Jacksonville, Patuxent River, and Argentia, Newfoundland in the Atlantic Ocean; Moffett, Whidbey Island, and Barbers Point in the Pacific Ocean. These bases were on the front line of the Cold War against Russia.

Promoted to Section Head

There were many restaurants and bars along the K Street corridor. After business hours, colleagues would often ask me, "How about a drink?" These after-hours social gatherings were a part of culture of policy wonks in the K Street corridor. The drinking culture had changed when we moved to the McLean campus.

Six months after I joined the company, Sidney Kissin promoted me to section head, a first-line supervisor in charge of a dozen Members of Technical Staff (MTS). As a supervisor, I needed people skills to be successful as a manager. Being a foreign-born person, I had to overcome my shortcomings in dealing with human resource matters.

There was competition in the workplace. Each MTS was not given one's job assignment automatically but had to compete for it by showing superior performance. The company organized its structure in a matrix form. There were two dimensions in this management structure. One dimension was the program office, which managed the contract work. Washington Operations had several programs, each of which could require several hundred technical personnel to perform contract works. The other dimension was the functional skill center. The company maintained several skill centers, each of which fostered technical disciplines such as mathematics, signal processing, computer engineering, and communications. A technical skill center manager provided technical skills to project offices.

A project manager would select support personnel from technical skill centers. As a technical skill center manager, I had some idea of technical staffing requirements for each new project as I had participated in proposal preparations. These management structures were new to me. They might have been included in the curriculum of business schools, but certainly not in the curriculum of engineering schools.

The matrix organization is one of the management methods employed in a large corporation. A corporation, which was organized in the matrix form, was flexible, but it must bear the cost of a dual management structure and higher overhead.

I worked with several managers in the TRW ASW Program Office, like Curt Carter, Dr. John Gormally, and Chuck Clardy. Curt Carter was an able manager, and dealt efficiently with Navy customers as he was a retired Naval officer; and John Gormally came from Bell Laboratories, where he worked on the SOSUS project. These managers held a very tight grip on technical and business matters. The company hired several ex-Naval officers as managers, who provided their operational experience. John Gormally had the technical leadership to lead us in the area of SOSUS signal processing and contributed to supporting the undersea surveillance program to the U.S Navy.

13

Temporary Duty to South Korea

COUNTERING NORTH KOREAN COMMANDO RAIDS

For nearly seven decades, we have heard about troubles on the Korean Peninsula. Recently, we've heard about North Korean ambitions for building nuclear bombs and testing of long-range missiles. In the 1970s, we'd heard of small-scale North Korean armed provocations toward South Korea. After the cease-fire of the Korean War in 1953, North Korean commandos frequently raided South Korea. In January 1968, a North Korean irregular unit crossed the Demilitarized Zone (DMZ) and infiltrated to a northern outskirt of Seoul and attempted to assassinate President Park Chung-hi. Several times, North Korean commandos raided the East Coast towns of Uljin and Jumunjin, resulting in South Korean civilian and military casualties. There were infiltrations across the 150-mile long DMZ. The North Koreans also dug several tunnels[3] under DMZ, which the South Korean Army discovered in Dongducheon, Cheorwon, and Sokcho.

These provocations prompted the U.S. and South Korean Defense Ministers to launch the Korean Counter Infiltration System (KCIS) program. Both South Korea and the U.S. were concerned with potential infiltration by North Korean insurgents on the east and west coasts of the peninsula, which might disrupt South Korean industries on both coasts. Management responsibility for the program was delegated to the Defense Advanced Research Projects Agency (DARPA).

KCIS PROJECT

In July 1971, I received a telephone call from Jerome Schwarzbach of TRW Systems Group in Los Angeles. He knew about a forthcoming DARPA Request for Proposal on the Korean Counter Infiltration System (KCIS). He asked me to help him prepare the TRW proposal. I got approval from my department manager for a temporary assignment in South Korea. When DARPA awarded the KCIS contract to TRW, Jerry Schwarzbach had asked me to become his Deputy and support him on KCIS Project as he needed to work closely with the South Korean defense establishment.

While I was preparing for my trip to South Korea, I received several letters from Schwarzbach, which described the status of the KCIS project. He said that the team was settled at the Chosun Hotel, which became both offices and accommodations for team members. Both the U.S. Armed Forces Headquarters in South Korea and the South Korean Ministry of National Defense had a dim view of the project team staying in a four-star hotel. DARPA-Korea suggested that the team moves into the Yongsan garrison compound but never moved to Yongsan. Here are letters I received from Jerry Schwarzbach just before I left for Seoul, and which give some idea of what was going on with the KCIS project in South Korea. (see photo 48)

CHOSUN HOTEL
87 SOKONGDONG, CHUNG-KU, IPO BOX 3706,
SEOUL, KOREA

Seoul
January 23, 1972

Dear Dr. Kim:

I have waited to write until things settled down enough so that the scope of the job was determined. The team left Los Angeles on January 3, arriving in Seoul on January 10, after stopovers for a briefing to and from in Japan and Hawaii. Our

office spaces—except for a safe and reading desk in the United Nations Command Headquarters building in Yongsan—and our rooms are in a wing on the ninth floor of the Chosun Hotel. The two secretaries are in Room 934; I am in Room 933. Our rates are very good.

The study team has grown to ten Americans plus seven ROK officers. The ten Americans include Lt. Col. Olson of Air Force Electronics Systems Division communication officer, three MITRE engineers, three TRW engineers, and two communication officers from the Pacific Command. The South Korean team includes all services plus Korean National Police. The team appears quite compatible. The MITRE people are new to counter infiltration, and they are a computer CRT[4] display system oriented, but it is an intelligent, enthusiastic group.

The South Korean Ministry of National Defense is enthusiastically supporting the study. The ROK team leader is Air Force Col. Cho, Il-dong. Our first week here we met and briefed the Chief of Staff of the United Nations Command, the U.S. Navy Command in Korea (USNKCOM) and the Chief of the US-ROK Operations Planning Staff.

The next week we will brief the ROK Joint Chiefs of Staff and the Director of the JCS Counter Infiltration Operations Center informally. We spent this week further organizing, defining and allowing the ROK team member to start the visit coordination. Next week we will visit all the Headquarters of the South Korean Military Services: Army, Navy, Air Force, Marine Corps, Fishery Service, Ministry of Commerce, and National Police. Next is a week of study of available documentation and preparations for the data gathering field trips which will cover the next five weeks. After two or three weeks of data compilation, we will return to the U.S. The team comprised of three subgroups plus a special steering group plus a commu-

nications specialist group. There are eight field trips planned divided up amongst the three subgroups. The least essential tours have been scheduled last in case we meet more than the expected delay. There has been much discussion of the scope and purpose of the study. Some of the ROK want it expanded beyond Command, Control, and Communications (C3), but we are going to limit it mainly to that. We will consider the effectiveness of a few potential new elements, C3, and other counter infiltration system elements but this will be limited.

The approach is as follows: In South Korea, the team will describe the present system (and situations). On return to the U.S. in 1972, the team will analyze the current equipment, information flow, and decision-making nodes, other support & operation factors affecting system use (training, etc.). The team will identify deficiencies in the present system. Then, the team will postulate change, evaluate changes, recommend a system configuration and implementation plan. Finally, the team will procure and test requirements of the recommended system. This contract does not cover the next phase.

If the product were right, we would present it to President Park, who will fund, if required, out of ROK funds. The fact of a joint US-ROK working so close at this level is unprecedented. So it should be particularly interesting to you. I expected to leave here the weekend of February 12, 1972, after the first week of field trips. I expect you should plan to meet with me in Los Angeles for a day either during the week or on the weekend, so you arrive in Korea during the early part of the week of March 6, 1972. This schedule will allow you to participate in a field trip and work on compiling the data and requirement and constraint base for the U.S. analysis.

We are trying to produce useful and implementable outputs. The basic analysis approach is information, function, decision, operational plan, as in our C3 proposal. There will be lots of attention paid to details of how the system operates; training, procedures support, etc. The Air Force Electronics Systems Division Technical Plan, which I sent you, should not be considered the bible as it was put together on the assumptions by ESD that this job was to design and procure a new C3 system a la American style. It was almost a carbon copy of a previous plan for another system. ESD now understands the job as less ambitious, and it is more like the task described in our C3 proposal. I will send you the TRW project plan. Your assignment is the same. Your Personnel Department people and ours will arrange for your trip. I have multiple copies of ESD travel orders for you, which I will send back to Los Angeles to send to you and to use as a basis for obtaining tickets. We traveled by Category Z[5] and assumed you would do likewise.

Now to other matters. I got the phone number of your friend, Dr. Bong-seo Lee,[6] and will call him for a social get together. It has been unseasonably warm here—above freezing—but yesterday the temperature dropped, and there was a layer of snow on the ground when I awoke. So winter has arrived.

The team looks forward to your arrival and participation. You have my address in Korea. Write if you have questions, or I can help in any way.

Regards,
Jerome Schwarzbach

❄ ❄ ❄

CHOSUN HOTEL
87 SOKONGDONG, CHUNG-KU, IPO BOX 3706,
SEOUL, KOREA

Seoul
February 14, 1972

Dear John:

My last letter was sent on Jan. 23, 1972. Since then we have
finalized the study scope and did the necessary South Korean
coordination & planning for the data gathering field trips. We
went on the first set of week-long trips. This week we collated
the data obtained and prepared for the set of trips next week.

Since my last letter, we visited the National Counter Infiltration Operations Center[7] and Headquarters of Military Services, and National Police. The first three field trips were to the
Inchon area out to Baekryeon Island, to the Kimpo Peninsula
and the Han River Estuary, and to the South Chung-Cheong
Province area.

I went on this last trip. We looked at the system all the way
from the Provincial Counter Infiltration Units at Taejon and
the South Korean 51st Division Headquarters at Jochiwon
through intermediate levels to the coast watchers, coastal
radar, and road checkpoints. We ate and stayed at Korean
inns/eating places. One night, we stayed in Mang-Il-San Forward Reporting Center. We were in the hot spring at Onyang,
Kyunggi Province.

DARPA-Korea told us that there might some changes in
the scope of the project. Before embarking to Korea, we had
envisioned an analysis of a C3 portion of the counter-infiltration system with emphasis on sea infiltration strictly. It now

appears that the ROK needs a somewhat more comprehensive look at the overall counter infiltration system. ROKs feel strong that the study should also include a determination of the effectiveness of the radar sensors, patrol aircraft, reaction force deployment & tactics, etc. They feel that improvement in the C3 networks is important. Procedures alone will not measurably increase the overall effectiveness, and they have looked for a more comprehensive definition of C3 to include some looking at these elements. We will briefly look at air threat. We will not consider DMZ, internal security, base defense, or special security area problems. We hope to use one of our company models from past studies approved to this study. I'll discuss the whole thing in detail in a few weeks with you in Los Angeles.

In my Jan. 23, 1972 letter I said I expected to leave the weekend of Feb. 12, 1972. I now plan to leave on Feb. 17, 1972, arriving in L.A. at work the following Monday. I'll call you on Monday. I stayed later to help collate the gathered data, discuss our Statement of Work for possible changes, set down some preliminary thoughts on the "Requirements Baseline" document, and put down some initial analysis thoughts.

I would expect you might plan to see me in Los Angele on about March 4, 5, or 6, arriving in Korea on Mar. 8 or earlier. I expect the total trip will last for about one month. The full team will leave Korea between Mar 25 and April 1, 1972. You will have a room at the Chosun with the rest of the team.

We have two full Colonels on the team; Il-dong Cho and Byeong-cheol Koh. We all are looking forward to your visit. We had breakfast with your friend, Dr. Bong-seo Lee.

Regard,
Jerry Schwarzbach

�֎ �֎ ✖

Jerry's letter of February 14, 1972 described the project activities. The team was to work within the scope of the Statement of Work (SOW) in the DARPA contract. While the South Korean government was interested in a comprehensive study of the counter-infiltration system, DARPA drew a line in the sand and limited the scope of the project to what had been described in the SOW.

In his letter, Jerry mentioned the American base defense issue. In 1972, there were several U.S. Army garrison posts in South Korea: Camp Casey,[8] Camp Red Cloud,[9] and Camp Page.[10] However, the defense of these Army bases was excluded from the project since, at division strength, the forces could protect themselves.

After preparing for extended temporary duty (TDY), I boarded Northwest Airlines flights to Seoul. From a personal standpoint, it was my homecoming after fourteen years since I left South Korea. When I arrived at Kimpo International Airport, it was guarded by fully armed South Korean soldiers. The atmosphere was definitely different from that of U.S. airports. This was in the wake of North Korean commandos hijacking KAL domestic flights at Gangneung in February, 1972.

There were not many travelers, and the airport was quiet and almost empty. My father and Lieutenant Colonel Don Olson of the DARPA-Korea Office were there waiting for me. We got into a waiting company car, an International Scout jeep, at the sparse parking lot in the airport and drove along rice paddies on both sides of the highway. I felt at home with the gray and mud-colored landscapes and the smells of the countryside. The road was narrow and rough with pot-holes. As we approached the city center, I noticed buildings were gloomier and somewhat smaller than what I had remembered.

I thought about two distinct impressions of the city. The first was Seoul in 1945 when I entered Seoul escaping from Pyongyang; the second was Seoul in 1972 when I came to Seoul from Washington. I remembered the city of Seoul in 1945 brighter and taller than in 1972. I am sure streets and buildings of Seoul were not shrunken, but I was disappointed with what I found in good old Seoul.

My journal entries, which I had recorded on my travel from Washington to South Korea, and during my TDY in South Korea, are as follows:

Los Angeles, March 3, 1972 - I received a Transportation Authorization issued by the U.S. Air Force Electronic Systems Command. The paper stated the purpose of travel, the security clearance data, the authority for theater clearance, the DARPA contract information, the authorization to the travel by Military Airlift Command and military aircraft in the Korean theater, travel by Category Z (Government travelers on official business) and the itinerary. The itinerary included Los Angeles, Camp Smith in Hawaii, Fuchu Air Station in Tokyo, Yongsan, and several field sites in South Korea. Jerry Schwarzbach filled me in on the reimbursement policy of the temporary duty.

Tokyo, March 5-6, 1972 - It was long flights from Los Angeles to Tokyo on Northwest Airlines Boeing 727 flights, which were quieter and more pleasant than the DC-6 when I traveled from Tokyo to Seattle in 1958. I arrived at Haneda International Airport in Tokyo and checked in at the Hilton Hotel in Shinjuku. Jerry Schwarzbach asked me to meet with Dean Lowry at our TRW company office in Roppongi Precinct in Tokyo; Lowry is the TRW Marketing Manager in Japan. In the next morning, I met with him at his office.

I explained the KCIS project to him. Lowry already asked Ray Harlan, the TRW Seoul Office Manager, to arrange a meeting with Colonel John V. Patterson, Jr., the Director of the DARPA-Korea. Lowry wanted to visit Seoul to get acquainted with the KCIS project and planned to visit the South Korean Agency for Defense Development (ADD) for marketing.. He acted like an early 20th century White Russian in East Asia, doing business for colonial powers. He carried a cane and smoked a cigarette held on a holder and wore a Havana hat.

Seoul, March 7, 2972 - Ray Harlan showed me my office and my hotel room and introduced me to fellow project team members, including Korean secretaries who were surprised when I greeted them in Korean. They thought I was a second-generation Korean American. The KCIS project occupied the entire ninth floor with 36 rooms of the Chosun Hotel, where five rooms were set aside for the office and the remainder as accommodations.[11] Then, in the afternoon, Ray and I went to the Yongsan Garrison, where I met with Air Force Colonel John Patterson. I also received a U.S. Air Force uniform. Project personnel must wear a uniform whenever we go to military bases such that we would blend into the background. We received an instruction to report at the Seoul Yeouido K-16 Air Base the next morning.[12]

K-16 Yeouido (Seoul) Air Base, March 8, 1972 - Early in the morning, our guide, Colonel Byung-Cheol Koh, South Korean Marine Corps, came to Chosun Hotel and led three of the KCIS project personnel to K-16 Air Base. Colonel Koh was a veteran of the Vietnam War and is the Operations Chief of the MoND Counter Infiltration Operations Center. I found him to be friendly but a battle-hardened Marine. (see photo 46)

I saw the control tower of the Army Air Base, where one DC-6 transport plane and several Army helicopters were on the tarmac. Colonel Koh met with the operations officer of the U.S. Army Aviation Regiment, and Koh escorted us to board a Bell UH-1D "Huey" Iroquois helicopter. The Huey was the VIP transportation for us. The rotor made cracking noises. I though rotor was about to break off from the helicopter. (see photo 47)

K-2 Taegu, March 8, 1972 - After a one-hour helicopter ride, the pilot told us that he would land at K-2 Taegu Air Base for refueling. I saw high ridge mountains surrounded the air base. The helicopter landing pad looked like a small doormat from our Huey helicopter at the altitude of 400 feet. Then, the pilot banked the helicopter blade at a sharp angle. The chopper descended vertically straight down to the landing pad with unabated speed and landed in less than three minutes. It was like a free fall. When the Huey touched down on the landing pad, I could feel strong, bouncy shocks on the tires. The helicopter must have good shock absorbers and struts. According to Koh, K-2 Taegu Air Base shares the air traffic control facilities with the USAF 51st Fighter Wing and commercial airlines, and in the event of a conflict, K-2 Taegu Air Base would become a full-scale combat unit.

K-3 Pohang, March 8, 1972 - We continued our travel and, in the afternoon, landed at K-3 Pohang Airdrome. Colonel Koh led us to our inspection site, the South Korean First Marine Division Headquarters. Colonel Koh wanted to conduct an unannounced inspection, but he found out that they were expecting us. The Division Chief of Staff and a small contingent of the honor guards were lined up at the gate. We inspected the counter-infiltration unit at Pohang Base and the coastal radars (the Raytheon navigation radar LN-66). At the Division Headquarters, the Operations Officer briefed us about the situation and demonstrated their radar operations.

K-18 Gangneung, March 8, 1972 - After lunch, we again flew the helicopter north to K-18 Gangneung Air Base for refueling and continued to K-50 Sokcho Air Base. We rode on jeeps and followed the desolate coastal area to the South Korean East Coast Defense Command in Sokcho, where they briefed us on the situation in their sector of DMZ.

Heavy snow started to fall in the evening. We attempted to return to the Yongsan Garrison, but there was a blizzard in the mountains. Our helicopter was grounded, and we decided to stay overnight at a local hotel.

Seoul, March 10, 1972 - The blizzard continued until the next day, and we could not return to Seoul by the helicopter. Col. Koh decided to go back to Seoul by Korean Air Lines (KAL) flights. Two plainclothed air marshals stopped us while we were boarding the airplane. The tight security measure was due to a KAL plane being hijacked and flown to North Korea in December of 1969. Col. Koh told us that each KAL airplane had been protected by air marshals ever since this incident. The KCIS team carried equipment and sensitive documents, which the air marshals insisted on inspecting. Col. Koh would not comply, and called the Commanding Officer of the South Korean K-18 Air Base, who vouched for the team. The team returned to Seoul Kimpo Airport in the afternoon without a hitch. Over the past three days, I had traveled 600 air miles altogether. During that time, our helicopter flew at low altitudes so that I could see many tombs in the mountains. This is something that I did not realize from the ground level.

Seoul, March 11, 1972 - In the afternoon, we visited the office of the Chief of the U.S.-South Korean Operational Planning Staff (USKOPS), who was rather skeptical of the outcome of KCIS team efforts. He recommended that DARPA-K should hand the project over to USKOPS. Don Olson and Jerry Schwarzbach reported to Col. John Patterson of DARPA-K about the USKOPS request. Colonel Patterson summarily dismissed the USKOPS request.

Seoul, March 11, 1972 - Rahn and children arrived in Seoul. The family settled down in the Chosun Hotel. The South Korean Ministry of National Defense sent security personnel to check the entry of the ninth floor.

Yongsan Garrison - During our stay in Seoul, the project team, had a rental car, an International Harvester Scout off-road vehicle, with a semi-diplomatic license plate. To go in and out of the U.S. Mission Compound in the Yongsan Garrison, our rental car needed either a military or a semi-diplomatic license plate according to the Status of Forces Agreement. Janet and William liked the International Harvester Scout car with the top down.

The Yongsan Garrison was an enclave that looked almost like a small American town grafted in the middle of Seoul. People cynically nicknamed the district as the "Republic of Yongsan." Yongsan has an interesting history as a military base. In 1904, the Imperial Japanese Army in Korea established its head-quarters in Yongsan, and in1945 it became the South Korean Army Headquarters. When I served in the South Korean Army Headquarters, our office and barracks occupied the northwest corner of the compound. This sprawling 800-acre base then became the military complex for the South Korean and American military high commands.

Seoul, March 16, 1972 - This morning, my mother-in-law called me to pay a visit to the office of my father-in-law during lunchtime. His office was about three blocks from the Chosun Hotel. He was the President of Korea Shipping Corporation, which is one of the largest shipping companies in Korea then. He is also the CEO of the Daehan Daily newspaper and writes two editorials every week. In his seventies, it was remarkable that he runs two businesses at the same time. He told me that he went home at lunchtime and enjoys 30-minute mid-day

nap. Then he returns to the office and works well into the evening. (see photos 51 and 52)

Seoul, March 17, 1972 - The KCIS team developed several threat scenarios staged in the southern coastal region including South Cholla Province. This coastal area has numerous islands, promontories, and estuaries, which could be the next target for North Korean commandos.

Seoul, March 19, 1972 - This afternoon, I went to Insa shopping district, where I found several art galleries and antique stores. Insa district was then known as "Mary's Alley." It is so named because one could find a Mary, meaning an American or European tourist, always there. At the Hyundai Art Gallery, I bought two woodcut etching drawings, Flute and Terracotta (Couple) by Wha-ju. I also bought two paintings from the gallery. One was a painting, Hwa-gyeong Kim's "Farm hut with a thatched roof in the snow" and the other Ju-young Lee's "Cityscape in the snow." A few days later, a friend of mine, Hwan-soo Kim, gave me an etching print by Yoong Bae, the Autumn Harvest Moon. These artworks became part of my collection. (see photos 85 through 89)

Seoul, March 27, 1972 - It was time for us to leave Korea. In the afternoon, we bid farewell to all who came to Kimpo Airport. Our Northwest Airlines flights took off from Kimpo Airport and arrived at Honolulu Airport. We went to the main terminal. Janet and William were exhausted. It was very humid. William, who is three years old, laid down on the floor of the main terminal, and said, "Dad! I don't want to go anymore." I knew how William felt, but we had to continue our trip; we flew to Los Angeles and to Washington Dulles Airport. We were glad to be back home.

The KCIS Team Comes to Boston

In the fall of 1972, the South Korean memebers of the KCIS team came to America and set up their office at the USAF Electronic Systems Division in Boston. They conducted evaluations in the MITRE facility in Bedford, Massachusetts. I also participated in these efforts in Boston. In December 1972, the Korean team members paid a courtesy call to the Korean Embassy in Washington. I invited them to the company in McLean and showed them our workplace. Dr. James Larkin, the Manager of Washington Operation, gave them a briefing on our business for DoD.

The KCIS team prepared the final report of the study in Boston and provided their first-hand knowledge of counter infiltration operations. For example, a high-speed agent boat crossed the Northern Limit Line in the East Sea, which coastal radars detected and reported as a contact to the Operations Center, which dispatched South Korean Navy and Air Force assets to the area to interdict agent boats. Jerry Schwarzbach told us,

"At the end of the day, we produced a report which was much more than we had expected.

"Both South Korean MoND and DARPA-K appreciated the excellent result."

In November 1972, after the completion of the KCIS project, Jerry Schwarzbach sent me a letter of commendation.

**TRW SYSTEMS GROUP
INTEROFFICE CORRESPONDENCE**

Redondo Beach, California
Nov. 21, 1972

6640.0.5-151

TO: J. C. Kim   cc: See below

DATE: 21 November 1972

SUBJECT: Commendation on Your Contribution
to the ICIS (Korea) Study (SN 21976.000)

FROM: J. M. Schwarzbach

BLDG: R2   MAIL Sta.: 2170   EXT: 52152

Reference 1: Draft Technical Report, "Quantitative Evalua-
tion Methodology for the ROK Counter Infiltration System
Study (U), "TRW Rpt. No. 21976-W002-R3-00, dated 26
May 1972.

The purpose of this memorandum is to convey to you personally and to memorialize for the TRW management, my
appreciation for your significant contribution to the success
of the ICIS Study, which we supported under contract to
the USAF Electronic Systems Division (ESD). Lt. Col. Don
Olson's management at ESD, Colonel Fernandez (USMC),
Mr. Doane, and others were so pleased with the final report
that they delayed its distribution so that Maj. Gen. Shiely,
ESD Commander, could see the work and sign the letter of
transmittal to the sponsor, DARPA—an unusual thing for a
project of this small size. We achieved our TRW objectives of
making the program a success and helping to create a favorable
opinion of TRW in command and control.

The nine-month study—three months in South Korea to
obtain data, followed by six months at Bedford to analyze the
data—was to study KCIS and recommend changes. The study

team consisted of ten U.S. and ten South Korean members in South Korea, and about the same number of U.S. and four South Korean members in Bedford for the analysis. Military, MITRE, and TRW personnel had to work together, as well as with the South Korean people from the four military services and the national police. TRW's effort was at about a three-man level outputs were in rough draft or input form to go into the ESD final report.

Your assignment was to develop the evaluation methodology. This evaluation, you did, based on a three-week visit to Korea in early 1972 while the team was gathering data, and on your background in command and control. Your knowledge of Korea, combined with your understanding of C3, was instrumental in gathering the team to follow the proper road.

The draft document (see Reference 1) so produced was much more than I had expected, in-depth and example, and was a basis for the quantitative methodology. Also, you helped direct the TRW analyst assigned to Bedford for the analysis phase, and you reviewed and made contributions to the full team's work from time to time (when you thought you were needed). I appreciate that much of this was on your own time; for example, the review trips were scheduled for you to Bedford for Friday so that you could work Saturday morning and return to Washington, thus minimizing time away from your other work. And finally, you provided counsel to help us (and me) over the difficult part of KCIS, where it now involved two countries and eight organizations.

Thanks.
J. M. Schwarzbach
JMS:cj

Cc: John Bryant, Chuck Clardy, H. T. Hayes, Martin Kamhi, Sidney Kissin, James Larkin, Dean Lowry, Robert Meyer, Art Sommer Personnel File

❊ ❊ ❊

LETTERS FROM MY ACTING SECTION HEAD

During my TDY in South Korea, I delegated my responsibility to Maynard Fader to be the acting section head. He sent me several letters about what was going on in the section during that time.

McLean, Virginia
March 10, 1972

Dear John:

This letter report will be brief, but I think it will cover the important items. This week has been the usual kind. Bill Richter was committed to the Levine task 50% of the time, and Tom Durek being requested again by Jimmy Logan to go to Keflavik. But Sidney Kissin did not approve his proposed assignment because of too much work to accomplish in the near-term.

We had a crash effort to produce a reliability and maintainability proposal and to do the pre-proposal task, which Curt Carter has given us. Jim Lam has completed the draft of the test results. We resolved the "inconsistency" problem raised by Pat Summerill and Rob Silverstein, but a couple of other modes have not operated as planned. Bob Benson has not called for the communications link support. Curt Carter has talked to him, and I have been instructed just to wait until Benson contacts me. Frank Crotty told Bill Richter that he has accepted our offer and would report on March 27, 1972.

Bob Meyer came down to find out what we are doing in the modeling and simulation area. Len Franz asked Meyer if we had any discussions with Moe Rosen's people. I assured him that we talked with Joe Anspach, Jim Byrne, and Bob Molander and that we were going to capitalize on their efforts in this simulation area. The general feeling left by Meyer is that this simulation is too ambitious an undertaking. I suggested that since we don't know this, we are going to do the job regardless.

The Laboratory management reviewed the project with their usual lack of flair. The simulation, reviewed by Joe Cornwell, has not been completed since Joe went skiing for a week out west. Tom Tarantino called just today and indicated that the task that Bill Richter is working for Curt Carter requires a delivery presentation to the Panel on April 3. Bill Richter's new work may affect our ability to carry out the scope of activities that we had planned for the Task 12 item.

I hope that your activities are about as expected and that you have good weather. Everything else here is going very well.

Will write again,
Maynard

I need to explain terminologies used by Maynard in his letter. During the Cold War, Keflavik in Iceland became one of the important Naval Facilities (NAVFAC) with a SOSUS Station and a Tactical Support Center (TSC) for the ASW Patrol Squadron. These stations monitored Soviet submarines passing through the Greenland-Iceland-U.K. (GIUK) gap, the maritime choke points in the northern Atlantic Ocean fenced by the Greenland, Iceland, and U.K. land masses. Maynard Fader mentioned Tom Derek, who was a computer scientist in my section and an Air Force reserve officer. He was a weekend warrior, assigned to Andrews Air Force Base.

Here is the second letter from Maynard Fader to me:

McLean, Virginia
March 15, 1972

Dear John:

Sidney Kissin wanted to know about your TDY schedule. There is an interest by John Bryant in your stopping off in Los Angeles on your way back home. It seems that there are people on the West Coast who are interested in your consulting with them and reviewing some of their efforts concerning the 427M program.[13] I guess that they wanted you to work out there for some extended period. However, John Bryant said that that was not possible, but that you may be available for a few hours or a day of consultation.

If you plan to come back to Los Angeles on a weekday or to stop over in Los Angeles, then they would like to be able to advise Rudy Kuehn of your availability. If you do not find it possible to stop off on your return trip, then John Bryant may ask you to go back out there after you have returned here. I do not know what kind of schedule they are working on, so I have no idea of how important the visit might be.

Yesterday Rob Silverstein came to ask when you would be returning. He apparently has an expanded pre-proposal task to encompass the development of an off-line test bed inclusion in his program proposal. This task would include the job input simulation functions in addition to the current software activity.

Most everything else is the same as usual with too much to do and not enough time to do it all the way we would like to do it.

Let us know of your returning plans as soon as they are firmed up.

Thanks,
Maynard

Maynard mentioned the 427M program, which was an Air Force program to improve the North American Air Defense Command (NORAD) Computer System in the 1970's.

I received the third letter report from Maynard.

McLean, Virginia
March 17, 1972

Dear John:

We are still afloat and working hard. I had a discussion with Curt Carter regarding the Interim Towed Array Surveillance System (ITASS) study. We completed the Anti-Ballistic Missile Defense (ABMD) test result report, but we are sitting on it for a few days until the due date gets closer than now. The support for Rob Silverstein in the near-term is going pretty well; he is going out to the West Coast next week so that Pat Summerill will be able to work more on the simulation. Joe Cornwell on his return to Washington asked that he puts together our technical approach to the simulation, input data requirements, and sources. He wishes to present the details of his "spec" report. Joe will go to Los Angeles sometime next week to present an algorithm approach to the SOSUS Improved Processing System (IPS) to some people out there, at Dr. James Larkin's request.

While Bill Richter has contacted the two Melpar applicants, we do not yet have an acceptance from either of them. Sidney Kissin is going to contact John Welchel direct.

Tom Durek has done well in pulling all of the essential material together for the Fixed Distributed System (FDS) report. He is in the process of boiling it down to a consistent level of detail.

I don't remember if I told you that some Bell Laboratory man, Barry Weyland, has been contacting the Navy regarding the Reliability/Maintainability (R/M) type of effort. Dr. Martin Kamhi was quite upset since he didn't know that it was going on, but they stopped it, and they identified Curt Carter as the official TRW point of contact for all surveillance activities.

Nothing has ever happened to the Bob Benson support to Commander Earl Eckert of Naval Electronic Systems Command (SPAWAR). We have not been asked to provide any at this time. Curt Carter has said that he has talked to Benson and that we should do nothing until we hear from him or Benson.

The SPAWAR Command had designated Captain Vern Anderson as SPAWAR ASW SOSUS Program Manager. He will become the primary control point in the Navy's surveillance development world. Since he is a "friend of TRW's" along with Jerry Cann, we stand a good chance of getting a significant segment of any future action in the area.

Rob Silverstein has registered interest in getting greater breadth in programming capability in-house in support of his program. Apparently, Bob Meyer has set up a programming section under Tom Barkley, which Rob Silverstein had intended to use. I talked to Sidney Kissin about this and suggested that it would be better if the additional programming support that Rob Silverstein's program may need would come from Bill Hewitt's shop. The assigned man out of Bob Meyer's group is fresh out of school, so there is apparently

no historical background or experience advantage to using Bob Meyer as a source. They did not decide what to do yet. However, Bill Hewitt and Rob Silverstein have been in contact with the subject.

Nothing yet has been done on the R/M pre-proposal study effort since I have been trying to get the ITASS thing straightened out and moved, and the Levine support has cut into Bill Richter's availability part of the time.

Soltys seems to be working out very well. He has been concentrating on testing of the Fixed Distributed System (FDS) programming. Tom thinks that he will do all right and will be able to be a good job after he gets his feet on the ground.

See you soon, I hope,
Maynard

(p.s.) I almost forgot. Per a request from Curt Carter to Dr. Jimmy Logan, Joe Yardumian, and John Nowacek came down to give us all the low-down that they could on the near-term task that Bill Richter is working on. It appeared that they did it as a command decision and were most cooperative. They didn't tell us anything we didn't already know, but they did confirm some of our understanding of the operational situation. Joe Yardumian is on his way to London, but John Nowacek said that he would get all the help that he can.

In the third letter, he mentioned three SOSUS-related projects, which engineers of my section had been working on. Those projects were the Improved Processing System (IPS), the Interim Towed Array Sound System (ITASS), and the Fixed Distributed System (FDS). These systems were the ASW-related projects that were intended to improve the submarine detection system, SOSUS.

The IPS project was part of the U.S. Navy ASW program, which developed

improved software programs at the SOSUS station.

The ITASS was a gap-filler effort for the fixed SOSUS system. A dozen SOSUS stations sometimes failed to detect or lose track of Russian submarines in some part of the Pacific and the Atlantic Oceans. The Navy deployed ships with towed sonar sensors. The U.S. Navy operated these ships in the ocean areas on an ad-hoc basis. This mobile sonar system became known as ITASS. In the 1980's, based on the ITASS experiment, SPAWAR developed a Surveillance Towed Array System (SURTASS), the USNS Able (T-AGOS-20). The USNS Able was a Small-Waterplane-Area Twin Hull (SWATH) vessel (or a motored catamaran). Later, Dr. Eugen Muehldorf and I participated in the development of the data relay system of SURTASS, which used the Super High Frequency (SHF) Satellite Communications System (SATCOM) called Defense Satellite Communications System Phase II (DSCS II).

The third project was the Fixed Distributed System (FDS). In the 1970's, SPAWAR developed a distributed passive sonar system in several key areas of the oceans such as the GIUK gap. The sonar system used low-frequency hydrophones. This sonar surveillance was known as FDS, and it provided cueing information vital to the Atlantic Fleet Headquarters.

More Travel to South Korea in 1973

When I went to South Korea for TDY in 1972, I spent most of my time on the KCIS project. As my father was then 65 years old, I was concerned about my parents living alone in Seoul. One year later, I traveled to Seoul to discuss their eventual reunion with all of their children in America. I could not kick the can down the road any longer. I urged my parents to come to America and live near their five grown-up children. My parents had to bite the bullet and decided to immigrate to America.

During my visit to Seoul in 1973, I stayed at my parents' new house in Dongsoong Precinct. I invited Dr. Justin Seong-joo Kim to my parent's new home. Justin Kim was then the Vice-President for International Investment of Tongyang Cement Corporation, and he was considering reverse immigration, but he decided not to return to Korea. I too thought about returning to Korea, but my experience in South Korea during my TDY convinced me to dismiss the idea.

With the members of the MSU Korean Student Association, 1960.
I was the president of the association. (Front row from left): Joong
Lee, EdD (2nd), John Kim, PhD (3rd), Charlie Chi Han Chyung
(6th). (Second row from left): Thomas Keun Mo Chung, PhD (1st),
Ken Chi Kwon Chyung (3rd), Hee Kyung Park (4th), Man Hyung
Yoo, PhD (6th). The doctorate degrees listed were the degrees each
member earned. The rest of the members earned master's degrees.
We Korean students excelled academically at MSU in the 1960s.

23

I received my Master of Science in Electrical Engineering. Ken Chyung and I were preparing for the commencement ceremony of MSU in June 1960.

24

I wore my academic gown when I received my doctorate from MSU in December 1962. This photo was taken at Woody and Dee-Dee Atkinson's home in Okemos, Michigan.

25

Colleagues of mine from the Applied Mathematics Department at Systems Research Laboratories in Dayton, Ohio, c. 1964. Clarence Ross (fourth from left) explained to us his missile defense system using the galactic coordinates. I was lost, Dave Brandt (second from left) was amused, and Daniel de Salvo (third from left) was unconvinced.

26

I was golfing in Dayton, Ohio, c. 1964. I played golf for several years and my score was over 100 most of the time. I don't understand why grownups chase small white balls all over the field. I quit hitting white balls after a few years.

27

I was skiing in Eau Claire, Wisconsin, c. 1964. I was an intermediate skier, parallel turning with my Head skis.

28

I bought a new car, a 1964 American Motors Rambler 550, in Angola, Indiana. Later in 1965, Rahn named the car Rocinante, *after Don Quixote's horse.*

29

Rahn, as a high school girl in Seoul, c. 1956.

I hosted a Christmas party at my apartment in Minneapolis, Minnesota, c. 1964. (From left): Me, Rahn, Mrs. Roh, Dr. Won-Chang Park (sitting on the floor), In-Kyu Roh, and Phil Kim.

I attended the wedding of my cousin, Won-Chang Park, MD, and served as his best man. Rahn was the maid of honor, and we met during the wedding preparation. (From left) John Kim, Rahn, Deok-Ja Roh, and Won-Chang Park.

32

Rahn in Rock Creek Park, Washington in 1965.

33

Rahn and I exchanged rings during our wedding ceremony at Fairfax Presbyterian Church. (From left): Dr. Chan-Mo Park, me, Rahn, and Pastor Henry Bauman.

34

Our wedding party photo. (From left): Dr. Tong-He Koh (Rahn's sister and the matron of honor), Rahn, me, and Dr. Chan-Mo Park (the best man).

35

At the wedding reception, Rahn and I appeared in traditional Korean costumes. Our guests were colleagues at Melpar, and their spouses. (From left): Dr. Jenny Bramley (4th), Rahn (5th), Grace Kissin (6th), Dr. Sidney Kissin (7th), I (8th), Mary Hanson (9th), Ed Connolly (11th), and Mary Connolly (12th).

The Kim and Chu families celebrated the wedding in the Diplomat's Club in Seoul, South Korea in 1965, without the bride or groom. (From left): Sun-Bok Choe (Rahn's mother), Yo-Han Chu (Rahn's father), and Pastor Shin-Myeong Kang.

37

Our honeymoon in Williamsburg, Virginia in 1965.

Rahn was driving a 1965 Ford Falcon, my wedding gift to her.

39

Yo-han Chu, visiting the Parthenon in Athens, Greece. He was the Head of the South Korean Delegation at the UNCTAD meeting held in Athens in 1966.

SNU Engineering College Alumni meeting in Washington, D.C., c. 1967. (The second row, from left) Dr. Chan-Mo Park (4th), John Kim (5th), Dr. Jung-Muk Lee (6th), Dr. Su-Young Lee (9th). (The front row, from left) Dr. Ho-Gil Kim (5th), Dr. Young-Suh Kim (7th).

대한의 아들아 딸들아
나오라 뭉쳐라 지켜라
자유의 삼천리를
영원무궁토록

4279년 설날
일에게 한

(유일하게 남은 선생의 肉筆로 二男 東日에게 써 준것임. 선생이 창안한 한글 풀어쓰기에 따라 쓰여졌음.)

Yo-han Chu proposed linear writing of Korean language (Hangul) in a way similar to the writing of European languages. The brush writing in the upper portion is written in the proposed linear writing. The traditionally spelled text is shown in the lower portion.

With friends at a Christmas holiday in Fairfax. (From left) Harry Oh, Jong-ran Oh, Dr. Sook-il Kwon, Rahm and I, 1965.

A dinner party at our house in 1966, in honor of Suk-Rai Cho. (The front row, from left): Rahn, Linda Lee, Suk-Rai Cho, Ye-Young Kim. (The second row, from left): John Kim, Dr. Bong-Suh Lee, Peter Choe, Duck-Jun Lee, Dr. Chan-Mo Park, and Jang-Soon Kwak.

I painted my 1962 sports coupe Volvo P1800 with my air compressor. The original color was white. I painted it metallic gray.

I was lifting the engine block from my 1962 Volvo P1800 sports coupe. I later overhauled the P1800-18B engine.

46

Colonel Byeong-Cheol Koh, South Korean Marine Corps, and I visiting a front line Radar Reporting Post near Sokcho, South Korea in 1972. He was the Director of Counter-Infiltration Operations, ROK Ministry of National Defense. Colonel Koh was a battle-hardened Vietnam veteran.

47

Standing in front of our VIP transportation, a U.S. Army Huey helicopter, at K-2 Taegu Air Base, South Korea in 1972. The air base was located within a river valley between two major mountain chains, seen here. The pilot banked the helicopter blade at a sharp angle. The chopper descended vertically straight down to the landing pad with unabated speed, and landed in less than three minutes. We felt like we were in free fall. I could feel strong, bouncy shocks on the skids.

48

(From left) Me, Colonel John V. Patterson, Jr., U.S. Air Force, the Director of DARPA-Korea, and Bob Beagle of TRW, at the Officer's Club, Yongsan, Seoul in 1972.

49

A memorial stone table of my father, Ke-Jun Kim, in our Kim clan memorial park, Cheong-won County, Seoul, Korea.

50

My father offered a cup of rice wine at the dedication ceremony of the tomb renovation of our twenty-third generation ancestor, Ik-Yeom Kim, c. 1500.

DR. CHAN-MO PARK

Some of my contemporaries did return to South Korea, one of whom was Chan-Mo Park. He was my best man at our wedding. He returned to South Korea to teach at the Korea Advanced Institute of Science and Technology (KAIST). In 1973, before I went to Seoul, I exchanged letters with Chan-Mo.

The Korea Advanced Institute of Science and Technology
P.O. Box 150 Chong-yang-ri, Seoul, Korea

Seoul

February 13, 1973

Dear John,

I cannot believe that three weeks have passed since we arrived in Seoul. We came to Seoul on January 21, 1973, and I went to my office at the Korean Advanced Institute of Science and Technology (KAIST) the next day. After arriving here, our children have had their shares of diarrhea and colds.

As I was busy in my new position, I found no time to meet with old friends and acquaintances. Our apartment is empty as our furniture did not get here yet. I am finding out every day how good life had been in America. I earnestly hope things will improve in the coming months.

KAIST will start its inaugural class with 106 students in the fall. The school will be ready to receive students. In the meantime, all students will be in the Reserve Officer Training Corps (ROTC) camp, which is a mandatory course in all South Korean universities. Also, KAIST plans to give individual tutoring to those incoming students who may need help in basic science and mathematics. Whether we will be ready or not, I am eager to meet these students in September.

By the way, I want to ask your advice. I am interested in recruiting our mutual friend, Dr. Heon-seo Park. Can you inquire for me if he would be interested in joining KAIST as a faculty member? It would be awkward for me to ask him directly. The Computer Science Department needs one professor specializing in computer hardware. If he is not interested in a position, could you suggest one or two potential candidates?

With Regards,
Chan-mo
(Translated by John Kim)

Chan-mo Park mentioned Heon-seo Park. He was a colleague of mine in TRW, who developed a Korean Hangul word processor.

In 1973, one month before I visited Seoul, I sent a letter to Chan-mo, and he replied. (see photo 40)

The Korea Advanced Institute of Science and Technology
P.O. Box 150 Chong-yang-ri, Seoul, Korea

Seoul
October 14, 1973

Dear John,

I am delighted to hear from you and looking forward to seeing you in November. I will be traveling to Europe in December for business. Please call me when you arrive in Seoul. My office phone number at KAIST is 96-xxxx-2844, and the apartment phone number is 97-xxxx-1703.

Best,
Chan-mo
(Translated by John Kim)

During my visit in November, Chan-mo and his wife invited me to a dinner at their new apartment. He told me KAIST was trying its best to accommodate repatriating faculty members. KAIST also provided fringe benefits by offering him a car and health insurance policy through an American insurance company. He said the returning faculty's salary was almost twice of Korean faculty's. This salary disparity became a cause of resentment within the university community. From his standpoint, Chan-mo and his wife had to endure inconvenience in their everyday life in Seoul, like ever-present air pollution and the rampant common cold.

Later, Chan-mo had a distinguished career in both South and North Korea. He became the President of the Pohang University of Science and Technology, South Korea, in 2004-2008, and the Science Advisor to President Myung-bak Lee in 2008. In 2010, he became the Chancellor of the Pyongyang University of Science and Technology (PUST). He stayed in Pyongyang during the school term and then returned to Seoul and Bethesda, Maryland in-between terms.

The Family Burial Ground

During my visit in 1973, my father, the Kim clan elders, and I went to our ancestorial tomb in Yeon-gi county. The tomb was located 40 miles south of Seoul. According to our clan genealogy book, there were several ancestors' tombs in Yeon-gi. A year before, my father had commissioned a search party to find the grave. When the search party had found the tomb, the inscription on the 450-year-old headstone was word-for-word the same as written in the genealogy book.[14] To their amazement, genealogy records were so accurate. I photographed the 450-year-old stone table at the dedication ceremony (see photo 50).

During the dedication ceremony, several youths from the village carried the last piece of the newly chiseled stone roof to the marker. They brought one day earlier the granite foundation and the main polished black granite column. The engraved commemorative citation had already been put in place. The group of village young men carrying the stone roof was moving up the hill. They stepped forward only whenever my cousin had put down some cash in their path. After several minutes of the push-and-pull with these young men, I wanted to speed

up the process. I pulled aside the leader of the group and made a deal with him. I would give him all at once my cousin's envelope filled with cash if they would finish their procession and place the stone roof on the black stone column. The leader looked at the thick envelope with money. He took the envelope, and the rest of the village youth put the roof on the stone column promptly as promised. Later, my father told me that I should have sprinkled the cash in front of them for the amusement of villagers instead of giving them the cash envelope all at once.

My father knelt on a straw mat placed in front of the new tombstone and read a prepared memorial message. After the ceremony, we had a bowl of hot beef soup and a cup of rice wine. We enjoyed them to warm our bodies on that chilly spring day on the hilltop.

My father also bought a two-and-one-half-acre property in Cheong-won County on a hill, not far from the tomb in Yeong-gi,[15] with the intention of building a family burial ground. (see photo 49) After he had moved to America, he was thinking of this hill as his final resting place. But we children suggested a nearby burial place in the Washington area. We suggested a plot at Parklawn Memorial Park in Rockville, Maryland. My parents were buried in the Parklawn as their final resting place.

14

Personal Miscellany II

MOVE TO A NEWLY BUILT HOUSE IN MCLEAN

Rahn and I decided to buy a house near my office in McLean. We were looking for a house in a good school district, which would provide good public school education. We found a newly built house in the McLean Hunt Estate Subdivision, which was a five-minute drive from my office. The subdivision was in the Langley High School district. Langley High School had an excellent reputation in the Fairfax County public school system. In this subdivision, the builder carved out a parcel of the farmland to make a 12.5-acre park. The Fairfax County Park Authority received the park property from the builder and agreed to maintain it. On the remaining 12.5 acres, the builder constructed 25 colonial style houses. In the bygone days, builders would develop a subdivision and would retain some green space for the community. (see photo 74)

When my parents came to America for the second time, my father was eager to see our new house. As soon as he arrived at our home from the airport, he looked around the front and back of the house and evaluated the land, the structure, and the layout of the house. He conducted his "Feng-shui"[16] of the house. He then said,

"I like the front of the house facing south. I also like that the house is built on the high ground."

Indeed, the elevation at the house was 400 feet, one of the higher places in Fairfax County.

KOREAN UNITED METHODIST CHURCH

After Rahn and I got married, we attended the Korean Church at the Foundry United Methodist Church. Pastor Andrew J. Hwang and Pastor Jacob S. Kim of the Korean Church baptized our three children. The Korean United Methodist Church (KUMC) moved its place of worship.[17] As the congregation grew, the church experienced growing pains, which resulted in the congregation dividing into two churches; one became KUMC, and the other the Korean Presbyterian Church in McLean. This breakup was painful, but it was a necessary cross to bear for the progress of the two congregations. The physical sign of the improvement was that the congregations owned their church properties, instead of renting a meeting place at the Foundry United Methodist Church and other churches.

As KUMC experienced growing pains, Rahn and I were looking for a more stable English speaking neighborhood church in McLean for our children. We found a well-run Sunday school at Trinity United Methodist Church and began to attend services there. In addition to spiritual life, the family participated in other church activities like the Charter Organization Representative of Boy Scout Troop 869. I acted as the representative from 1985 to 2003. For many years in the church, Rahn and I shared fellowship with friends like Dr. Edward and Phyllis King, who was the granddaughter of Dr. Sherwood Hall[18] an early missionary in Korea. Edward and Phyllis were the co-editors of Dr. Sherwood Hall's autobiography, *With the Stethoscope to Asia: Korea*.[19] The book describes the life of American and Canadian missionaries and their medical mission in Korea in the late 19th and the early 20th centuries.

MY RELIGIOUS VIEWS

Today, at KUMC, my friends, and acquaintances in the congregation are mostly in their jubilee years. Among church members, I can recognize fewer faces each year. My high school classmate Suk-kih Min used to be a choir member in KUMC, and every Sunday I used to see him standing in the choir loft. As I looked at his gray hair on every Sunday morning, I thought I saw a reflection of my own gray hair.

When Rahn and I became empty nesters, we returned to KUMC, where services were conducted in Korean. Every Sunday for the last 40 years I have attended Sunday services, whether at Trinity UMC (in English) or KUMC (in Korean). I have received steady spiritual diets from sermons delivered by the pastors, Andrew J. Hwang, Jacob S. Kim, Yun-gyeong Seon, Ferd Wagner, David Balcom, James Sprouse, Young-jin Cho, Young-bong Kim, and Han-sung Kim.

These pastors helped me to form the framework of my spiritual life and my worldview, some parts of which I attained by reasoning and others by faith.

For a long time, I asked:

"Does God exist?"

I once had asked this question to my Uncle Heon Sunwu, who was an ordained Presbyterian minister. He replied:

"John, if you try to understand the existence of God by your human reasoning, God would be too enormous an entity for your infinitesimally small cognitive reasoning capability to fathom and understand."

I did not like his answer to my question at the time. I thought his answer was insufficient. I continued to dwell on this thesis for a long time. My thesis of God's existence was influenced by two approaches: reason and faith. I began to realize that it would be tough to answer this question through an algorithmic method. I selected a heuristic method to address the question and relied on my faith for an affirmative answer as to the existence of God.

The second question I've pondered upon was: "What is the property of God?"

Christian God is said to be the Trinity, that is, the unity of Father, Son, and Holy Spirit. I believe in the Trinity Doctrine taught in the Christian Church. I accept this doctrine to depict the omnipotent God by early Christian fathers to teach one God in three positions.

I may as well touch on the third question: "What are the nature and the origin of the Universe?"

I consider the nature of the Universe to be composed of matter, energy, and an omnipotent Spirit. I came to this conclusion by both scientific reasoning and faith. I accept the Universe consists of matter and energy, based on what I learned through physical science. But what is the engine that kicked energy into matter, or vice versa? I think this is the question, which had stumped scientists and cosmologists. I like to believe that energy is emanated from the matter by the omnipotent Spirit, or the matter creates energy according to the formula pre-determined by the omnipotent Spirit.

My fourth question is: "What does this possibility mean to me? The possibility is that He who believes in God, though he may die, he shall live." (John: 3:16)[20]

I would never know how the Universe had started and how it will end. But I like to believe in the possibility of eternal life. The other possibility, of being non-existent and nothingness after my death, is too pathetic. Yes, I know others may disagree with epistemology as it is not logical and defies reasoning. But I am talking about my faith, not my reasoning.

Now that I have stated my understanding of the Universe, I ask myself: "What are the nature and the origin of man?" I think the nature of man is the composite of the physical body and the God-bestowed Spirit. The physical body is the result of the conception of my parents and my subsequent growth, which then leads to the end of life, my death. But at the same time, my spirit was bestowed by God. All this might be too simplistic, but I wanted to write down my thoughts on these challenging theses.

This I want to believe, as John's testimony in the Bible (John 11:26) stated, "Whosoever lives and believes in me shall never die. Do you believe this?"

I want to stop my religious speculations and metaphysical musings here. The above statements and expositions are what I understood and what I believe.

For a quarter of the century, from 1945 to 1970, my parents worked hard day after day. I do not think they took any holiday vacationing away from home. They sacrificed themselves for their family, providing five of their children decent living and education. I once had a chance to sit down and ask them,

"Thank you, Mom and Dad, for providing us the roof over our heads, clothes to keep us warm, and three meals on our table every day, and sending us to good schools."

"John, there is no need for you to thank us because we have done our duty as parents to you and your brothers and sister. Instead, there is something you could do for us."

"What is it? I would like to know."

"Oh, just give your children your love and guide them along the right paths. You don't have to pay us back anything."

"If you could provide your children the same kind of the roof, the clothes, meals, and schooling, which will be good enough for us."

That was excellent advice, and I tried to abide by their advice with my own children.

"The Lord provided me steady work for over 80 years. I was not idle.

"The Lord provided me with enough food on my table. I was not hungry.

"The Lord provided me with adequate means. I was able to send our children to a good school.

"The Lord provided me with reasonable health and vitality. I have reached the ripe old age and counting more."

I Never Was Any Good in Golf

I was a mediocre golfer, and could seldom break 100. In the 1970s, on a summer afternoon, my golf mates and I used to go to Pinecrest Golf Course in Annandale, Virginia to play golf.

One weekend we went to Algonquian Golf Course in Sterling, Virginia. We invited a colleague, Raj Edwards. He was reluctant to join us, as he had never played golf, but he agreed to join us.

"O.K. Raj. Here is a tee for you. You place your ball on the tee."

"Use this club, a three-iron, and hit the ball." When he swung his club, and

the ball flew off the tee and landed 180 yards away straight ahead. Our jaws dropped in disbelief.

"Raj, that is an excellent shot.

"Are you sure this is your first time on a golf course?"

"John, yes, it is the first time."

"Yeah, but, you swung the club like a pro."

"I played field hockey in India. The club looks similar."

That explains it. For his second shot, we saw him placing his ball on the tee again.

"Raj, you cannot use the tee in the fairway. You use the tee at the teeing ground only."

Then for his third shot, he was not able to see beyond a hill, so he began to walk ahead of us in the fairway, trying to locate the green and the flag.

"You can't walk toward the green.

"You stay behind everyone's balls until all of us hit the ball."

Then, we were convinced that he had never played golf before.

Now it has been many years since I golfed. Instead, I took up running and walking as my daily exercise. I never understood why grown-ups chased a small white ball all over the golf course. (see photo 26)

The Cars I have owned over the Past 50 Years

"How many cars have I owned in my lifetime?

"I have owned about 20 cars since I bought my first one in 1960.

"My first car was a 1954 Pontiac Chieftain, which was a two-tone car, yellow and green."

"It was a two-door sedan with a V-8 engine.

"I paid $340 (my monthly salary was $500) for it at a Lansing used car lot.

"I bought my second car, a 1958 American Motors Corp. Rambler two-door sedan.

"It had an automatic transmission, but I shifted the gear by pushing buttons instead of a gear stick."

One Saturday morning I was driving from Dayton to East Lansing. My Rambler suddenly just stopped running, of all places, on a railroad crossing in

Lima, Ohio. The engine was running, but the car would not move forward. I knew that this railroad track was one of the busiest tracks in Ohio. I panicked. I tried almost everything, but the car would not move. I heard grinding noise in the powertrain as I shifted the gear to several positions. Suddenly, I was able to drive the car in reverse. I parked it on the side road, breathing a sigh of relief. Fifteen minutes later, a diesel locomotive passed by on the track. A repair shop mechanic found the problem; the rear axle differential gearbox was dry and needed grease.

In 1965, as my wedding gift to Rahn, I gave her a Ford Falcon; it was a two-door, leaf-green car with a 4-cylinder engine. (see photo 38) After a dozen years of use, I painted the Falcon by myself "competition orange" color. Once, Rahn drove the Falcon to a state inspection station. A young mechanic asked her if she would sell it. Rahn told him that her car was like a family member and declined the offer, to his disappointment. This Falcon provided transportation to all my brothers and my sister and my children for over 20 years. They learned how to drive with that car, and certainly added to wear and tear on the clutch plate of the manual transmission. After 20 years of service, the floor on the passenger side of the old clunker was rusted through. I covered a gaping hole with a piece of plywood and sealed the interior.

Under the hood of the Falcon, I could easily access and remove any parts and assemblies. I rebuilt the engine of the Falcon by lifting the engine block out of the car and removed the rocker arm assembly, the engine head, the oil pan, the timing gear belt, the pistons, the crankshaft, and the piston rings. I took the stripped engine block to a machine shop, and had them reconditioned the cylinders and the engine block; then I reassembled and put the engine back. I enjoyed working on car engines. I was always interested in tinkering with automobiles. I finally sold the good old faulty Falcon and was sorry to see it go.

I have owned several foreign-made cars. I owned six Volvos of various models, including a P1800 sports coupe. The British actor Roger Moore starred in the television series, *The Saint*, in which he drove a Volvo P1800 sports coupe. I found a P1800 car in a classified ad and bought it for $1,550.[21] The sports coupe had a four-cylinder engine with a displacement of 1,800 cubic centimeters, and dual-Skinners Union (SU) carburetors on the engine. It had a manual gearbox with an electrically actuated overdrive, which functioned as a fifth gear,

but the overdrive gear did not work. The first repair work I did on the car was to fix the overdrive gear. I jerry-rigged a hydraulic pressure gauge to the overdrive. The oil pressure gauge I used was an oil pressure meter from an old boiler, with which I could measure hydraulic pressure. After some tests, I figured out the cause of the overdrive problem. There was a 1/8-inch scratch in the hydraulic piston. The previous owner, who probably worked on the solenoid actuator, damaged the cylinder. After I had fixed the scratch, I restored the oil pressure, and the overdrive gear worked. (see photo 44)

My father and I took the P1800 for a spin to Leesburg and Warrenton along the sparsely traveled U.S. Route 15 in 1978. The car's center of gravity was low, and father, being a knowledgeable automobile driver, appreciated the sports coupe and enjoyed the ride. Then, I painted the P1800 myself in metallic silver. The most frequently recurring problem of the P1800 was malfunctioning electrical instruments. I enjoyed driving the P1800, but finally, in 1988, I sold it to a young man for $1,200. I am sure he enjoyed the car as much as I did for a decade. I was sorry to see it leave my garage.

Nowadays, it would be difficult for me to fix latest model cars. It used to be a simple task to remove an alternator or some other parts from the engine block. These days, I wouldn't be able to reach an alternator without removing several adjacent parts or assemblies. I would need an automobile diagnostic computer and expensive software, which is beyond the means of a weekend mechanic. I have read "do-it-yourself" Haynes automobile repair manuals, which listed computerized diagnostic codes, which tells me what the issue is with the car. Knowing the repair code is one thing, but I cannot do anything about it as one needs a specialized computer to repair automobiles. Modern automobiles were embedded with many electronic chips. I have given up "do-it-yourself" car repair work. The time has come for me to quit car tinkering on the weekend altogether.

My Carpentry Hobby

One day a friend of mine, Dr. Alfred Schuler, dropped by my home. When he was drinking iced tea, he noticed a beautiful cupboard made of cherry in our dining room. Then he asked me:

"John, where did you buy this cupboard?"

"I did not buy it. I made it myself."

"You are kidding me."

"No, I am not."

"Do you have your carpentry shop here in the house?"

"Yes, I do."

"Would you like to see the shop?"

"Yes."

"Let me show you my tools in the garage and the workshop in the basement. I have a power saw, a lathe, a planer, a router, a drill machine, a band saw, and a jointer."

"Well, John, I can't believe it. Now, what is that thing hung on the ceiling?"

"Oh, that one. It is an air filter."

"It is a dust collecting system."

"You know it gets quite dusty in this garage."

"You want to see my workshop in the basement?"

"Sure."

"They are the spindle sander, the belt sander, the mortise, and the hand sander."

"When did you get all these stuffs?"

"Al, I bought these tools over the course of several decades. And I probably invested four or five grand. To build fine furniture like what you've seen in the dining room, I need all these tools.

"I used to make simple furniture like desks, dressers, and lawn chairs. Then I gained enough skill and began to build fine furniture. Carpentry and woodworking became my hobby."

"John, I saw a planer and a jointer in the garage."

"Yes, you did."

"Tell me why do you need both the planer and a jointer?"

"Aren't they both doing planing wood?"

"Why can't you use just one of them?"

"I use mostly cherry wood to build my furniture. I like cherry. It is easy to cut and finish the surface. But it is too expensive to have someone mill a piece of lumber for me. That would simply be cost prohibitive."

"So you buy lumber?"

"Yes, I go to a hardwood lumber company in Manassas to buy materials."

"They sell lumbers in different lengths, widths, and thicknesses."

"Then I first plane it to a half-inch or three-quarter-inch thickness."

"I then produce a flat surface with the jointer."

"John, I am impressed with your tools, furniture you have built, and the whole setup."

I often thought about why I took up woodworking as my hobby. During five decades of my career, I moved up my career ladders in TRW and ONR. As I advanced in the career ladder and became engineering managers, I had no opportunities to work on hands-on tasks as I did in my junior positions. Gradually woodworking became a substitute. I like to build things with my hands.

In this memoir, I have included three photographs of my carpentry works: my Canadian step-back cupboards (see photo 117), a Winthrop secretary's desk (see photo 118), and a deacon's bench (see photo 116). My Canadian step-back cupboard has a well-balanced upper and lower section. I built three of them and gave each of them to my three children.

On the weekend, Rahn and I often visit woodworking shops and furniture factories in the Shenandoah Valley, and the Thomas Moser furniture store in Georgetown. Joan Chu Reese, Rahn's niece, who saw my Canadian step-back cupboard at my son William's home, asked me,

"Uncle John, the cupboard is beautiful.

What is the asking price of a cupboard like this?"

"Joan, I saw a cupboard like this one at Thomas Moser's store in Georgetown. The price tag showed $6,000."

"You are kidding me."

"No, I am not. These factories may spend 7 man-days (56 man-hours) to build one like this.

"The labor cost, the overhead, and the cherry lumber cost add up to $3,500.

"If they spend more than 56 man-hours to build it, they would lose money."

"How long did it take you to build this cupboard?"

"Oh, it took me about 300 man-hours. I usually work two or three hours per day, two days per week, and it adds up to be three months."

The furniture factories we visit in the Virginia countryside are often housed in an old railroad depot or a nearby warehouse. They usually have ample space. I would like to have a workshop like that.

I built my deacon's bench with 20 dowels in the back of the bench, which distributes the weight of several persons sitting on the bench. My bench is like a bridge with trusses. If it were built with just one dowel each at the end, it would bend with a 40-pound load placed in the middle, but it would break if I doubled the weight. The wood is subjected to tension force at the bottom of the dowels and compression force at the top of the dowel. It permanently changes its form, and it would break. If I add two more dowels in the middle of the bench, it might hold more weight. But if I add 18 dowels equally spaced, the bench could hold tenfold of the weight. This "stress and strain" analysis was what I learned in college physics.

The Winthrop secretary's desk, which I've built, is a moderately complicated structure, featuring a folding desktop and even a secret compartment. I explained the process of making it to Doug, who became the owner of the secretary's desk. I finished these furniture pieces with Danish oil by the wet-sanding method in three successive steps with 220-, 400-, and 600-grit sandpapers.

One afternoon in 2011, I was sawing a piece of plywood on the table saw. In an unguarded moment, I injured my left, index finger and left thumb. A piece of wood I was cutting went out of control, and I severed a half-inch tip and the nail of my index finger and severely bruised my thumb. "Ouch!" I wished I took that moment back and handled my saw more carefully, but it was too late. Rahn called an ambulance to take me to the Fairfax Hospital emergency room. My primary care doctor recommended Dr. Amir Saba, a hand and plastic surgeon, who stitched up the injured finger and thumb. He told me to lift my left arm above my heart for several weeks, which helped ease the throbbing pain of the

finger and the thumb. I got the stitches removed after four weeks. Dr. Saba prescribed three months of physical therapy to rehabilitate my finger and thumb. At first, I had a minor problem using my computer keyboard, but I got used to striking some keys using my other fingers instead. After about a year of practice, I did not feel any inconvenience. But playing my flute became difficult as I could not close the high C key. On cold wintry days, there is not enough circulation at the extremity of my index finger, and it becomes cold.

FAMILY CAMPING

A cotton canvas tent I bought from Montgomery-Ward smelled like industrial shop rags. The tent reminded me of the classroom of my Pusan refugee high school where the air inside the U.S. Army surplus tent was thick with moisture brought by the monsoon air.

For one camping trip, we headed to Great Smoky Mountains National Park and pitched our tent at Big Creek Campground. Near the campground, the flow of coldwater streams was rapid. Moisture from the Gulf of Mexico moved up to the Appalachians. It dumped rain almost every afternoon in the park. The water flowed fast in Big Creek. I built a waterwheel with twigs, branches, and plastic blades, which the children liked to play with. Big Creek was a place where one could encounter bears. Sure enough, when I pulled into a parking lot, I heard a quiet voice from nearby, saying "Bear! Bear!" About 20 feet ahead of us a black bear was searching for food in a garbage can.

Blue smoke covers the Smoky Mountains. It is an optical phenomenon, caused by vapor released by the dense tree cover and other vegetation, as it brings out blue spectrum. Think of how a prism scatters light, and, scatters blue light. That scattering of light produces a hazy effect over the mountains. The blue color was there even in the Colonial days; it has nothing to do with modern-day emissions.

LITTLE LEAGUE BASEBALL

One summer afternoon, my eldest grandson, Keaton, was playing a baseball game in the McLean Little League field. When he stepped up to the plate and was ready to bat, he got hit in the mouth by the ball, and his lip was cut and bleeding. His mom and I took him to an emergency care center in McLean. The good doctor advised his mom to send Keaton back to the ball field right away so he could shake off any fear of playing baseball later. Keaton returned to the field and continued to play the game. "You should never catch the ball with your mouth," I told him on the way back to the ball field.

At the start of baseball season, we paraded on Westmoreland Street to the McLean Little League field with Keaton's baseball team. As I was marching with kids, someone behind me said,

"Hello, Mr. Kim."

"Hi, who are you?"

"I am one of Johnson boys."

"Oh, that is right."

"What is your name, is it Jason?"

"Yes, I am Jason, Mr. Kim."

"I am Keaton's coach this year.

How is William?"

"He lives in Great Falls, and he is well."

Forty years ago, William and Jason had been teammates, and now Jason has several kids of his own. William and Jason's team had been coached by Jason's Dad. I was glad to see our second generation was playing on the same little league field. When Rahn and I became parents and were raising our kids, everything was new to us as we never experienced anything like the little league in Korea. Now our grandchildren were repeating what their parents had gone through some thirty years ago, and it was a déjà-vu, the same baseball field, the same soccer field, and the same school system. Life was predictable for the generation of my children, unlike mine, who wandered through four capitals in my lifetime.

One summer, Tony, Keaton's father, got three tickets to a Baltimore Orioles game. Keaton was then four years old. When we drove to Camden Yards, Keaton kept asking his dad how much longer it would take to get to the

ballpark. From McLean to the Camden Yards ballpark was about an hour's drive. Tony told Keaton that we would be there in half of the time needed to watch the Caillou.[22] Keaton understood the length being fifteen minutes as the "Caillou" program was a thirty-minute program. I was amused by this concept of measuring the time interval. Finally, we got to the ballpark and settled in our seats. Below, lights flooded the green field. Excitement was in the air. We bought hot dogs and popcorns and had a good time. Between innings, I went to a souvenir shop and bought a baseball. When a batter popped up a ball toward us, I stretched out my glove, pretending to catch the ball. Then I produced a ball. Keaton was impressed by grandpa's feat of catching a foul ball.

15

TRW Projects (1975-1980)

During the Cold War, the U.S. Navy SOSUS stations listened vigilantly for any sign of Soviet submarines in the Atlantic and Pacific Oceans and the Mediterranean Sea. These Soviet submarines would transit from one place to the other or would patrol in the oceans. The SOSUS sonar system listened to subsurface and surface vessels of both friend and foe, and detected, classified, and tracked ships.

Occasionally, the sonar system could lose track of a submarine as the target moved outside of the SOSUS detection range. Then, patrol aircraft took over tracking operations. The ASW Operations Center (ASWOC) would dispatch a shore patrol aircraft (Lockheed Orion P-3C) to the location of the last report, and it would continue search operations from the air. The P-3C would drop a sonar buoy called DIFAR on the last known site, which would self-activate and try to reacquire the sound of interest and then transmit recorded signals to the P-3C via the HF data link to ASWOC for analysis. I became one of the engineers performing the contract work for the U.S. Navy to develop this search activity.

AN/USC-32 Digital HF Radio and VADAC Vocoder

The Naval Electronic Command (NAVELEX) tasked TRW to develop a new digital HF transmitter-receiver, which could send sonobuoy signals from a patrol aircraft P-3C to ASWOC. My Navy customer was Commander Earl Eckert, who was the NAVELEX manager in charge of the new digital HF radio development. This HF radio became known as the SEcure Transmission of Acoustic Data (SETAD). (see photo 53) The recorded sonar signals were

transmitted in a digital form to improve quality of HF radio communications. The speed of digital transmission was at the rate of 2,400 bits-per-second, which was the fastest transmission speed achievable at that time. The use of HF in radio communications went through several changes over the years. From 1920 to 1950, HF radio, also known as the shortwave radio, was popular with amateur radio and broadcasting but not usable in military operations. With the advent of digitized signal transmission, military users returned to HF radio. Most air-to-ground tactical radios were limited to an operational range of at most 40 nautical miles, while HF radio could extend the range to beyond 600 nautical miles. However, HF radio must use a digitized signal with a forward error correction system. The SETAD development demonstrated the feasibility of using the HF band.

NAVELEX awarded Harris Corporation a contract to manufacture digital HF radio according to the specifications developed by Earl Eckert and me. Nine months later, we received the SETAD prototype equipment. Earl and I tested HF radio at ASWOC-NAS Patuxent River. After the successful operational test and evaluation, we obtained the approval for service use, and the U.S. Navy designated HF radio as the AN/USC-32 HF digital data set.

Eckert and I also worked on a vocoder associated with SETAD for voice coordination during ASW operations between a P-3C pilot and an ASWOC sonar operator. This project was to convert the E-System's existing commercial VADAC vocoder to a fully militarized vocoder. I developed specifications for the newly militarized vocoder according to the standards for the militarization of electronic equipment. Today, almost all audio signals on telephones, computers, and movies are digitized and then converted back to an analog format.

A TDY AT THE U.S. NAVY NAVFAC BERMUDA

My Navy project manager, Commander Earl Eckert and I went to Bermuda on TDY to NAVFAC Bermuda to install and test the newly developed HF radio set. When we arrived at the Bermuda airport, we heard the airport public announcement system blared:

"Commander Eckert, Commander Eckert, please come to the information desk."

So we approached the information desk and found a U.S. Navy sailor.

"I am Commander Eckert. Did you page me?"

"Aye, aye, sir. Welcome to Bermuda.

"My captain sent his greetings to you and your party, sir.

"I will drive you to the Pampano Beach Hotel." (see photo 55)

It was my first travel to Bermuda in the Atlantic. My initial impression of Bermuda in the lobby of Bermuda Airport was very British with a proper accent of Queen's English but was Hawaiian atmosphere permeated with warm and breezy subtropical air. The hotel was on the southwestern corner of the island, which was like a causeway that's one-mile wide and 20-mile long. I felt as though I was on a huge ship because I could see the ocean on the port and the starboard sides. The buildings were mostly stucco, painted in pastel shades of white or pink. Many shops lined up on Front Street, and huge cruise ships towered over the Royal Dockyard. On the street, I saw men dressed in long-sleeve shirts with ties but wearing Bermuda shorts, stockings, and leather shoes. There were many compact white cars, but there were more bicycles than cars.

We checked into the hotel, which was a country club with a golf course. I saw two big barracudas swimming in the emerald sea off the beach.

"I will pick you up here in the morning.

"Just give me a buzz if you need to go to any place on the island," the sailor said.

The next morning, we went to NAVFAC BDA, where we met Commander Lou Alderson, Commanding Officer of the U.S. Navy NAVFAC BDA. He was addressed as Captain although his rank was Commander. It was a time old Navy tradition to address a commanding officer of Naval Facilities or Naval vessels as Captain, even if he would be a Lieutenant, who could be the skipper of a motorboat.

According to Earl, Lou Alderson was his Executive Officer when Earl was the Commanding Officer of the ASW Patrol Wing at NAS Argentia in Newfoundland. Alderson invited us to the morning situation briefing, which included the whereabouts of Soviet nuclear submarines in the mid-Atlantic Ocean that day. A large-screen display showed the tracks and the courses of ships in the Atlantic Ocean and the Mediterranean Sea.

ANOTHER TDY AT FORD ISLAND, HAWAII

I accompanied Earl on another TDY to Oahu, Hawaii. We went to NAS Barbers Point and the Ocean Surveillance Station-Pacific on Ford Island to install an HF SETAD radio set at the technical control facility of ASWOC. One afternoon, Earl said,

"John, why don't we climb to Diamond Head in the tomorrow afternoon."

"Have you been there?"

"Oh, ya, I climbed it a few years ago.

"It is quite a landmark on Oahu.

From Diamond Head, you can see the mountain range formed by ancient volcanoes."

"O.K. I will go."

Next day, we drove to Diamond Head National Monument and to the interior of the crater through a tunnel. Inside the crater, we found Ft. Ruger, the oldest U.S. Army fort in Hawaii. Diamond Head is a bowl-like crater. The diameter of the crater is one mile, and its elevation is 672 feet.

"Earl, are you sure we could find the trail."

"John, don't worry. You will like the climb."

From the trail, I could see Diamond Head. We arrived at the top an hour later. To the west, I could see long white sand of Waikiki Beach, and further west Ford Island and Hickam AFB, green lush mountain ranges, and the tropical clouds hovering halfway up the mountains. Hawaiians call the mountains "pu'u." After taking some photos, we headed back to the parking lot. It was getting dark, and we got lost halfway down. We somehow got off the trail but found the parking lot two hours later.

I visited Ford Island in the summer of 2003 again when my family trav-

eled to Honolulu to attend David Kim's (my nephew) wedding. We stayed at the Navy Lodge on Ford Island. I earlier told you that I visited Ford Island some thirty years ago. At that time, Ford Island was a bustling operational naval base. But in 2003, the island became an idle government-owned real estate. I thought the island was waiting for another war in which it may serve the nation as it did during the World War II. The Navy had abandoned much of Ford Island, except for a newly renovated Navy Lodge and Navy officer's quarters. There used to be a ferry boat which connected the island to the Oahu, but now a bridge connected the island to Oahu. The Navy security still guarded the Ford Island premise 24 hours a day, so it was a very secure place to stay.

The Fleet Command Center (FCC) Data Network

When I entered the computer room at the TRW McLean building, I found a general-purpose mainframe computer, the Honeywell World-Wide Military Command and Control System (WWMCCS) H-6000. Operators were busy at their consoles, and the reel-to-reel tape recorders were continually repeating "stop-go" spooling. Using this computer, TRW developed the FCC software system. We used Datanet-355 to connect 200 terminals to the WWMCCS network for data communications.

In 1981, the FCC program manager was Jim McCurry; I became his senior staff engineer. The TRW FCC program office was in a bay in the McLean W-1 building. The bay faced south, and it was very cozy and warm in the winter months, except that it attracted insects, which died on the window sills after a while. Jim was a Scot with a dry sense of humor. He told us,

"Don't eat those raisins on the window sill. They aren't raisins."

Jim assigned me to build a prototype data communications terminal between the WWMCCS development site in the TRW McLean and the other computer site at the U.S. Army War College in Carlisle Barracks, Pennsylvania. The WWMCCS computer system included a Honeywell H-6000 mainframe computer, a Datanet 355 front-end processor, and peripheral terminals.

I obtained a pair of the commercial modems, Rixon Sebit-24B, for providing data communications over plain old telephone service (POTS) at the

transmission rate of 2,400 bits per second. This was a far cry from today's transmission speed of 400 gigabits per second using fiber optic cables. That was not the only antique museum piece I had to deal with. Unlike today's computer communication, I had to use a data communications test set to monitor the protocol to handshake the transmitter and receiver terminals. Today, a computer is ready to be plugged into a home telephone jack with any handshake protocol. My team installed a data transmission device at the computer center in McLean, and another device in Carlisle Barracks. An Army signal corps man monitored his communication device.

In 1973, Jim McCurry came from TRW, in Los Angeles, and became the FCC Program Manager. The business of the Washington Operations was all Navy projects then. But Jim had been working on the cutting-edge NASA Gemini-3 Spacecraft Project. He was working with astronauts Gus Grissom and John Young at Cape Canaveral.[23] He was not very happy with the FCC program assignment.

Once, I traveled with him to Los Angeles. He invited me to dinner at his home in Rancho Palos Verdes, an upscale suburb of Los Angeles. The house was at the top of a hill, facing northwest. From his house, one could see the glistening Pacific Ocean in the afternoon and the sparkling lights from Los Angeles downtown in the evening. The region was smog-free, as Pacific Ocean breezes blow the smog out to the sea daily.

"Our house is on a quarter-acre lot,

"We built a mini-swimming pool," Jim told me.

The price of the home was worth several times that of a comparable home in the Washington area.

BALLISTIC MISSILE DEFENSE PROJECTS

During the first Iraq War in 1991, on the TV set in my living room, I saw reports of missile attacks from Saddam Hussein's Iraq to two populous cities in Israel, Tel Aviv and Haifa. Russian-made SCUDs were propelled into Israeli airspace. Until then, I had never seen an armed conflict, where one country attacked the other country with missiles. In turn, she countered and defended herself with her Ballistic Missile Defense (BMD) system.

The Israeli missile defense system consisted of American-made Patriot Advanced Capability-3 (PAC-3). I worked for two decades on and off, on various aspects of BMD projects. What I saw on TV was the reality of a missile attack being countered by Air Defense Artillery (ADA); it was a new kind of warfare, which we could watch in our living room on the TV news. It was scary!

The first time I had worked on an Anti-Ballistic Missile Defense (ABMD) project was in 1975 when TRW received an Army contract to develop an ABM system. Dr. Bill Besserer became the Project Manager, and Rob Silverstein became his Deputy. They needed my help to analyze the processing speed of application programs, required for the computer in the ABM system.

A typical timeline of a missile attack from the launch to the impact was about thirty minutes. TRW sought to build application programs, which must process in near real-time to detect incoming hostile missiles via a satellite surveillance system. The first opportunity to detect a missile was during the booster phase, which was the portion of an attacking ballistic missile track when it reached the peak velocity. After this phase, the incoming threat data would be handed over to the Engagement Control Station, equipped with the Perimeter Acquisition Radar (PAR). When PAR had reacquired re-entry vehicles, the system aimed the target. I studied computer requirements to determine how much capacity would be required to process application programs.

The next missile defense project I was associated with was the Joint Theater Missile Defense (JTMD) Project. In 1993, the TRW Albuquerque Operations received a contract on the JTMD project from the Air Force Operational Test and Evaluation Center (AFOTEC), Kirtland AFB, Albuquerque. JTMD was a joint program to develop a theater ballistic missile defense system.

Keith Beaver, the Manager of the TRW Albuquerque Operations, asked me to review a concept of operation by which the Navy defined its role in the first phase of theater missile defense. The Navy assets like the Aegis battle group would be the most mobile assets for theater missile defense with the Standard Missile-3. The Navy assets could arrive at the conflict area within weeks, if not days. Keith Beaver and I met with TRW's Air Force customer, Colonel John Carlile of AFOTEC.

During one of my briefings, Colonel Carlile asked me,

"What is meant by 'Ulchi' in the joint command post exercise, and Ulchi-Focus Lens, in South Korea?I knew the answer, and told him that "

Ulchi was the 7th-century Korean general who successfully defended the invading Chinese army across the Yalu River.

John Carlile and his staff appreciated my short history lesson. Ulchi-Focus Lens was a U.S.-R.O.K. combined forces exercise. The exercises still continue today and are a thorn in the eyes of the North Korean regime.

❋ ❋ ❋

The third missile defense project, in which I participated, was the National Missile Defense (NMD) project. In 1998, I supported Jim Larson, who was the TRW NMD program manager. The company became a subcontractor for the NMD Lead Systems Integration project. Boeing Company was the prime contractor. TRW supported the Battle Management Command, Control, and Communication (BMC3) subsystem. Jim Larson was interested in the NMD data center. I performed a network simulation of the data center using the BoNES simulation tool. Juanita Ford and I simulated the data center and performed an analysis of the end-to-end delay of files traversing the Ballistic Missile Defense Organization (BMDO) network. I published the result, "BMDO Virtual Data Center Network Traffic Analysis," in *Proceedings of IEEE 1998 MILCOM Conference.*[24]

I BECOME MANAGER OF THE UNDERSEA SURVEILLANCE DEPARTMENT

One day, John Bryant, the Manager of the Systems Engineering Laboratory, asked me to drop by his office. When I got there, he surprised me by saying:

"John, we will reorganize the Washington Operations in the coming weeks. Jim Larkin and I have decided to promote you to head a newly established department. It will be known as the Undersea Surveillance Department. Your department will have three sections and thirty MTS's."

"I am touched by the news of the promotion. I thank you and Jim Larkin for the confidence you have placed in me. But, why does company need reorganization?"

"Who knows? The company felt that we need a new alignment of business and skill centers.

"Or, as they say when in doubt of business expansion, reorganize.

That way all evil may disappear."

I was about to ask more questions.

"Don't ask more. Just accept the promotion.

You earned it."

During the Cold War, Russian nuclear submarines continued to be the most imminent threat to America. The Navy spent a substantial amount of its budgets on the anti-submarine warfare program. There were several classes of Russian submarines, such as the Charlie-, Victor-, and November-classes, which had become quieter to avoid detection by the U.S. Navy underwater acoustic surveillance network.

I assisted Navy engineers in drafting the research and development plan for the satellite communications device to the new cable-towing ships, called the Surveillance Towed Array Sensor System (SURTASS). The TRW engineers helped the Navy to improve NAVFAC operations. The improvement of ASW operations was quantified by the metric of deci-Bell (dB), which was the unit of acoustic power in sonar. We called these conflicts between Americans and Soviets "the battle of dB," a battle of keeping one's submarine propeller and other machine noise quieter than the adversary's.

How I Managed the Workforce Stability

In the days of the boom-and-bust business cycle of the aerospace industry, I saw a rapid expansion of the aerospace industry in Southern California, which reached $20 billion funding out of the total Pentagon and NASA budget of $300 billion. I traveled to the Space Park campus in Redondo Beach, where TRW was conducting most of the research and development, and manufacturing of spacecraft, missiles, and electronics.

Every now and then, I heard about a large-scale layoff of the workforce in the aerospace industry in Southern California when a company completed a large project or lost a large contract. The trailers of the winning company's human resources department would come to the parking lot of the losing

company to hire laid-off employees. Such was the scene in the aerospace industry. To prevent such fluctuation of the workforce, our company and other well-managed companies tried to devise a management method to smooth workforce fluctuation.

I learned to manage workforce fluctuation in my department of thirty technical and administrative staff members. All of them were gainfully employed, most of the time. However, there were times when staff numbers were disrupted by the completion of projects.

Needless to say, employees sought assurance that the company would continue to provide them the job security. An MTS in-between-jobs might get an assignment to the proposal preparation. A large corporation like TRW always had proposals to prepare, an activity which was funded with Bids and Proposal (B&P) funds. This was an overhead budget, allowed by the government procurement regulations as the cost of doing business. At the end of each fiscal year, the Government reimbursed B&P funds, which was about 3 percent of the company's annual budgets. In 1979, TRW Systems Integration Group had an annual budget of $1 billion, from which $30 million was set aside as B&P funds. The Systems Integration Group management adjusted the personnel hiring quota according to the labor force forecast and the B&P overhead budget allocation.

When I joined TRW in 1969, the Washington operations were a one-project business organization with 200 employees. The operations became well-established with the ASW Program. However, the operations needed more than one project and sought to diversify its business. The operations found new programs by offering its technical expertise to the World-Wide Military Command and Control System (WWMCCS) Program to support the Defense Information Systems Agency (DISA)[25] and to the aviation business to support the Federal Aviation Administration (FAA). Two decades later, the Washington operations became a full-fledged group with three divisions with John Stenbit at the helm of the group; it had annual sales of $1 billion in 1990.

Secure Voice Conferencing System and Mobile Command Center Project

Until the end of the 1950s, DoD had sufficient and necessary in-house capabilities to manage most of its R&D programs with government employees. However, from the 1960s on, DoD managed its programs through the significant amount of support contractors.[26] A portion of program budgets was set aside for contractor supports. During my tenure in TRW, I was an engineer in the private sector, who worked on Government Systems Engineering and Technical Assistance (SETA) contracts. From 2001 to 2013, during my ONR tenure, I had been sitting on the other side of the table, and I had hired SETA contractor, Dr. Bill Stachnik, as my staff. (see photo 107)

My first task in support of a DoD SETA contract was the Secure Voice and Graphics Conference (SVGC) project for DISA. Earlier, I supported SPAWAR (which used to be called NAVELEX) to redesign and build the CV-3332 vocoder using the existing E-Systems's VADAC vocoder. Until the 1970s all voice communications were in analog forms, like the signal in POTS. But military voice communications were gradually converted to a digital form, which became a precursor of today's telephone communications in wireline and wireless phones. In the early days of the vocoder, analog voice signals were not digitized by analog-to-digital conversation. Voice signals were digitized by the formant vocoder with voice pitch and sound synthesis.

For the SVGC project, I helped the DISA manager Lieutenant Colonel Earl Williams to develop a conferencing bridge connecting several voices. Using telephone technology of the day, we found that a conference bridge of digitized voice signals was a technical challenge. An older conferencing bridge using analog voice was easier to implement than a conference switch using digital voice. An analog voice conference bridge could easily combine several participating analog voice signals. However, digital voice signals could not readily be combined with a bridge but needed more complicated signal processing at the conference bridge.

16

Personal Miscellany III

As the old Sage Confucius said in his Analects:

"At 50, I became a mandarin of my country, and I understood
the mandate of Heaven."

But for me, when I had reached the age of 50, did I understand the mandate
of Heaven? No, but I think I knew the purpose of life. Perhaps I felt I needed
to contribute to the community.

SERVING AS A NATIONAL JUDGE FOR THE MATHCOUNTS COMPETITION

For many years, I served as a judge in STEM-related competition called
Mathcounts. Mathcounts is a mathematics competition for junior high school
students; it promotes interest in mathematics, and it is a mathematics version
of the spelling bee competition. As the National Judge of the Mathcounts, I
reviewed all math questions to determine whether each was solvable or not.
What was amazing was that these middle school students sometimes figured
out the solution before they heard the full question. There were six of us who
served as the judges every year, and we discussed the importance of teaching and
learning mathematics.

"We viewed mathematics as the backbone of STEM.

"Mathematics is called 'the queen of all sciences.'

"Does it mean that studying physics, chemistry, or biology is not as important as studying mathematics?

"No, it does not mean that.

"But, without mathematics, there could be no exact science of physics, chemistry, or biology."

We judges had discussions on whether the American school system was doing enough for mathematics education. We saw the results of annual international mathematics competitions for high school students. The Asian nations, notably China, Japan, Singapore, and South Korea, tended to rank high on the competition list, while the ranking of the U.S. and European nations comes behind the Asian nations. Does this ranking mean that our mathematics education was not good enough in quality? Some judges disagreed that the results of math competitions tell the whole story, considering that the teaching in Asia tends to foster memorization, but not enough reasoning and out-of-box thinking. The Asian students were indeed excellent in solving mathematical problems by numerical methods. But computer programming languages and operating systems were mostly invented by mathematicians produced by American computer science education. Perhaps we should have more faith in American mathematics education and give more credits to them. (see photo 92)

BOY SCOUTS

In the winter of 1975, in the cafeteria of Springhill Elementary School, my son William, a cub scout, held a shoebox, in which he had placed his pinewood derby model car. He had been working on this car for two months. The excitement of racing was in the air, and cub scouts were milling around in the cafeteria as their families sat and waited for the race to start. In the middle of the cafeteria was a 50-foot long race track manned by racing officials, assisted by several older Boy Scouts.

William had gotten a pinewood derby kit and cut and shaped the block of wood with help from me. He carefully pushed the axles into four slots. He then painted it in metallic silver and named it the "silver bullet." The cars ran down the track powered by gravity. In the first race, his car was the first to cross the finish line and the first place again in the next two races, and he won the championship. A few years later, Doug also participated in the derby contest, and he, too, won the championship.

Four decades later, William's son, Matthew, also built his pinewood derby

car and won the first place in his pack. I posted a photograph of Matthew, William, and me on the Facebook with the following caption:

"Three generations of the pinewood derby."

A day later, Jinny Lee, the mother of another cub scout, commented on this posted picture,

"John, my son Andrew needs tips from you.

"Andrew's pinewood derby will be held in two weeks."

Several decades after, the pinewood derby joined the computer age. Now, an electronic sensor at the finish line displays race results in real-time, replacing judges who stood at the finish line to declare the race results. This eliminated human errors in judging derby races.

In October in 1977, William and I woke up in a pup tent at Monocacy Aqueduct Park near the Chesapeake and Ohio (C&O) Canal in Maryland. The night before we drove to this park to join a cub scout overnight father-and-son camping. We brought with us a pup tent with sleeping bags, cooking gear, and groceries. The park was situated on the 184-mile long C&O Canal, from Georgetown in Washington, D.C., to Cumberland, Maryland. The canal has been known as the "Grand Old Ditch" along the Potomac River. In a bygone era, horses pulled barges carrying freight. Today, there are no boats in the canal. Hurricane Agnes damaged the aqueduct 30 years ago.

The Chesapeake and Ohio Canal

In the bygone era, horses pulled barges
Carrying bacon and coals,
Now no more cargoes, nor boats, nor boatmen,
Just a few rusted machines once lifted the lock.
The infrastructure of the 19th century, in America,
Are gone, and no restoration, How sad it is!

By John Kim

One cub scout Josh Levine and his father did not bring pots and pans and groceries. William and I were cooking a piece of Spam and eggs in our skillet, and it smelled good in the fresh autumn morning in the park. Josh followed the cooking smell and came to our picnic table. As we shared our breakfast with him, his father came and told Josh;

"You should not eat someone else's breakfast."

What he meant was not to eat Spam, which was a pork product not allowed in their religion, so poor Josh had to retreat to his tent.

My son William joined Boy Scout Troop 865, which had been chartered by Lewinsville Presbyterian Church in McLean. The Scoutmaster, LeRoy Parnell, was a dedicated Scouter for many years. I became his Assistant Scoutmaster. A few months later, when Roy Parnell suddenly died, the Scout Troop Committee appointed me as the new Scoutmaster. During my tenure as the Scoutmaster, I guided four senior scouts, John Scuddi, William Kim, Dave Kildee, and David Hsu, to attain their Eagle Scout ranks.

In 1982, I led a four-car convoy of Boy Scout Troop 865 and drove from McLean to Norfolk Naval Base, for a field trip. Two sea patrols met us at the submarine base gate and asked us to state our business at the base. From my briefcase, I took out a letter stating that seven scouts of Troop 865 and their parents, including Congressman Dale Kildee and Mrs. Gayle Killdee, who were parents of a scout, were visiting *USS Birmingham* (SSN 695). We were the guests of Rear Admiral William O'Connor, who was the grandfather of the scout, Kevin O'Connor, in the troop. After confirming from *USS Birmingham*, the sea patrol lets us pass through the gate, and we proceeded to the entrance of Submarine Berth S-3 with the arched sign "SS Birmingham-SSN 695". The gangplank connected from the entrance upward to the deck of the submarine, moored alongside to port, where the skipper of the submarine, Commander Dennis Jones, greeted us. We walked up the elevated gangplank to the deck level and entered the boat by the hatch door at the rear of the conning tower. It was early March, and the air on the waterfront was nippy, but the interior of the submarine was warm and cozy. That afternoon, most of the sailors were on liberty. The skipper let Congressman Kildee and me shoot two empty torpedo tubes. When I pushed the big button to fire a dummy torpedo, I could feel the reaction of the submarine lurching backward as the launcher pushed out a significant amount of water under high pressure. In the galley, there was free ice

cream, and t scouts enjoyed soft serve ice cream. The skipper gave us permission to look through the periscope. He trained the periscope on a ship about two miles away and showed us how we could see a magnified bolt on the mast of the ship, also shown on the video monitor.

From the National Mall, the white U.S. Capitol dome looks grand, but it was less grand from inside of the dome, as we discovered it to be a rusted steel structure. One winter day, scouts of Boy Scouts Troop 865 toured the dome, which Congressman Kildee had arranged for us. Our tour guide, the Architect of the Capitol, took us to the freight elevator and guided us inside the dome, from which we saw a panoramic view of Washington. The dome was a huge shell, which covered the steel and brick structures; we walked around the interior of the dome on scaffolds, which circled the dome. After that tour, I think of the Capitol dome as the drafty and windy space, whenever I look at the massive white dome.

Whenever I hear a Swahili greeting "Jambo" in movies on Africa, I think of the Boy Scouts gathering known as the Jamboree, which resembles a boisterous African tribal gathering. I led my troop to the 1985 National Scout Jamboree, held at Ft. A. P. Hill, Virginia. It was the 75th Anniversary of BSA, which attracted 30,000 scouts and scouters at the week-long event. We parked our cars near the Army garrison headquarters, which had a large Army parade ground. At the Scoutmasters' powwow in the evening, scouters, who had camped out in Ft. A. P. Hill before, warned us about infamous mosquitos swarm around and near the several large ponds, a breeding ground for pests. Our troop traveled heavy. Each scout carried their gear to the designated camp area, where we pitched our tents. The Senior Patrol Leader and the quartermaster went to the Jamboree headquarters and fetched our food ration, including chicken, onions, celeries, potatoes, and carrots. The troop cook details poured the chicken meats, curries, onions, celeries, potatoes, water, and everything else in a Dutch oven, and boiled everything for dinner. At six o'clock we heard the

camp bugler sounding off the mess call, "Tata Tata tah-tah," but our troop had begun eating our supper a half-hour earlier as we didn't know about the mess call. We had cookies for dessert. Imagine yourself served this kind of chow for several days, and you will be hungry enough to wolf down anything.

Every Tuesday of the week during the scout year, the troop met in the basement of Lewinsville Presbyterian Church. They would usually horse around for most of the time during two-hour evening meetings. The evening activities were boring to them sometime. But at the National Jamboree, all scouts helped Senior Patrol Leader John Scuddi without anyone's prompting. They all pitched in to carry troop equipment and became a well-trained scout troop, not a motley crew of pirates as they usually were at our church meeting. They surprised me with their disciplined behaviors. I thought that was one of the values of attending a Jamboree. The scouts rose to the occasion and shined.

In addition to the National Jamboree, the National Capital Area Boy Scout Council held a Camporee at Ft. Belvoir, Virginia, every year, and our troop also participated in several competitions and activities. The U.S. Army gave the Boy Scouts permission to use part of the Army base. I remember that one year the competition was pioneering.

"What did scouts do in the pioneering competition?"

"Well, scouts must build an eight-foot-tall tripod gate, on which we would hoist the troop color and the gate sign, "Troop 865, McLean, VA."

"To make it, we needed some rope and six 8-foot long poles.

"The Senior Patrol Leader knew that there were some leftover materials in the basement.

"We found poles, ropes, and woods, which were leftovers from a pioneering competition several years earlier.

"For a month, the scouts practiced constructing the gate.

"They laid three poles on the table, started a claw hitch, and made a square lashing with three poles.

"They half-hitched the end of the rope.

"Then, they spread the tripod's legs and lashed a cross member pole on the ground and also another tripod at the gate.

"They tied the sign with a scaffold hitch, and hung the sign. "Troop 865, McLean, VA." on it.

"I was not sure the scouts would ever get it right.

The weekend of the Camporee, it rained for three days. The scouts re-enacted their pioneering practice and tried very hard to build the tripods. One of the judges then did a chin-up on our tripods, and it was sturdy enough to bear his weight for the required two minutes. Later, the Camporee Head-quarters announced the results, and our pioneering made the third place in the competition. The scouts' hard work had paid off. In the rain, they started to chant,

"Mr. Kim, Mr. Kim, 865, 865; we are the best."

I was grateful that no scout got pneumonia. But I heard plenty of com-plaints from their mothers on the amount of red clay mud they brought home out of their clothes and gears that weekend.

"Well, you win some, and you lose some."

The following fall, the competition in the District Camporee was to build a wooden catapult and shot a tennis ball with it. The catapult was like a slingshot on a forked branch. We built a catapult and a cart so that we could transport it. (see photo 61) It had a hinged throwing arm, on which we attached two three-foot bicycle inner tubes, and a can for holding a tennis ball. It took us one month to build and test the catapult.

So how did we do? Our goal was to throw the ball for a good distance by the catapult. In the outdoors, a Scout might need to throw a line across a stream. Or, Sea Scouts might have to throw a lifeline farther than you could launch it by hand. For materials, we bought five 2-by-4 studs, a sheet of half-inch-thick plywood, a bicycle inner tube, carriage bolts, and screws. For tools, we used a table saw, a jigsaw, and a hammer. We built it in my workshop and tested it in the parkland in the back of our home. To be safe, I did the cutting the studs and the plywood.

The Council Headquarters instructed us to bring our catapult to the campo-ree. Assistant Scoutmaster Pete Johnson carried it in his pickup truck. We placed four cinder blocks to secure the catapult. To operate the catapult, two older scouts pulled back the throwing arm and secured it with a pin at the middle hole, and place a tennis ball in the can. Then, the Senior Patrol Leader shouted "Fire!" A scout pulled the pin to release the throwing arm. After the

ball was launched, we would measure the distance. Here came the physics of launching a projectile. I told the scouts:

"You know the objective is to throw the ball as far as possible."

"Now, do you know how to get the distance?"

"You don't know."

"O.K. One way to find out is to try different angles. Pretend that you are an outfielder throwing a baseball to the home plate."

"Yeah, I have to lob the ball."

"Yes, that's right. But what makes the ball go farther?"

"You throw hard."

"Yes, that's right.

"But what else makes the ball go farther?"

"The angle, I guess," another scout said tentatively.

"That's right. I will tell you what I've learned in college physics. You can get the farthest distance by throwing the ball at the angle of forty-five degrees."

"Really! How do we get the angle?"

"By testing it out."

So my scouts adjusted the lever arm angle, mark the pin position on the lever arm, launch the ball, and measure the distance. The scouts kept a record of the experiment and figured out which angle yielded the farthest distance. On the day of the competition, I could see that scouts of Troop 865 were excited. I have never seen them so intense in their competition. After several heats, Troop 865 placed fifth out of 24 entries. One scout asked me,

"Mr. Kim, why can't we go further than 20 yards."

"I think we needed a better rubber tube. The other team used a better rubber tube. We did pretty well with our catapult. Let's go home."

We got a big yellow ribbon, which they tied on the Troop flagstaff, and returned home.

How do Boy Scouts learn their scouting skills? One way was through their experience whether good or bad. In the following fall, our troop went another weekend camping to the Washington National Forest in the Blue Ridge Mountains. Scout Dave Hsu brought several bags of Asian ramen noodles but a limited quantity of water. Ramen noodles were very convenient to prepare as you just poured boiling water into a cup of ramen noodles, simmered for three minutes, and it was ready to eat. I warned scouts that ramen was salty, as one bag contained 30% of a person's daily sodium intake allowance. By Saturday afternoon, David had drunken much of drinking water in his canteen. Suddenly the troop was running out of water. The Senior Patrol Leader (SPL) had a U.S. Geological Survey map that indicated a spring was nearby. Scouts searched the area but could not find any spring. I then ordered SPL to collect all water canteens. From then on, until Sunday morning, SPL should strictly ration the water. David Hsu learned his lesson, how precious water was, the Boy Scout way.

In 1975, Doug went to the Boy Scout summer camp in Goshen, Virginia for one week. Scoutmaster Mark Van Raden asked me to give a straggler scout, who missed the previous day's bus ride to the Goshen Scout Camp, a ride to join his troop. On the way to the camp, at Lexington, Virginia, I bought a watermelon at a roadside market for our scouts. As I carried the watermelon from the parking lot to the campsite, some passing scouts congratulated me on winning the watermelon. Apparently, there was a competition in the morning, and the prize was watermelons. Boys thought my troop had won the contest. I found Doug and his buddy Eric Behrens sitting on the top of a picnic table, looking bored when we arrived at the campsite. When they saw me and the watermelon, they perked up. The troop had a feast with the watermelon.

BOARD OF DIRECTORS OF THE FAIRFAX COUNTY VOLUNTEER CENTER

For many years, TRW was active in several community outreach programs as its employees had a significant presence in Fairfax County and neighboring jurisdictions in Virginia, the District of Columbia, and Maryland. Each year the company contributed funds to the Fairfax County Volunteer Center (FCVC). The company asked me to represent as a board member of FCVC. I presumed that the volunteer center wished one of its major donors to be active in their board activities.

As part of the commitment to promote volunteerism, FCVC administered the Alternative Community Service (ACS) program, which placed a broad range of court-ordered clients in community services instead of serving a jail term. Each year nearly 700 clients completed more than 34,300 hours of service at over 100 local nonprofit organizations and public agencies. According to the Virginia Employment Commission, ACS clients contributed the equivalent of $676,000 each year with their community service.

Until I became an FCVC board member, I had no idea about the number of people incarcerated in America. Statistics showed that America had the highest rate of incarceration in the world. In other words, America was, and still is, a nation of jailers. I began to realize that what FCVC did was not just volunteerism to help poor, or underprivileged people, but also sought to divert people from our prison by placing court-referred clients in community service. During our orientation session at the Fairfax County Court, the chief judge told us about the number of ever-increasing court cases and overcrowded prisons. I was overwhelmed by the statistics presented by the judge.

THE CHESAPEAKE BAY AND THE POTOMAC RIVER

One summer day, I went on a fishing trip on a charter boat in the Chesapeake Bay with fellow members of the KUMC Methodist Men's Club. I drove to the South River pier near Annapolis, where we boarded a 40-foot charter boat. When our boat went to the mid-channel in the Bay, the skipper used his sonar equipment to find for fish; he also exchanged information with captains of other fishing boats over the VHF marine radiophone. Around ten o'clock in

the morning, our boat finally hit a school of bluefish; the school was so large that the water below us became dark with fish. I didn't even need to use bait to catch fish; I just yanked the line and hooked fish. I could not believe that I could catch fish that way. After two hours of fishing, we filled our 32-gallon plastic container with fish, and we called it a day. We returned to the pier where the fishermen cleaned fish and divided the catch; Rahn stored fish in the freezer and ate them for over several months.

I enjoyed boating in the Chesapeake Bay. It reminded me of boating with my father on the Daedong River in Pyongyang when I was ten years old. My dad took me to Goat's Horn Island and crossed the Daedong River in a rented rowboat; in the mid-channel, small waves in the dark blue water of the river lapped against the wooden boat.

A year after the fishing trip, I bought a 19-foot green-and-white Winner powerboat (see photo 59) with a 105-horsepower inboard-outboard engine for $1,400. I hauled it to marinas up and down the Potomac River. We had a good time, riding the boat down the river to the Wilson Bridge in Alexandria and sometimes up the Anacostia River or the Potomac River to the Key Bridge. Since my boat took too much space in our garage, I rented a slip at the Columbia Island Marina, which was just in front of the Pentagon River Entrance. Then in 1979, came Hurricane David, and the weather station forecasted six inches of rain. Fellow boat owners at the marina warned me about giving slack to my boat lines as the Potomac River would rise during the night. During two days of rain, I went to the marina several times to check the boat line. Even though the pier was almost below water, my boat survived, but the marina became a disaster area, clogged with wood debris in the river. The first year I took the boat out two or three times every month, but my boating enthusiasm waned. Then, I lost interest and sold the boat for $1,200.

One day in 1982, Eugene Kaiser invited Rahn and me, along with our mutual friend Commander Pete Stogis, on a sailing trip in Annapolis. He had rented a 28-foot sailboat at the South River Boat Rentals in Annapolis. Eugene had been sailing in the Chesapeake Bay and had a required license to handle the 28-foot sailboat powered by a small outboard motor. He could drive the boat from the slip down the narrow channel in the South River. He could drive the sailboat. On that day, the wind was blowing at 10 knots, gusting to 15 knots, and we could see white caps on the bay. It was the first time that Rahn and I

had experienced the sailing boat on the Bay. Eugene anchored the boat in a cove for lunch, and we opened our lunch basket filled with sandwiches and wine.

After this sailing excursion, Rahn and I decided to buy a sailboat. We bought an 18-foot O'Day Daysailer. We took sailing lessons at the Annapolis Sailing School. We had fun learning the basics of sailing.

On summer days, we would launch our sailboat at the Potomac sailboat marina and sail her down the Potomac River near the Naval Research Laboratory (NRL). From the river, I could see Building No. 43, NRL Headquarters, on the left bank as I went downstream. (see photo 60) Next to it was a large gray Building No. 210, where I occasionally worked.

JANET GOES TO NORTHWESTERN UNIVERSITY

When Janet was a junior at Langley High School, she started to search for her college. In 1982, we traveled to Chicago to visit Northwestern University in Evanston. She liked the university and the town of Evanston, so she applied and accepted by Northwestern University, where she majored in Electrical Engineering. In her senior year at Northwestern, Janet joined a summer internship program for overseas Korean American students. There were three sponsoring organizations for this internship: (1) the South Korean Government, (2) the Korean Scientists and Engineers Association, and (3) the South Korean industries. The internship program office assigned her to work in the South Korean Nuclear Research Institute. During the summer, she had an opportunity to immerse herself in Korean culture. She mingled at her colleagues' team-building gatherings, where participants drank Korean rice wine.

In the fall of 1988, she entered the graduate program at Northwestern University. During her winter recess, she and I discussed her Master's degree program. I found out that she did not select her Master's thesis topic yet. As she was finishing up her coursework in the spring quarter, she had better ask her academic advisor to give her a research topic. After the winter recess, she received her research topic, which was on the metal fracture analysis using ultra-violet light. She completed her research, and in June 1989, she received her Master of Science degree in Electrical Engineering. Later that year, she started her doctoral program at the University of Virginia, which awarded her

a graduate fellowship. Her academic advisor was Professor James McVey. When she finished her coursework for her doctoral program, she began her research in neural net computation. In May 1992, Janet received her Ph.D. degree in Electrical Engineering from UVA. Her doctoral dissertation was "Translation, Rotation, and Scale Invariant Pattern Recognition Using Multilayered Third Order Neural Network (MTONN).[27] Her research was part of Professor McVey's project with the U.S. Army. After graduation, she was employed by Booz-Allen Hamilton in McLean.

DAE-JOONG KIM'S POLITICAL RALLY

As Washington is the center of politics in the World, South Korean political events were occasionally staged in the area. Rahn and I did not attend any political gatherings, but in 1997, we inadvertently found ourselves involved in a South Korean political event. It was a political rally for Dae-joong Kim, held at the Sheraton Premier Hotel in McLean, Virginia. It was a fund-raising effort. A few days earlier, I had received a call from a friend, Young-jak Lee, who was Dae-joong Kim's nephew. He asked Rahn and me if we could share the head table at the fundraising occasion. Dae-joong Kim was one of the protégés of my father-in-law, Yo-han Chu, in South Korean politics for many years. It appeared to be a benign event when we accepted it.

At the head table, Rahn and I found our nameplates on both sides of Dae-joong Kim. When we sat, Dae-joong Kim asked me what I was doing in Washington. To the question, I replied that I was a Technical Fellow in the defense and electronics company TRW. I tried to explain what a fellow was since I could not think of a proper word in Korean. Then, he told me:

"John, you need not explain what a fellow is.

"I am a Fellow at Harvard Center for International Affairs, and a Fellow of Clare Hall College of Cambridge University." I was humbled.

After the successful campaign, Dae-joong Kim became President of South Korea (1998-2003). He also received the Nobel Peace Prize for the year 2000. At the end of the rally that afternoon, I saw Kim walking down the aisle, taking short shuffling steps. It was the painful sign of torture he had received at the hands of the military junta several decades earlier. The next morning a local

Korean TV station in Washington broadcast the event, and showed Dae-joong Kim prominently, but, also to our dismay, the broadcast showed Rahn and me sitting at the head table. We received several telephone calls about us sharing the head table with the presidential candidate but declined to answer all media calls that week because we did not have anything to say. I do not think we will have an opportunity like that in the future, but if we ever have another occasion like that, we shall stay away from it.

MY PRIMARY CARE DOCTORS AND MY HEALTH ISSUES

Several primary care doctors had looked after my health over the past 50 years. The first was Dr. Leo LaRow, who diagnosed my lactose intolerance symptom. This was not a serious medical issue, but it was a significant medical diagnosis for me as, up until that time, no physician had been able to detect this condition, which had persisted throughout my early life. Dr. LaRow had a small facility in Fairfax. It was the time when the American medical profession and the healthcare system were civilized and efficient, unlike today's healthcare system. I remember a sign in Dr. LaRow's office, *"Only God heals; doctors just collect money."* Whenever I visited his office for general malaise, our conversation was usually no more than five sentences about his findings on my health condition. However, he became quite interested in my profession of electrical engineering when one of his sons became an MIT undergraduate majoring in Electrical Engineering. He became a concerned father of an undergraduate, with questions about his son's study and future job prospects of electrical engineering students. I was more than happy to answer his questions, but I told him I would send him a bill for the consultation. For that joke, he chuckled.

In 1976, when we moved to McLean, I found two new doctors, Dr. Fred Hubach and Dr. Allen Horne, who became my primary care physicians. On one occasion, I told Dr. Hubach about the insurance company refusing to pay for one of the medical procedures he had performed. He warned me health insurance companies would take over the role of a medical doctor by telling him what medical procedures he could and could not do. His prediction proved to be right as I struggled to get some of my claims reimbursed by insurance companies.

During a health checkup visit, Dr. Hubach expressed some concern about my hypertension readings creeping up each year, so he prescribed drugs to keep my blood pressure at the reasonable level. After Dr. Hubach had retired, Dr. Allen Horne became my primary care doctor. He cared for me when two significant health issues occurred. I ask your indulgence of telling stories about my pains and aches. I recorded them for posterity, but not for the joy of reciting them. I was reminding myself of the seventeenth century Unanimous Nun's Prayer, which admonishes to curb my stories of ache and pain.

"There were more aches and pains as I got older. I wanted to seal my lips about them, but they were increasing as the years go by. I could not refrain from repeating them to friends and family and enjoyed rehearsing them. I dare not ask for grace enough to enjoy the tales of other's pains, but help me to endure them with patience."

One day in July 1996, I was riding a bicycle in our neighborhood and felt pain in my butt. I thought I might have hurt myself on the hard seat of the bike and complained about my pain to Dr. Horne. After an examination, he recommended that I see the colon specialist, Dr. Donald Colvin. To my dismay, Dr. Colvin found early-stage cancerous polyps in my colon, and on July 21, 1996, he performed a colectomy procedure. Thanks to modern medicine and anesthesia, all I remember about the operation was the beginning of anesthesia while I was counting backward from 100,

"100, 99, 98, 97, ..."

The next thing I remember was part of a conversation between Dr. Colvin and his attending nurses,

"........sixty-one years old. He is an electrical engineer at TRW."

"John, you are awake now. The operation was a success."

Dr. Colvin sent me to Dr. Arthur Kales, an oncologist, for chemotherapy. During that time I was on medical leave from the company for convalescence. Dr. Horne subsequently recommended colonoscopy tests every five years, all of which had shown no issue with my colon thus far. When Dr. Colvin first told me about the polyps, I blamed myself with anger and asked him:

"Dr. Colvin, what could have caused this."

"I cannot tell you what caused it, but with all the pollutants in our foods and air, the body sometimes just cannot handle it."

Gradually, I reconciled with myself that only God knows about the cause.

In March 1997, I returned to my office in good health.

Later I had another serious medical episode. After I had retired from ONR, I noticed that my heart rate was low. One day I visited Dr. Horne's office and complained about it. He ran an EKG test, the result of which alarmed him. He called the Fairfax Hospital Emergency Room (ER) and, immediately, an ambulance came to his office to take me to the ER. I asked Rahn to take me to the hospital, but Dr. Horne insisted that I ride in the ambulance and enter the hospital through the ER so that I would receive faster medical attention. A few hours later, Dr. Robert Shapiro, a cardiologist, and Dr. David Strouse, an electrophysiologist, implanted a pacemaker in my chest. It maintained my heart rate at the proper level and made me feel comfortable. Since then I have visited Dr. Shapiro's and Dr. Strouse's offices regularly so that they could monitor my cardiological health.

I much appreciate all my doctors for maintaining my health. In the meantime, my medical bills have become a uniformly increasing function. From time to time, I heard from my doctors' offices that the doctor was on vacation, and I felt that I helped finance their vacations. However, I am not complaining and so far continue to count my blessings.

Janet's Wedding

In April 1995, Janet told Rahn and me that she received a marriage proposal from Tony Lee. She had met him in Seoul in 1988 when she was in South Korea for three months. During her stay in Seoul, Janet and Tony met through a mutual friend, Timothy.

On May 11, 1996, their wedding ceremony was held at Trinity UMC, McLean, officiated by Pastor David Balcom and Pastor Teresa Smith. As a prelude, Eugene Kaiser played Bach's *Sheep may safely graze* and *Jesu, Joy of Man's Desiring*, Handel's *Air from Water Music Suite No. 1* and Pachabel's *Canon in D* on the flute. A brass ensemble accompanied by the organ played John Stanley's *Trumpet Voluntary*. Then, with "Bridal Chorus" by Wagner being played, the bride's attendants entered the sanctuary. Her attendants included Meredith LaRoche Wilson, Angelica Oviedo, Joy Reba Gerber, Irene Huang Shiu, and Janice Brewster Weiser. The bride and I walked down the aisle by the music

of Wagner's wedding march. Pastor Balcom delivered the invocation and conducted the wedding ceremony, assisted by Pastor Smith. During the ceremony, the congregation sang Beethoven's "*Ode to Joy*." As tokens of the matrimonial vows, the couple exchanged beautiful double rings. Pastor Balcom then announced the bride and groom as husband and wife. The organist Jerry Rich played Mendelssohn's *Wedding March*. When the wedding party and the guests were heading for the reception, there was a sudden summer shower, pouring down in earnest. Everyone had to scramble to their cars. The wedding reception was held at Marriott-Fairview Park, Falls Church, Virginia. Tom Cunningham's orchestra played on musics. (see photo 76)

Four Sons-in-law of Yo-han Chu

In November 1987, all four sons-in-law of Yo-han Chu happened to be in Chicago; we dined together at the Korean restaurant, Shilla. We called it a team-building party of Yo-han Chu's sons-in-law, and all chuckled and enjoyed the each other's company. This occasion was the first and the last time that the four of us got together in one place.

The eldest was Byung-lim Roh, MD (1922-2009), who was a retired physician from Wood Veteran's Hospital in Milwaukee. He did early pioneering work in proving that the kidney produced erythropoietin and identified the cells in the kidney which produce erythropoietin, a hormone for red blood cells. The second was Dr. Soon-deok Koh (1917-1990), a psychologist[28] who received his doctorate in experimental psychology from Harvard University and was an Adjunct Professor of Psychology at the University of Illinois-Chicago. I was the third. The youngest was Jong-hyeon Choe, MD, who was a neurosurgeon in Seoul and was visiting Chicago that week. Now in 2017, the two elder brothers have passed away. Indeed, the relationship is long; life is short. I ponder a Korean proverb, "Life is like a long springtime dream." It came, and it was gone, but will remain in my heart and memory as long as I live. I miss the gentle, smiling face of Byung-lim and I miss the penetrating psychologist stares of Soon-deok. (see photo 68)

CLASSICAL MUSIC AND THE NATIONAL SYMPHONY ORCHESTRA

Since 1992, the foursome (my brother Dong-Kyu, his wife Ki-Nam, Rahn, and I) had bought season tickets of the National Symphony Orchestra (NSO) and had met seven times a year to attend NSO concerts. For many years, I made an effort to buy CDs of music NSO performed as much as I could. I had collected more than 350 CDs when I counted last in 2017. In 1992, Maestro Mstislav Rostropovich was the conductor. He was followed by Leonard Slatkin, Ivan Fischer, and Christoph Eschenbach as maestros. In 2018, NSO selected a new music director, an Italian, Gianandrea Noseda, to improve NSO. He was a music director with a reputation for conducting symphony as well as operatic music.

The previous six music directors occasionally included avant-garde music either commissioned by NSO or composed by contemporary composers, in the programs. The NSO from time to time sent out questionnaires asking musical preferences of the audience. They preferred fewer contemporary pieces than classical.

In 2005, Rahn and I visited Doug in Boston and attended a concert given by the Boston Symphony Orchestra (BSO). A young violin soloist was to play the Beethoven violin concerto, conducted by Maestro Pierre Boulez. Before his performance, the soloist was nervously tweaking his strings, and Maestro Boulez was dismayed and prompted him to get started, the violin soloist began. To the surprise of the audience, one of his strings snapped a minute into his play. Quickly, the soloist put down his broken violin and grabbed the concertmaster's violin and continued without missing a beat. The concertmaster grabbed his assistant's violin, and he too continued. The audience applauded.

On the other visit to Boston, Rahn, Doug, and I went to the BSO summer concert at the Tanglewood Music Center, which was 100 miles west of Boston in Berkshire County in western Massachusetts. On the way, we dined at the German Restaurant named "Student Prince" in Springfield, Massachusetts, where I ordered Wiener schnitzel and enjoyed it. In the evening, we arrived at Tanglewood. We sat on the lawn and heard the wind passing through pine trees under the moon, blended with the sound of musical instruments. We enjoyed our excursion to Tanglewood.

MY BROTHER-IN-LAW TONG-SUL VISITS OUR HOUSE IN MCLEAN

We had two visitors from Seoul, Rahn's brother Tong-sul and his wife, Young-ok. Tong-sul was the retired CEO of Hanna Shipping Corporation, Seoul. After his father passed away, Tong-sul undertook editing and publishing task of *The Collected Literary Works of Yo-han Chu: The Dawn.*[29] This book was in two volumes and 1,805 pages long.

In May 1991, I received a letter from Tong-Sul that he and his wife would like to visit us in Washington. A few days later, he and I talked on the phone.

"John, last year when the mother returned from America, she told me about her visit to the Library of Congress."

"That's right. Mother, Rahn, and I visited the Library."

"She saw and read several of father's books."

"Is that right?"

"Yes, there were two dozen of father's old books, published in the 1920s and 1930s.

"Some time ago, I discovered his collection on the bookshelf of the Library of Congress with the help of a staff librarian Dae-wook Chang in the East Asian Section.

"He showed me father's books, cataloged and kept in the East Asian Section.

"So during her stay in Washington, I checked out father's books, and we spent one afternoon browsing through them at the reading room.

"She was quite moved when she saw the old books.

"She thought she touched the father himself."

"That was fantastic."

"I also checked out Uncle Yo-seop's books.

"But we were surprised to find the book published by Uncle Young-seop.

"As you know, Uncle Young-seop was the youngest of father's three brothers."

"Sure I do.

"John, he stayed in Pyongyang and never came to South Korea.

"He was a playwright."

"Well, I found a book he has authored in the Library.

"The book was *Introduction to Scenario Writing*[30]

"The paper was coarse dark brown papers."

"John, it is fantastic.

"I would like to ask you to make another arrangement like what you have done for the mother since 1989."

"Sure, I will see to it that his books will be on the shelf when you will visit the Library of Congress."

"To my knowledge, the father's books published in the 1920s and the 1930s had not survived in South Korea."

"They were all destroyed during the Korean War."

A few days before their arrival, I arranged for the books to be delivered to the reading room of the East Asian Section. The day before Tong-sul's visit to the East Asia Section, the staff librarian sent me a note saying that the requested books would be on hold for four days. Like his mother's reaction a year earlier, I could see Tong-sul's excitement when he held the books.

Doug Ate a Fish Head

My son Doug told me the following story about an evening he spent with Tong-sul.

"You know, in 1992, I went to Korea to work as a summer intern at SNU College of Agriculture and Life Sciences."

"One evening, Uncle Tong-sul invited Mom and me to an upscale Korean restaurant in Seoul.

"Doug, that was very nice of him."

"My food at the SNU cafeteria was barely edible.

"I liked fish grilled on charcoal in the upscale restaurant."

"Then, Uncle Tong-sul challenged me to eat the fish head as most Koreans do.

"Of course, I had never eaten a fish head.

"Most of the fish, which Mom put on our table, was a fish fillet."

"I know.

"No bones and no head."

"So, did you eat the fish head?"

"I rose to the occasion and ate the offending fish head!"

"Then, do you know what Uncle said?"

"No, what did he say?"

"You have now demonstrated that you are a true Korean."
"I took his compliment in stride."

17

TRW Projects (1987-2001)

Navy Communications Project

When the U.S. Navy constructed a new ship class, or newly developed equipment was delivered from the Navy procurement system, the Space and Naval Warfare Systems Command (SPAWAR) installed communication, radar, sonar, or electronic equipment on a ship just like one furnishes a house. NAVSEA constructed, converted, or repaired ships, while SPAWAR installed equipment on them.

Ron Deblois was a Navy engineer who managed the Communications Engineering Branch (PME-110-1) of the Naval Electronic Systems Command (NAVELEX). Through a grapevine of a NAVELEX, I found out that the Communications Engineering Branch was looking for a technical support contractor. I told the TRW management about this new business opportunity, and the management encouraged me to pursue the forthcoming procurement. Three months later, the Navy Communications Branch announced a Request for Proposal in the Commerce Business Daily. I prepared the technical and cost proposals, and TRW won the contract.

Then I got mired in office politics. The business area manager Chuck Denton told me that I would not become the manager of the new TRW Navy Communications Project. I was quite surprised that I would not manage the new project. He was planning to appoint Pete Atkins as the project manager and asked if I could work with Pete as his deputy. I told him that Ron Deblois was expecting me to work as the manager of the new project. The next day, I met with the Washington operations manager, Dr. James Larkin, to tell him my grievance, and that I could not support Pete Atkins as the manager. A week later, Denton announced that the new manager would be a third person,

Brian Jones, who had no experience in communications engineering but was an aeronautical engineer. I would become his deputy manager. There was no logic at all to this decision. It was outright cronyism. What a disappointment it was to be passed over.

After a few days of licking my wounded pride, I met with Ron Deblois to work on one of his tasks. He was responsible for the engineering work for all Naval Communications Master Stations (NAVCAMS)[31] A Naval Communication Station (NAVCOMMSTA) provided the connectivity to the fleets worldwide via RF and satellite communications links. Operationally, the Naval Telecommunications Command (COMNAVTELCOM), located in Northwest Washington, managed twelve NAVCAMS and NAVCOMMSTAs deployed around the world. I visited COMNAVTELCOM to coordinate the acquisition and maintenance of equipment for the Naval Telecommunications System. From NAVTELCOM, I exchanged telephone conversations with most commanding officers on a first-name basis. It was exciting to work in the worldwide community of NAVTELCOM at places like Wahiawa, Lago di Patria (Naples), Keflavik, Adak, Stockton, and Harry Holt (near Exmouth, Australia).

LANDING CRAFT AIR CUSHIONED (LCAC) PROJECT

One November morning in 1986, Dick Klein of Unisys and I were standing at the hangar of the LCAC Assault Craft Unit (ACU)-4, in the Little Creek Amphibious Base, Norfolk. As we approached the hanger from the ACU-4 quarterdeck, an LCAC turned on its four diesel engines and was ready to slide forward on the concrete driveway. Then slowly, the large air cushion vehicle went down Little Creek to the mouth of the Chesapeake Bay. The craft master zigzagged his craft for a warm-up, spewing sand on the creek. Then, as it made contact with the water, a massive spray of water, known as a "bird bath," around the craft with deafening noise. Then, one-by-one, three other LCACs moved onto the water, cushioned by air. The craft moved fast, easily overtaking a small power boat. It seemed to me LCACs were making 30 knots. Dick Klein and I were impressed by the spectacle. Marine Sgt. Jorge Romero welcomed us to the ACU-4. We had driven down to Little Creek the night before and had checked into the base BOQ. Dick Klein, the manager of the LCAC Combat System

project, and I met with Marine First Lieutenant Dave Flynn to discuss the requirements for the speed log, the surface-search radar, the collision avoidance system, and HF and VHF radios.

The U.S. Navy acquired all amphibious warfare ships through the NAVSEA PMS-377 program office. The amphibious ship classes included LHA, LSD, LCAC, and LHD. The program office had an annual budget of $820M. TRW became the SETA contractor supporting the Amphibious Ship Acquisition Program (PMS-377) of NAVSEA. I gradually learned how the U.S. Navy managed the ship acquisition business. I supported Unisys, the prime contractor, to provide the combat system to LCAC. My task was to support the Unisys design and installation. The TRW LCAC team included Herb Graham and me, and two engineers from Band, Lavis, and Associates. The NAVSEA program office selected the off-the-shelf combat system, which was the one installed on the U.S. Coast Guard Medium Endurance Cutter-270. It is called the Command Display and Control (COMDAC) system, which includes an LN-66 surface search radar, and HF, VHF and UHF radios, and a Singer-Kearfott Attitude Heading and Reference System. I worked on communication, navigation, and surveillance devices. Also, I worked on a navigation device incorporating newly emerging technology, GPS.

MY FIRST GLOBAL POSITIONING SYSTEM (GPS) PROJECT
FOR THE FLEET

Today, I navigate my car using a GPS receiver, and solve for my position in real-time. But, about 30 years ago, when I received the first-generation GPS equipment as government furnished equipment for one of my projects, it was a bulky and cumbersome apparatus. The first GPS receiver I used was a single channel receiver, such that I had to fix three positions sequentially, which took several minutes to solve for position. NAVSEA gave us a Rockwell-Collins prototype GPS receiver, known as the AN/WRN-6. It was a rack-mounted unit, suitable for helicopters, ships, and vehicles. The GPS receiver sequentially acquired and tracked four GPS satellite signal readings from the same satellite. Today, GPS receives signals from four or more GPS satellites simultaneously, thereby enabling a faster fix of position and time.

For the next two decades, I spent much of my time working on GPS, especially on mitigating man-made and natural risks. I was the Program Officer in charge of basic and applied research on Navigation and Timekeeping technologies of the U.S. Navy. But when I started on GPS 30 years ago, it was a humble beginning. At the meeting with the combat system engineers, they told us that the primary navigation equipment would be the Marconi LN-66 radar, the Singer-Kearfott Attitude and Heading Reference System (AHRS), and the Doppler radar speed log. GPS would update a periodic position fix. GPS provided a periodic update to the primary navigation system via an interface system like the Navigation Sensor System Interface (NAVSSI).

In 1984, Herb Graham of TRW and I performed operations research on LCAC navigation using LN-66 and GPS, I co-authored a technical paper on LCAC navigation. It was published in the May 1985 issue of the *Naval Engineers Journal*.[32] The GPS program was still in the concept validation phase.

Following are some of the findings described in the technical paper.

"Air cushion vehicles have operated successfully on commercial routes for about twenty years. The courses are usually quite short; the craft is equipped with radar and radio navigation aids, which maintain continuous contact with their terminals. Navigation of this craft, therefore, does not present any unusual difficulty. The introduction of air cushion vehicles like LCAC into military service, however, can give a very different picture, when external navigation aids are not available, and the craft must navigate by dead reckoning. John Kim and his co-authors consider the problems involved when navigating a high-speed air cushion vehicle by dead reckoning in conditions of poor visibility. A method is presented to assess the LCAC's navigational capability under these circumstances. A figure of merit is used to determine the sensitivity of factors that affect navigation such as the range of visibility, point-to-point distance, speed, turning radius, and accuracy of the onboard equipment. The method provides simple but adequate answers and can be used effectively to compare the capability and the cost of alternative navigation concepts."

When I worked on the AN/WRN-6 prototype GPS receiver, I did not know that it would become a household item three decades later. I could not imagine that almost every automobile would someday have a GPS receiver.

ROYAL SAUDI NAVAL EXPANSION PROGRAM

A decade before the Middle East wars engulfed the region, I worked on the Saudi Naval Command Post project. Ron Deblois of NAVELEX asked me to provide technical support to him in a Foreign Military Sales (FMS) program. Under the FMS agreement, the U.S. Navy would provide the construction of three Royal Saudi Naval Force (RSNF) Command Centers, one in the capital Riyadh, a second at the Western Fleet Command in Jeddah in the Red Sea, and the third at the Eastern Fleet Command in Jubail in the Persian Gulf. NAVELEX awarded the prime contract for building these three RSNF Command Centers to Science Applications International Corporation (SAIC).

I became an Independent Test and Evaluation (T&E) agent for the RSNF Command Center project. SAIC built the RSNF command centers in two steps.

The first step involved assembling and integrating the RSNF command center equipment in a McLean facility and making sure that the hardware and software systems were operational. I observed the T&E task conducted by SAIC personnel in their McLean facility. Commander Youssef al-Saeed, the Director of Command and Control of RSNF, dictated operational requirements of the command centers, from which I developed an operational test plan. A dozen Saudi Naval officers also collaborated with me during the acceptance tests. SAIC equipped much of the command centers with mahogany furniture and Persian carpets, befitting for princes, but I was not so sure if these furnishings enhanced warfighting capabilities. I heard from U.S. Navy advisors that RSNF ships have blue ocean capability, but they stay near the Arabian Sea, the Persian Gulf, and the Red Sea coasts, never out of sight of land. Come to think of it, the Saudis were once the Bedouins of the Arabian desert.

The second step was to cross-deck the equipment from McLean to three locations in Saudi Arabia. Among Saudi Naval officers, there was a lieutenant who happened to be a Saudi Royal Prince. Youssef al-Saeed, while outranking the lieutenant, was always deferential to the Prince.

One day during a coffee break I asked Youssef,
"Who is senior in rank in the Saudi Navy, Commander or Lieutenant?"
"John, in the Saudi Navy, Prince outranks Commander anytime."

Three European Projects: The U.S. European Alternate Command Post, BRASS, and NMOS

From 1990 to 1992, Johnny Johnson and I went to Brussels, London, and Munich to work on three European defense-related projects as part of the program development effort for the TRW Navy Systems Business Area. The three projects were: the U.S. European Alternate Command Post, the NATO Broadcast and Ship-to-shore (BRASS) Network, and the NATO Maritime OPINTEL System (NMOS).

The U.S. European Alternate Command Post Project, August 4, 1990

On August 4, 1990, we arrived at Brussels Airport and went to the Hotel Metropole by subway. Tom Baird, the company's international marketing representative in Brussels, guided us during our travel through European cities. The previous evening, when Johnny Johnson and I went to Dulles Airport, practically no one was flying to Europe because the first Iraq War, Operation Desert Storm, had begun two days earlier. Every place we went the security was tight. In Brussels Airport, a security agent asked me to open my camera, which ruined the film. The clothes we wore gave security folks an impression that we were military, as I wore an Army green jacket and Johnny wore his Navy Mil Spec G-1 leather jacket. We did not blend well with the background. (see photo 73)

Tom took us to his office in Brussels, a four-story, brick townhouse in the Brussels embassy row. I felt at home in the office, located at 12 Avenue Franklin Roosevelt, Brussels. Avenue Franklin Roosevelt was in the middle of the diplomatic community of Brussels, with embassies and NATO agencies.

The U.S. European Alternate Command Post Program was aimed at build-

ing the wartime EUCOM Alternate Command Post in the U.K. There were four parties in the team, which included TRW, the lead company, Plessey of the U.K., Siemens of Germany, and Alenia of Italy. We had our first meeting with the team members at TRW's Brussels office. I observed interesting dynamics of how these multinational companies interacted with each other during discussions of technical and business matters. Italians had the propensity to agree first with TRW on anything, and, then, they complained much after the initial agreement was made. On the other hand, the German company representative was inclined not to commit to a position on any issues. The Plessey representative usually supported the TRW position. Plessey became the wholly-owned subsidiary of Siemens, the German company.

We had a virtual fifth team member, Michel Ribaud of Thomson-CSF. Thomson-CSF was a French company which expressed its interest in our project, and determined to get its foot in the door. The French company's dilemma was that France was not a member of NATO, then, although it was a member of the European Union. President Charles de Gaule had pulled out of the NATO membership in 1966 after a series of disputes over the dominant role of the U.S. in NATO. I was amused that some sensitive procurement information, which should not have been available for any party outside of NATO, was accessible to the French company. Many European companies were interrelated to each other through mergers and subsidiary arrangements. These convoluted business relationships allowed Thomson-CSF to stay informed of the proposed plan of our team. I began to realize that it was difficult doing business with NATO. The NATO procurement agency preferred the distribution of the contractual work to all member-nation companies. But only a handful of NATO countries funded the procurement, and the U.S. funding was the largest of them all.

During these meetings, Thomson-CSF pushed back anything TRW proposed, although it participated only as an observer. At the end of the day, the team dismissed the Thomson-CSF participation.

The team visited NATO HQ in Brussels, where I made another interesting observation. I saw member companies in European countries were well-guided by their national staffs. The U.S. international staffs at NATO HQ were not supportive of us, and I got the distinct impression that they were working against us. The U.S. companies were disadvantaged in the procurement com-

petition as its support staffs conducted their business by the book.

Doing business with NATO was a challenge. The contractual work had to be distributed to several national companies regardless of the procurement objectives. Another issue was language. All written and oral business was conducted in English, as it is the most commonly used language in European and NATO countries. But French must be used in official documents. I attended several NATO Research and Technology Agency (RTA) Sensors and Electronics Technology (SET) panel meetings which dealt with navigation and timekeeping. These meetings were held in countries like Canada, France, Spain, Turkey, the U.K., and the U.S. Technical reports, agendas, and proceedings of these meetings were required to be translated into French. For one meeting, the documents were duly prepared in French, but not a single French representative attended.

DAY TRIP TO AACHEN TECHNICAL UNIVERSITY

During the weekend, I made a short day-trip by train from Brussels to Aachen, Germany, to visit my old friend from Michigan State University days, Heinrich Vogt. Before I left Washington, I made an arrangement to meet him at Aachen Technical University. Aachen was a German border town near Belgium and the Netherlands. It was 90 miles from Brussels, and the train rides were pleasant. Charlemagne established Aachen, from where he ruled the Frankish kingdom in the 9th century. Heinrich was waiting for me at the Computer and Electronics Department. We were glad to see each other. He lost much of his blonde hair and gained weight in the middle. He gave me a tour of the university. When I was a student in the double-E department of MSU, there were quite a few Prussian names such as Professor Lawrence von Tersch, the Department Chair, Professor Herman Koenig, my academic advisor, and fellow students like Heinrich.

What I saw in Aachen lived up to my expectations. The laboratory building was old but well-maintained and more importantly, equipped with the state-of-the-art electrical engineering laboratories, equipment, and computers. The library was also efficiently run. However, graffiti on walls in the campus were alarming. Turkish workers and students voiced their protest against the host country's injustice. From the 1950s on, West Germany enjoyed rapid economic

progress, which created demand for labor. This demand was met by so-called guest workers or immigrant laborers in the coal mines. Turkey provided a large number of workers.

✷ ✷ ✷

During this trip, we flew to Munich and checked into a five-star hotel, the Bayerischer Hof Hotel in Marienplatz. I was impressed with the workmanship of the doors and hinges, machined with precision. Later in the evening, we went to the Hofbräuhaus Beer Hall. During my high school and college years, I studied German for six years so I could carry on simple conversations in German. "I did not know you spoke German," Tom Baird said. I too was surprised with myself. In the evening, when I was passing the hotel gift shop, a young lady standing behind the counter sneezed. Without any thought, I uttered "*Gesundheit*," and she replied "*Danke schoen*."

We had a meeting at Siemens in Ismaning, a suburb of Munich. We had our lunch in the executive dining room, and they served us wine for lunch. Serving alcoholic beverages was a surprise to me, as American companies would not allow any alcohol on their premise. Hans Romeiser and Richard Strauss hosted the meeting at Siemens. Richard Strauss told us that he was no relation to the famous composer. At the meeting, the teaming agreement was signed by the four-nation team to pursue NMOS.

NATO BRASS Project

On January 22, 1991, Johnny Johnson, Tom Baird and I, went to Brussels and London again to get acquainted with another NATO project, the Broadcast and Ship-to-Shore (BRASS) Network. NATO navies planned to develop an HF network for ship-to-shore long-haul beyond-line-of-sight (BLOS) communications as a backup to SATCOM. In Brussels, three of us met with Prof. Mario Piccio of Telttra-Marconi and Hans Romeiser and Richard Strauss of Siemens, to discuss the NATO BRASS procurement.

We met with Commander John Marsh of the NATO Communications and Information Systems Agency (NACISA) to exchange ideas on BRASS. I told

them that the U.S. Navy had been using HF ship-to-shore broadcast since the 1930s. The U.S. Navy transmits fleet broadcasts from NAVCOMMSTA's and Broadcast Control Stations in the Pacific Ocean, the Atlantic Ocean, and the Mediterranean Sea. TRW was well-qualified to develop such HF equipment and message formats of the fleet broadcast.

In the afternoon the three of us flew from Brussels to London and checked into the Parklane Hotel (a four-star hotel) in the Mayfair district. Next day, from London, we drove to Christchurch, near Bournemouth on the southern coast of England and checked into Waterford Lodge. It was comfortable, and the price was about one-third of what we paid at the Parklane Hotel. When we visited the Plessey facility, I asked Commander Marsh,

"This facility looks like a military barrack, not like an industrial facility."

"You guessed it right.

"In 1938, this facility was the U.K. Air Defense Research and Development Establishment."

"Is that right? What happened, then?."

"The Ministry of Defense developed the radar system here.

"In 1957, the Army sold the facility to Plessey.

"They, in turn, sold the facility to Siemens.

"You see the Bavarian and Union Jack flags both hoisted on the flagpoles.

"We are not very proud of it." Paul Mors of Plessey said.

In the evening, the Plessey BRASS manager, Brian Curd, surprised us by inviting to dinner at a club in Christchurch. In the evening, a limousine came to our inn and gave us a ride to the club, which, we thought would be a commercial establishment. To our surprise, it was a private club in a former ducal palace. The car approached the palace on a circular, gravel entrance road, and stopped at the door of the great house, part of which had been converted into a clubhouse. A six-piece band was playing. Brian told us that the other half of the great house was still occupied by the Duke. The other team members, Paul Mors and Mike Champion of Plessey; Vincenzo Roselli and Roberto Morelli of Teletra, and Prof. Mario Piccio of Telttra-Marconi, were already settled down at sofas. Earlier, Tom had briefed Johnny and me about these team members. These U.K. managers, old toffs, had no technical background but conducted business without uttering a technical word in the course of the evening. Paul Mors, the Plessey engineer, seemed nothing more than a general factotum but, in fact, he

was the power behind the throne at Christchurch during our team meeting.

The next day, we returned to London and attended a meeting at the U.S. Embassy in Grosvenor Square in the Mayfair district. When I approached the embassy, I saw armed U.S. Marines and British soldiers at the four corners of the fortress-like embassy building. In front of the building was a large mall, where the statues of Dwight Eisenhower and Franklin Roosevelt stood. These statues were a contrast to the peaceful grand mansion, which surrounded the mall. I saw no pedestrians. We had a meeting with James Christianson and Collin Smith at the U.S. Naval Forces Europe (CINCUSNAVEUR). In the afternoon we visited Commander John Edwards's office at MoD in the White-hall, London. Edwards represented the Royal Navy's interests in BRASS.

There was a sequel to this evening entertainment. When BRASS team members came to McLean for a follow-up meeting, Johnny Johnson and I knew we needed to reciprocate the entertainment. We invited everyone to a French Restaurant, La Canard, in Vienna, Virginia. We knew these folks drink, which could ring up the bill to a thousand dollars easily. The problem is that libations were not an allowable business expense in DoD regulations. Jack Dreyfus, VP, gave us a special allowance for this evening entertainment. Oh, well, such were the government ethics regulations in America, but I was all for it.

NMOS Project, Meeting

Since the end of the World War II, the U.S. Navy has collected extensive information on maritime ship movements, especially Russian Naval forces, and provided intelligence support to U.S. Naval Fleets. This maritime information system was known as the Ocean Surveillance Information System (OSIS). In 1989, TRW had received a U.S. Navy contract to develop the OSIS Baseline Upgrade (OBU). Johnny Johnson found out that the NATO Maritime Command planned on expanding the NATO Maritime Operation Intelligence System and asked me to help his program development effort on NATO Maritime OPINTEL System (NMOS). We met with Lieutenant Commander Tom Morran, the Royal Navy Program Manager of NMOS. Tom Baird led us to the U.S. Mission at NATO HQ, where Johnny Johnson and I read NMOS documents in the conference room.

❋ ❋ ❋

On Feb 20, 1991, Saturday, I went to Cambridge by train and visited Cambridge University. A few days earlier, Johnny and I had done some sightseeing in London, including visiting Harrods Department Store in Kensington. The Harrods still carried catalogs of a number of items small and large. I supposed these catalogs supplied various household merchandises to far corners of the British Empire. In the basement, there was the famous food hall. When we entered the food hall, pleasing aromas permeated the entire basement. I took particular note of game fowl hanging on the beam.

COMMERCIAL SATELLITE COMMUNICATION INITIATIVE (CSCI) PROJECT

Over the last several decades, the American telecommunications sector had gone through changes brought about by technology. For example, in the 1960s, a walkie-talkie wireless telephone, designated in the military as AN/PRC-68, weighed 15 pounds and was about the size of a shoe box. In 2018, a mobile phone like the Apple iPhone-8 weighed 6 ounces and fitted in a coat pocket.

In the 1960s, I worked on several wireline telecommunication projects. At that time, the speed of data transmission was at the snail's pace of 150 bits per second (bps) on an analog (four-wire copper) telephone line. Later, I worked on Navy shipboard communications systems, which deliver data and digital voice communications via satellite and HF radios. Satellite communication systems included the Fleet Satellite Communications (FLTSATCOM) terminal AN/WSC-3 at the data transmission rate of 2,400 bps and the Defense Satellite Communications System (DSCS) terminal AN/WSC-6 at the data transmission rate of 32,000 bps. These long-haul satellite terminals provided a ship-to-shore link over several thousand miles. I also worked HF digital radio, AN/USC-32, called HF SETAD.

As technology advanced, the Defense Information Systems Agency (DISA) considered changing the way communications connectivity was provided for warfighters. Until then, DoD let the private sector develop and build warfighting communications satellite systems like FLTSAT and DSCS, but DoD owned and operated these satellites through military agencies such as DISA,

the Army Satellite Communications Agency, the Naval Telecommunication Command, and the Air Force Space Command.

DoD considered a business paradigm shift in long-haul communication links. In the new paradigm, DoD would lease military satellite capacity as it had been doing with terrestrial communications systems from common carriers like AT&T. To investigate the feasibility of a leased military satellite communication system, DISA invited three competing teams, Communications Satellite Corporation (COMSAT), Hughes Network Systems, and Loral Space Systems. In turn, COMSAT asked TRW to be its subcontractor and support their effort.

The TRW Electronics and Space Group (ESG) in Los Angeles appointed Raul Rey as the manager, who contacted Dr. Al Babbitt and told him ESG's plan to bid the DISA procurement on *Commercial Satellite Communication Initiative (CSCI)*. DISA included two military satellite communication services, one of which was the Fixed Satellite Services (FSS) and the other was the Mobile Satellite Services (MSS). These satellite terminals located at FSS (Army Corps and Division HQs) used a larger fixed but transportable antenna on-ground site; those satellite terminals located at MSS (vehicles and ships) used a smaller mobile dish antenna. The end of the feasibility study of three contractors recommended the system architecture, the acquisition strategy, the transition plan, vulnerability mitigation, the integrated logistics plan, the testbed demonstration, and the host nation approval plan.

Al Babbitt assigned me to assist Raul Rey in the proposal effort. My first task was to represent ESG at COMSAT Corporation in Gaithersburg, Maryland. The second task was to perform a study of the ground-based tactical communications interface from FSS and MSS stations to the existing DISA network. The third task was to represent TRW at International Maritime Satellite (INMARSAT) meetings; INMARSAT was a satellite system that offered global mobile services and a member of the COMSAT MSS team.

After the one-year study, the COMSAT team recommended using the Small Business Systems Corporation's satellites for FSS, which would provide transponders in the Ku-band. The Ku-band receivers required smaller, less expensive antenna dishes. For MSS, the COMSAT team recommended using INMARSAT, which operated in the C-band.

Here I need to explain the naming of the electromagnetic spectrum, with the letter-coded frequency bands in wireless radio and radar systems. The origin

of the designation came from the U. S. Army Signal Corps and was intended to confuse enemies during the World War II. Its original intent has long faded away, but the designations became part of radio engineering systems. The frequency for the C-band is 4-8 GHz; the Ku-band is 12-18 GHz, etc.

The CSCI study came up with four findings. The first was the substantial cost savings by placing the burden of R&D on the industry and cost savings achieved by bundling currently leased circuits to obtain volume pricing discounts. The second was the evaluation of the vulnerabilities associated with commercial satellite communications by jamming. The third was the data handling capabilities. There would be enough capacity in the low data rate (32 kbps and below) but not enough capacity in the high data rates for mobile terminals. The fourth finding was that satellite coverage would mostly be in the medium latitudes, between 70 degrees North to 70 degrees South around the Earth.

For one year, I frequently drove on the I-70 corridor to COMSAT, and to INMARSAT at Tenley Circle, including several trips to Space Park in Redondo Beach, California. I am thankful for the opportunity given to me by Raul Rey and Al Babbitt.

Air Combat Training Systems

I never imagined that I would go to the top of high mountains in Nevada, but that was what I did in the fall of 1992. I went to the top of Mt. Callaghan and Job Peak, the elevations of 10,187 and 8,785 feet, respectively, by a helicopter. Nor did I dream that I would drive through Death Valley in the Mojave Desert, but that's what I did in the hot summer of 1993. The basin was not exactly a valley, but a salt flat, appropriately called Badwater Basin. Badwater Basin was 286 feet below sea level, the lowest elevation in the U.S. During my trip, the temperature of the Badwater Basin hovered around 115 degrees F.

I was working on the Navy and Air Force tactical air combat training systems when I visited these Nevada mountains and deserts. How did I get involved with tactical air combat system projects? Two years earlier, TRW had acquired a company called BDM International Inc. BDM had been supporting the range instrumentation system at Fallon Naval Air Station (NAS), one of the Navy's tactical air combat training systems in Nevada and the home of

"Top Gun" of Navy aviators. Keith Beaver was the Manager of BDM's Fallon Range Support project; he told the company management about new business opportunities in Nevada. Keith knew that the Navy would soon announce a Request for Proposal (RFP) for upgrading the Naval Tactical Air Combat Training System (TACTS) at Fallon NAS. It was anticipated that the U.S. Air Force would also release an RFP for improving the Joint Air Combat Training System (JACTS) at Nellis Air Force Base, Nevada.

Dr. John Gormally became the Manager of the tactical air combat training projects, and I received an assignment to investigate the Fallon and Nellis range data communication infrastructure to record flight data and tracks of combat training aircraft. I went to Mt. Callahan and Job Peak by a helicopter and conducted a site survey of the Tower Information System (TIS) which was a part of the Air Combat Training range instrumentation system at NAS Fallon.

The air combat training ranges at Fallon and Nellis covered an area of 80 miles east-west and 60 miles north-south. This space could accommodate 40 fighter aircraft flying. That was the number of aircraft in a typical air combat operation in the Vietnam War era. But, during the first Gulf War, the number of combat aircraft increased threefold to 120 fighter aircraft, and the combat training range needed larger airspace and additional monitoring towers.

Another requirement of the Navy, Air Force, and Joint Air Combat Training systems was the introduction of new GPS pods for tracking time, space, and position information (TSPI) of training aircraft and the new supporting RF data link infrastructure. As I started to work on the GPS pod issue, I felt the need to bring in a subcontractor who could assist us with GPS pod technology. Jim Hartz, the TRW Marketing Manager, and I met with Bob Van Wechel and Pat Jerrel of L3-IEC at Anaheim. IEC was one of the major suppliers of GPS receivers and aircraft pods for the navigation and range instrumentation equipment. IEC became our subcontractor in support of the TACTS and JACTS projects, and Van Wechel briefed us on their approach to GPS technology on the two air combat training systems.

After the bidder's conference, the U.S. Navy invited representatives from prospective bidders to join a site survey to obtain first-hand knowledge of the training range and the new TIS network. I joined the site survey to fly to Mt. Callaghan and Job Peak, located 15 miles due east of NAS Fallon. The only way we could reach the mountain range was by helicopter,

which participants rented from the boondocks, somewhere in Ely, Nevada. We paid $1,500 for flights to the top and back. One cold morning, we met at the Centroid Heliport facility in NAS Fallon. I noticed the pilot wore a heavy flight suit. The pilot warned us about the low temperature at our destination. I was wearing a tweed jacket and a thin parka. None of us except the pilot wore clothes warm enough for the temperatures on the mountains. It was too late for us to find warmer clothes, and we decided to brave the elements. After takeoff from Centroid, the pilot followed a trail to the mountains. (see photos 80 and 81) To our surprise, we saw mule packers with two pack mule trains on the trail below. The pilot spoke loudly to me:

"Mr. Kim, look at these two guys down there.

"These guys happen to be your company technicians, carrying things to the Job Peak relay station."

"I know these guys.

"They rent my helicopter every once in a while.

"Yep, in this neck of the desert, we tend to know everyone.

"Also, everything must be carried either by pack mules or by Ely Helicopter Services.

"And everything including trash must be carried back by the same way you brought stuff into.

"Otherwise, you make BLM unhappy."

"Aren't off-road vehicles allowed on these trails."

"No, first of all, this trail is one of the least visited roads in the Great Basin.

"They want to keep it that way."

"Who are they?"

"Oh, you know the federal government.

"These mountain ranges belong to BLM, the Bureau of Land Management of the Interior Department.

"They prohibit any motorized vehicles in the mountains.

"BLM is not the only bureaucracy involved, just one of four agencies."

"What are the other three?"

"Oh, let's see.

"The second is the Forestry Service of the Agriculture Department.

"The third is the National Park Service of the Interior Department.

"The fourth is the Indian Bureau of the Interior Department."

"Really?"

"These four agencies manage two-thirds of public lands in the U.S.

"The land management is excellent from the standpoint of conservation.

"But, this bureaucracy can cause some dilemmas to the Navy, because the Navy has to construct TIS with hardware on these protected lands.

"That will become you fellows' problems down the road.

"Out here in the Nevada mountains, you do not rent a car from Hertz or Avis.

"You rent helicopters from Ely, or else you drive a donkey."

Along the way, I saw several TIS towers, which looked like today's mobile telephone towers. When we arrived at the TIS master station, the temperature was 30 degrees F at two o'clock in the afternoon, so I quickly collected information on the data link on the tower and went into the TIS Master Station. Fortunately, I found the TIS Master Station was heated and comfortable.

In January 1993, the procurement office of the Nellis Air Force Base invited company representatives who had interest in the RFP on the Joint Air Combat Training System (JACTS) to an air combat training exercise known as Exercise Red Flag.[33] My company again sent me to participate in Exercise Red Flag, which was a two-week long exercise. In the wee hours of the first morning, I sat in the balcony of the briefing room along with other company representatives and had an opportunity to hear the morning briefing conducted by the Red Flag staff on the simulated combat training operations of that day.

I later saw a 2004 DVD movie, *Fighter Pilot: Operation Red Flag*, directed by Stephen Law.[34] In the actual exercise, I have no way of knowing what pilots did in a dogfight, or what downed pilot did during Search And Rescue (SAR) operations. But the one-hour long DVD showed what pilots did in the simulated air combat training, flying real Air Force aircraft, such as F-15s, F-16s, F-117s, B-1Bs, B-2s, C-17s, U-2s, E-2Cs, and AWACS. Allied Air Force pilots also participated in Excercise Red Flag, flying the Harriers and the Tornados of the Royal Air Force, and the Hornets of the Royal Canadian Air Force. One sequence in the film showed the massive (the weight of 45,000-pounds or 22.5

ton) F-15 Eagle taking off from Nellis Runway-21, followed by another F-15 Eagle right behind. Two powerful jet engines with a thrust of 21,000 pounds (or 840 horsepower) pushed the aircraft forward with the red-whitish afterburner blazing. It was awesome.

I knew by common sense all pilots need training. But why do fighter pilots need such an extensive exercise like Excercise Red Flag? The Airboss of Excercise Red Flag explained the importance of the training this way:

"When an Air Force or Navy pilot comes out of fighter pilot training, his or her first ten missions are crucial to whether the pilot will make or break.

"If a fighter pilot makes it through the first ten training sessions, his or her learning curve shoots up exponentially and will most likely survive as a fighter pilot.

"These ten missions in the Red Flag Exercise provide that crucial learning curve."

The umpires and evaluation teams had monitored activities on the large screen display when the training exercise began. Sixty blue (friendly) and red (enemy) forces aircraft were flying in various sectors (with colorful names like Coyote Alpha, or Caliente Bravo) of the training range. The Red Flag staff displayed real-time three-dimensional positions of the aircraft by the GPS pod telemetry data received at TIS telemetry in Nellis Range.

These blue and red forces conducted dogfights using flares to confuse infrared-guided missiles. The Airboss monitored each hit via TIS telemetry. All I could see in the briefing room was a large screen display with Blue-, Red-, Green-, and Orange-colored combat aircraft moving around all over the range airspace. *Excercise Red Flag* showed actual film footage of dogfights and aerial combat of aircraft flying at speeds exceeding 600 mph. A Blue aircraft was trying to position his aircraft at the tail of a Red aircraft, while the Red aircraft attempted to shake the Blue aircraft off from his tail. At the end of the day, the Airboss and the Red Flag staffs debriefed noteworthy events of the day, both good and bad, and blatant mistakes some pilots had made. One debrief example of the Excercise Red Flag was:

"I want to talk about a near-miss mid-air collision here in the area Oscar today.

"Falcon Bravo you briefed us earlier today that you would egress the area Hotel through the area Tango."

"But you deviated from that flight plan. No one knew about it because you failed to report your change.

"Because of that deviation, we almost lost eight lives in the area Oscar. Don't make a mistake like that again."

The next day they gave us a tour of the Senior Scout SIGINT shelter on the tarmac. It was a unit that can be transported on C-130 aircraft. The Team Chief of the Senior Scout was a female Air Force major, and there I saw the future direction of Air Force personnel, with more woman becoming pilots.

After air combat training, Excercise Red Flag continued with three additional exercises. One was the live bombing of moving vehicles and tanks of the Red force. As we entered the Exhibit Hall of Nellis AFB, I saw an open area in the rear of the building where the Red Flag staff gave us a tour of the aircraft equipment and radar, a surface-to-air missile (SAM), and an array of Red Force assets used in the simulated training. The second exercise was to practice mid-air refueling, which could be a dangerous operation. The third exercise was an SAR operation for a downed pilot, which involved AWACS aircraft, E-2C Hawkeyes, and surveillance satellites. I gained a first-hand knowledge of how the military conducted air combat training while using the microwave network and GPS pods attached to each participating aircraft. It was helpful for me to prepare the combat training proposal.

NEXT-GENERATION ATTACK SUBMARINE, COMBAT CONTROL SYSTEM PROJECT

In March 1993, I found myself standing next to the two huge steel cylinders which were about 40 feet in diameter. I compared my height to the cylinder's diameter, which was about six to seven times my height. The length of the cylinders was about three times of the cylinder diameter. These two huge steel cylinders were standing in the shipyard and sitting on a wheeled platform to which 200 over-sized tires were attached. These steel cylinders were not ordinary cylinders; they were sections of a submarine hull. These cylinders were standing outside of a high-bay building in Groton, Connecticut. The incredible thing was that the high-bay building had sliding doors large enough to slide through the cylinders. A jumbo logo for the Electric Boat (EB) Company was

attached to the corrugated aluminum wall of the facility.

That day I was standing in the EB facility with two dozen fellow team members from TRW. An engineer from EB, who stood in front of us, said.

"You are looking at a portion of the hull, which will become the Navy's newest attack submarine."

"These cylinders were assembled in the facility of our EB Company Quonset Point two months ago.

"We had a keel laying ceremony for the ship.

"We transported each cylinder on a barge for about 60 miles on the Long Island Sound. "All four cylinders are for one submarine.

"We will assemble the four cylinders in the final assembly facility, the building just behind you."

The following day, TRW's Next Generation Attack Submarine (NSSN) project team, led by John Gormally, went to the EB Company's New London facility across the Thames River in Connecticut. EB will design and develop the submarine. Later, NSSN was named the Virginia Class attack submarine.

From 1993 to1996, I participated in the project to develop the Combat Control System (CCS) of the new Virginia Class attack submarine. The U.S. Navy wanted to use commercial-off-the-shelf (COTS) subsystems in CCS, which was a shift in the procurement paradigm. The maker of the attack submarine, EB, invited TRW to provide subsystems of CCS, which could be a candidate for Open System Critical Items (OSCIs). EB assumed that COTS would facilitate the use of state-of-the-art technology throughout the life of the submarine class and would help avoid obsolescence. The U.S. Navy had two CCS's for the previous classes of attack submarines, the Los Angeles Class (SSN-688) and the Sea Wolf Class (SSN-21). Those CCS's were AN/BSY-1 and AN/BSY-2. The suppliers of these systems never considered open systems architecture. Instead they built it as a stove-piped system. They built CCS with custom-made components, which often resulted in the late delivery and the increased cost. The Navy decided to build the new Virginia Class submarine CCS with open systems architecture as much as possible.

I received an assignment to provide OSCIs in the new CCS. After some discussions, I proposed two candidate OSCIs. The first was the improved connectivity of the twenty CCS subsystems (e.g., the command and control structure for fire control, navigation, electronic warfare, acoustic intelligence, radar,

sonar, radios, etc.) by a local area network. The second was the radar subsystem. I proposed that two components of the radar subsystem, the radar electronics, and the display indicator, would be interconnected by LAN.

For the first OSCI, I proposed to use a LAN connection with the high-speed fiber optic cable (Asynchronous Transport Mode (ATM)-Synchronous Optical Network (SONET)). I used the OPNET simulation tool to demonstrate the improved efficiency of the LAN system. This infrastructure also reduced the use of copper wires and provided a robust CCS connectivity.

What do smoke signals, the shipboard signal lamp, and the semaphore telegraph have in common? If your answer was the optical communication, you guessed it right. The signal lamp and the semaphore were useful but slow. Today optical communication uses optical fiber and transfers information at a much faster rate. How fast is optical communication? The speed of an old signal lamp was in the order of ten characters per minute, while the speed of optical fiber is 7 tera-characters per minute. The increase is one million-million times, which means 12 zeros after the comma.

For the second OSCI task, I proposed the application of the LAN to the radar subsystem. I recommended that the AN/BPS-16 X-band radar system would be connected to the radar indicator AN/SPA-25. I intended to transfer radar data via the high-speed combat system network. Based on the radar sub-system experiment, Phil Girardi and I wrote a technical paper "The Application of the ATM-SONET to New Attack Submarine (NSSN) Radar Subsystem,[35] which was published in *1997 IEEE MILCOM conference proceedings.* This article presented the 1995 NSSN OSCI test demonstration results in Newport, Rhode Island. The experimental results, comprised of a series of radar screen photographs, showed no discernible difference between the direct connect and the indirect connect using the LAN.

TRW Aviation Automation Projects

At the 1994 ATCA Conference, the conference organizer invited attendees to the Denver Airport control facility. When I entered the facility, I saw several air traffic controllers standing in front of their air traffic control consoles, looking at the Automated Radar Terminal System (ARTS) consoles. I heard constant communications between air traffic controllers and pilots, talking to each other.

Controller: "United 023. Denver tower controller. You are behind American 1297. Wind 8 knots at 010. Runway 16R. Clear for take-off."

United 023: "Roger. Denver controller. United 023. Taxiing to Runway 16R."

Controller: "United 023. Contact departure. Good flight!"

Controller: "American 1297. Climb and maintain 2000 feet. Turn left to 145."

American 1297: "Denver controller. Roger."

The controllers exchanged their conversations with pilots on air-to-ground radio. At first, it looked much like a video game, but this was not a game. Each number on the screen represented an aircraft. Passengers' lives depended on the air traffic controller's careful, decisive, constant instruction. The supervisor on duty told me that, for air traffic controllers, the pay was good, and the benefits were excellent, but the stress was high. Whether a controller worked at an air traffic control tower or at an en route center, the controller had to give instructions continuously to keep airplanes a safe distance apart during takeoffs and landings and en route flights.

Controller: "Southwest 289. Denver TRACON. Cessna 172. 10 O'clock direction. 4 miles at altitude 2800 feet."

Southwest 289: "Denver TRACON. Southwest 289. Cessna 172 in sight."

Controller: "Southwest 289. Climb and maintain 5000 feet altitude. Turn right to 240."

Southwest 289: "Denver control. Turn right to 240. Maintain 2000 feet. Vector 25 right into LAX."

Controller: "Southwest 289. Contact LAX center 132.9. Good day. Maintain flight level 240."

Southwest 289: "Denver TRACON. Roger. Good day."

LAX TRACON: "Southwest 289. Flight level 10."

LAX TRACON: "Southwest 289. Go ahead. Descend and maintain level 10."

Southwest 289: "Roger."

The supervisor told me that,

Whether it is at an airport control tower or an en route center, the controllers monitor aircraft traveling on the highway in the sky. The controllers must speak clearly, work in a team and be constantly alert.

※ ※ ※

From 1992 to 2001, I have been the senior staff engineer reporting to three successive managers in FAA-related projects. They were Dr, Wilson Felder, Steve Hertz, and John Dadiani. The TRW Air Traffic Automation Projects had its offices in a School Street building next to the FAA headquarters. For several years, I represented TRW in the Radio Technical Commission for Aeronautics (RTCA), which played an advisory role and build consensus based on recommendations on aviation issues. RTCA was a nonprofit organization charged with developing technical guidance related to FAA and advanced aviation technologies. RTCA had numerous special committees that developed recommendations in response to requests from FAA. Special committees addressed such areas as operational and safety performance requirements, interoperability requirements, and minimum operational performance standards. I participated in Special Committee SC-159 (Navigation Equipment Using GPS), SC-198 (Next-generation Air-to-ground Communication), and SC-172 (VHF Future Air-to-ground Communications for VHF Aeronautical Bands).

In one of the meetings, attendees introduced themselves. Almost everyone was a pilot at one time or another. They described what equipment they have flown, such as the Boeing 707. When it came to my turn, I knew I had to say something about flying, but I had never been a pilot. I told them:

"I fly American Airlines."

We all chuckled.

There was a meeting of the GPS special committee, members of which were representatives from the domestic and foreign aviation community in 1990.

Recommendations made by special committees would directly impact their respective businesses. The topic was navigation of both commercial aircraft and general aviation aircraft using GPS-augmentation. It was known first as Free Flight and, in 1977, was renamed to Flight 2000. GPS-augmented navigation between airports became known as the Wide Area Augmentation System (WAAS) while the terminal landing phase became known as the Local Area Augmentation System (LAAS). Primary motivation behind WAAS was to remove rigid flight plans in the U.S. airspace, thereby reducing fuel consumption. However, this approach raised safety issues. This GPS-augmented navigation and air traffic control operation became known as "Free Flight." Interestingly, during an RTCA meeting, a Romanian Air Force brigadier general made a not so humorous comment on the Free Flight program.

"I tell you, Romanian airspace is small, and the Romanian Air Force and the civil aviation fleet are modest in size as compared to American aviation. We do not need air traffic control for the military aircraft, and we have been doing free flights with our civil aviation successfully for many years."

In early years of American aviation, aircraft operated without a rigid flight plan, but it is a different story with more than 14,500 airplanes in U.S. airspace.

One winter morning, I walked through the not so busy lobby in the general aviation building at Reagan National Airport (DCA). I saw several small general aviation airplanes on the tarmac. General aviation encompasses other-than-scheduled air services. That morning I got a seat on the FAA-owned DC-6 aircraft to fly to the FAA Technical Center in Atlantic City, N.J. The FAA operated shuttle aircraft and allowed me to fly on shuttle flights since I was an FAA contractor on official business. I carried a hand-held GPS aviation receiver, Garmin GPSMAP-195. After the DC-6 propeller airplane took off, I followed the flight path along the coastline of the Chesapeake Bay. Then we flew over Baltimore, Wilmington, Philadelphia, and into Atlantic City. One hour later the airplane landed at Atlantic City Airport. It taxied to the hangar building, which housed several FAA research facilities. Air travel was like this in the old days. I remember regional airports like Fort Wayne or Albuquerque, where I could get off the airplane, carry my baggage with me, and just walk out

of the airport. How civilized air travel used to be.

I met with FAA Technical Center engineers to discuss LAAS technology, which was to be GPS-augmented navigation for the final landing phase. GPS LAAS provides an aircraft in the landing phase with critical corrections of GPS navigation errors to aircraft flying within 30 nautical miles of the airport runway in near real-time via VHF data links. One issue was multipath errors, that is, by the difference between actual and measured positional data at a LAAS receiver.

BUYING AND SELLING ELECTROMAGNETIC SPECTRUM AS A COMMODITY

"Did you know that one could buy and sell the formless and nonphysical entity called the Radio Frequency (RF) spectrum?"

"What is the RF spectrum?

"A wave in a pond propagates through a medium, the water.

"Classical physicists thought radio waves propagate through a medium called *aether*."

"Yes, aether as a medium,

"The Federal Communications Commission (FCC) sells the RF spectrum as a commodity like gold or crude oil.

"FCC issues a license to broadcast TV on the RF spectrum or a license to send and receive wireless ham radio signals.

"With the growth of the wireless business, which was two percent of the U.S. GDP in 2018, there were ever-increasing demands for the RF spectrum.

"In one case, the FCC allowed a TV broadcasting company to sell the unused spectrum to wireless telephone companies.

"They paid $19.8 billion for 70 MHz of the spectrum."

"What about the other RF band in the spectrum, which FCC controls?

"There is one particular RF spectrum band called the Industrial, Science, and Medical (ISM) radio band, which is in the 900 MHz to 2.4 GHz band.

"The FCC assigned this ISM band for non-communication use.

"Non-communication use means microwave ovens, short-range devices like bluetooth, garage door openers, video devices, and wi-fi networks.

"This band is the RF version of a waste dump.

"But this RF band is also used for non-ISM applications like wireless sensor networks, wireless LANs, and cordless phones."

"The spectrum-hungry wireless telephone industry invaded this band with GSM-900 for cell phones and the radio-frequency identification (RFID) application.

"One's cell phone frequency could be found in an RF dump."

"Needless to say, aviation communications also need the RF spectrum.

"What are supply and demand of the spectrum in the aviation world?

"Way back in 1943, FCC assigned 3 MHz in the 123-126 MHz frequency band for aviation communications.

"As the number of channels increased, FCC expanded this to 15 MHz in the frequency band of 118 to 136 MHz.

"There were several studies of channel requirements for the aircraft in U.S. airspace.

"There was no increase in supply.

"There was only the increase in demand.

"All trends indicated that required bandwidths were much larger than the spectrum assignment of 15 MHz.

"The bandwidth used for each VHF channel was 100 KHz with double-sideband amplitude modulation (AM).

"As the demand for the VHF radio increased, John R. Carson of Bell Laboratory and the U.S. Navy experimented with single-sideband (SSB) over their radio link.

"The SSB radio reduced the necessary bandwidth per channel by 50 KHz; then in 1972, it was further reduced to 25 KHz.

"These channels used the double-sideband AM waveform.

"Therefore, this scheme increased the bandwidth utilization by fourfold.

"AM was the radio modulation technique for transmitting AM radio, such as your car radio.

"When an AM radio modulated voice or music, it used two RF sidebands.

"One was on the upper side of the carrier frequency and the other on the

lower side.

"Why did AM use a double-sideband? This was based on the phenomenon of electromagnetism.

"The modulation produced two sidebands.

"A mirror image of the spectrum existed whether you like it not.

"But one half of the spectrum carried all the necessary information.

"All one had to do was to filter the one side of the spectrum.

"This approach was somewhat a simple solution and was quite adequate to handle the demand for VHF radio up to 1990.

In 2009, FAA initiated the development of technology that will integrate digital voice and data into air-to-ground communications as part of the next-generation air/ground communications (NEXCOM) program. NEXCOM radio used the 25 kHz bandwidth but needed more sophisticated technology for multiple access, coding, and the modulation that allowed more efficient use of bandwidth. The multiple access method enabled sharing of the bandwidth with several users simultaneously. Both the FAA and the Eurocontrol developed architecture for NEXCOM.[36]

At the 1999 World Aviation Congress, I presented a technical paper, "A Review of Enabling Technologies for NEXCOM." I published this technical paper in *American Institute of Aeronautics and Astronautics/Society of Automotive Engineers World Aviation Congress Proceedings.*[37] My technical paper presented a comprehensive review of several enabling technologies for NEXCOM.

18

Fine Art Collection, Cornell University, Stanford University, and Mt. Palomar

MY FINE ART COLLECTION

In 1971, during my TDY in South Korea, I bought two paintings at the Hyundai Art Gallery, in Insa precinct. The first one was *Farmhouse with a thatched roof in the snow,*(see photo 88) by Hwa-gyeong Kim (1922-1979). The painting was about a winter snow scene of a Korean farmhouse with a thatched roof. He painted several variations on this theme. The artist painted it with black and pastel color inks. His brushstroke was fast, and he exaggerated the thatched roof. The painting depicted a woman waiting for her family and a dog walking in the snow around a rustic farmhouse. I saw a similar painting by Hwa-gyeong Kim in the book, *A History of the Korean People.*[38] He studied at the Tokyo Imperial Fine Art School. He won the prestigious Korean National Fine Art Competition in the 1960s.

The second one was an oil painting *"Cityscape in the snow,"* by Ju-young Lee (1934-2008). (see photo 87). According to the gallery curator, the painter won the first-place award of the Shin Sang Fine Art Group competition in Seoul in 1962. Later, I discovered that the artist had an unfortunate experience during the Korean War. His son wrote the following article about his father's experience in the *Hankyoreh* newspaper in 2010.[39]

> "In 1950, the North Korean Army forced my father, who was then 18 years old, to join the North Korean People's Volunteer Army. In 1951, he was captured by the South Korean Army and interned in the Geojedo Prisoner Of War (POW) camp. It was in the prison camp where my father met one of the

notable Korean painters, Kwe-dae Lee (1913-1965), who was also a POW. My father got acquainted with Kwe-dae Lee, from whom my father learned to draw oil paintings. In July 1953, when the Korean War was ended, the South Korean Army freed my father from the camp, but not the elder Lee. My father survived the war, and, after the war, he gave me a few legacies, one of which was a 60-page sketchbook by his mentor Kwe-dae Lee, who drew a human anatomy as teaching materials for my father. In 2008, I donated this collection to the National Museum of Contemporary Art, Gwacheon, South Korea. The U.N. Command sent the elder Lee to North Korea, and he passed away in North Korean in 1965."

Whenever I look at Lee's painting *Cityscape in the snow*, it reminds me of the terrible war. What was the reason for his son's delayed publication of the above newspaper article? From the 1950s until recently, soldiers, who served in the North Korean People's Volunteer Army, were stigmatized in the South Korean society. They hid their dark past from public.

Now it is all but forgotten that the U.N. Command built the Geojedo POW camp in 1951 to incarcerate POW's during the war. The POW camp held 170,000 prisoners. One day in June 1953, one month before the armistice, then South Korean President Syngman Rhee released 25,000 non-Communist POWs, who wanted to remain in South Korea. In 1953, I lived in Pusan, and the POW camp was only 20 miles west from Pusan. Syngman Rhee was against the armistice, which would leave the country divided. He revolted against the American authority by releasing prisoners. Today historians judged his release of 25,000 non-Communist POWs favorably.

The younger Lee was one of released POWs and later painted *Cityscape in the snow*. The elder Lee had no such luck. The painting *Cityscape in the snow* hanging on my study wall, represented the intertwined lives of two artists in Korean history.

I owned a woodcut etching print *Autumn Harvest Moon* by Yoong Bae (1928-1992). It was a gift from my friend Hwan-soo Kim. The print had a full moon in gold and on red background (see photo 89). In the 1950s, Yoong Bae worked at the Public Affairs Office of the United States Information Service (USIS) in Seoul. During the period, he studied modern American and European woodcut etching print techniques. In 1968-1973, Yoong Bae led the Korean Contemporary Printmakers' Association, and which created a modern silk-screening technique group.[40] He created many prints, that formed modern European and American etching paint techniques with a spiritual motif of the East. In 1973, Yoong Bae immigrated to San Francisco and continued his woodcut printing activities. When I visited the Asian Art Museum in San Francisco, I saw one of his later prints, titled *Meditation,* in which I saw similar techniques as he used in *Autumn Harvest Moon.*

Rahn owned a watercolor painting by a notable Korean painter Sang-beom Lee (1897-1972). A clump of yellow chrysanthemums was hanging on a shrub with red flowers. (see photo 85). Rahn told me how she got the printing from Lee:

"I received *Autumn Chrysanthemum in the Field* as a gift from the painter Sang-beom Lee himself a few days before I left Seoul for America.

"My parents asked him to draw a painting to commemorate the occasion.

"Lee had been a good friend of my parents. My parents expressed their appreciation by giving him a bottle of his favorite Scotch whiskey."

In 2001, Sotheby's of New York auctioned the Marcus Scherbacher collection.[41] Scherbacher was a cultural attaché of the American embassy in South Korea in the 1950s. Sotheby's published a catalog for the auction, in which was another of Lee's paintings *Spring Landscape* was listed. The painting was listed at $2,000. Lee painted several variations of theme with four seasons. The plum, the orchid, the chrysanthemum, and the bamboo symbolizes the four seasons. The *Four Noble Ones (Seasons)* had been a well-known genre of Asian painting. The Scherbacher collection had one painting of spring, and Rahn had one painting of autumn. I wondered what happened to summer and winter.

❀ ❀ ❀

One of my favorite Asian paintings is *The Coming Winter as Birds Fly South* by Professor No-soo Park of SNU. Park created this watercolor painting, based on the theme of the Tang poem by Cen Shen (716-770) (see photo 86). Cen Shen was an 8th century Tang poet, who was famous for his poetry about bleak Chinese frontier and fortresses along the Silk Road in the western region of China. In the 8th century, the mighty Chinese dynasty stretched its sphere of influence in the western regions, where Cen Shen was a magistrate. He wrote desolate poems based on his experience. One poem depicted the frontier garrison, where Cen Shen was magistrate and commander,

The Coming Winter as Birds Fly South[42]

I am riding my horse to the West by the Imperial order,
And the horse 'giddy up' by the stirrups and whips,
Now it is September, and I am sending you to the north
of Jaohe,
I recite this poem with the snow on my back
And teardrops on my clothes.

By Cen Shen (716-770).[43]
Translated by John Kim.

I first saw this painting in the office of Professor Yong-gwon Kim. He was an exchange fellow at the University of Minnesota when I met him in 1964. He had received three Korean paintings by Professor No-soo Park, who wanted to teach a course on Asian painting at UM. Yong-gwon and I went to enquire Professor Thomas Cowette, the Head of the Fine Arts Department of UM, whether Park could teach a course on Asian brush painting. When Cowette made a survey on the brush painting course, he found not enough students to open a course in UM. Park told Yong-gwon Kim to sell paintings if he could. I bought one of them, which I own to this day (see photo 86).

WILLIAM GOES TO CORNELL UNIVERSITY

In 1989, our son William enrolled at Cornell University, and he thrived in school and enjoyed the college life in Ithaca, *Far Above Cayuga's Waters.* He studied mechanical and aerospace engineering and was very active in *The Cornellian* yearbook during his undergraduate years. Over one hundred photographs in the 1991 yearbook were credited to William. Most of the photographs were about the Cornell campus life, action-oriented sports, and nature around Ithaca.

In his sophomore year, William joined the Cornell University model airplane team. The Cornell team entered the model airplane competition, which was sponsored by the American Society of Mechanical Engineers (ASME). It was held at Wright Patterson Air Force Base (WPAFB) in Dayton, Ohio. William invited me to the competition. A model airplane has its challenges as it is a pilotless plane, a precursor of today's ubiquitous unmanned aerial vehicles (UAVs). More than 20 colleges, including Embry-Riddle Aeronautical University, Kansas State University, Cornell University, Princeton University, and Poland Technical University, participated in the competition. As it was held two months after the outbreak of the first Iraq War, security in WPAFB was tight. No spectators were allowed to attend the event; only participants were allowed to the base. It was cold and blustery days to fly model airplanes. William was in charge of the remote control system. On the first day, both of the Cornell team's model aircraft crashed. There were only two entries from Ivy League schools, Cornell and Princeton, and they were vying for Ivy League bragging rights. At the end of the first day, the score of the Princeton team was ahead of the Cornell team's. Knowing that the two Cornell model aircraft had crashed, the Princeton team returned home and did not participate in the second day of the competition. (see photos 69 and 70)

But, the Cornell team did not give up and decided to repair one of their model airplanes. They needed several parts for repair. It was Saturday afternoon, and there were no hobby shops open in the Dayton area. But I remembered a hobby shop near Springfield, Ohio, as I lived in nearby Xenia, Ohio, in 1964. I found the telephone number of the store in the Yellow Pages. After the shopkeeper heard of our predicament, he helped us with the necessary parts. The team repaired one airplane in the motel throughout the night and the early

Sunday morning. The Cornell team then flew the rebuilt model airplane on Sunday and scored enough to beat the Princeton team. It must have been a big surprise for the Princeton Tigers when they found out the final results!

A Cross-country Trip with William

In 1993, when William enrolled at Stanford University for his graduate study, he planned to drive his car to Palo Alto. He asked me to help him drive across the Continental United States. On August 24, William and I began our trip from McLean to Palo Alto. It took us 12 days and covered 3,000 miles on a northern route. On the first day we drove for eight hours on the Pennsylvania and Ohio Turnpikes. We then drove the flat countryside of the Midwest.

The area south of the Twin Cities in Minnesota, where I once lived, reminded me of another trip in 1964. My brother Phil and I were traveling from Minneapolis to Rolla, Missouri, where Phil began his graduate study. We drove my Rambler from the Twin Cities and passed through Rochester, Minnesota, along the endless cornfields all day long. Alfred Hitchcock filmed *North by Northwest* on these Iowa highways, in the middle of no place, where two roads would cross in the middle of cornfields. That trip in 1964 took about 12 hours, covering 670 miles, mostly through farmlands.

William and I headed west from the Twin Cities to South Dakota. We reached Badlands National Park, South Dakota. The landscape started to change to the tall grass prairie with rocky hills and occasional buttes. William wanted to photograph landscapes. We set up our camera on the tripod, waiting for diffused afternoon sunlight and tried to photograph the layer of the unusual sandstone formation. The layered hues of limestone deposits in pink, yellow, gray, and white were beautiful. While we were waiting for sundown, I thought I heard the clattering sound of a rattlesnake.

I whispered to William,

"Rattlesnake?"

"Where?"

There also were prairie dogs, which emerged from holes to peek at us while standing up on their hind legs.

Our next stop was Mount Rushmore National Memorial in Rapid City. We

also visited nearby Ellsworth AFB, home of the Air Force Bomber Wing and the Minuteman Intercontinental Ballistic Missile (ICBM) wing. There was, the South Dakota Air and Space Museum in the base. The museum exhibited a Rockwell B-1 B Lancer, a Boeing B-52 Stratofortress, and a Boeing B-29 Superfortress, and also displayed a Minuteman Intercontinental Ballistic Missile (ICBM) system. According to the poster, during the Cold War, there were 1,000 Minuteman silos in the Mountain States.

"Let's go find a Minuteman silo.

"There should be one nearby.

"William, when I was working on the National Missile Defense project in the 1980s, I heard that one could find a silo by following the power line."

We ventured into the surrounding area and found a power line near Ellsworth AFB. We followed the power line. After a 30 mile drive from the air base along the power line, we found a structure.

"William, what is that structure ahead of us."

"Keep driving."

"O.K. We found a missile launch facility."

We found a power line, a concrete slab, and antennas. There was a silo in the small village of Cottonwood, South Dakota. The plate said, "D-O1, Quinn Cottonwood Missile Flight Control Center."

After nine days of traveling, we entered Yellowstone National Park at the eastern entrance and crossed the continental divide, the elevation of which was 8,150 feet. The lodge in the park was full of weekend travelers, so we decided to pitch our pup tent at a nearby campground. In the next morning, we found out that it had snowed overnight. We then visited Grand Teton National Park, south of Yellowstone National Park. (see photo 79) William told me,

"Dad, you are looking at the most photographed mountain in America."

He meant the Grand Teton Mountains across Jackson Lake. We saw aspens near and far, which formed bright, gold screens at the foot of the mountains, their leaves quaking vibrant color of gold in the wind.

From Jackson Lake, we drove to Idaho Falls in the afternoon. Most cars and trucks we saw were American made: Ford, General Motors, and Chrysler. I sel-

dom saw any foreign-made vehicles on the road in this part of the country. In the Greater Washington area, when I park my car, it is surrounded by imported vehicles. But in mid-America, I see more Ford F-Series, Chevy Silverado, and Dodge Rams.

At the junction of two highways in Idaho Falls, I found a lone service station, where I filled the gas tank. A lanky cowboy stood next to me, filling gas into his pickup truck. I greeted him with,

"Hello."

He looked at me and did not respond. I told this story to a friend in the office when I returned from the trip, and he said,

"John, consider yourself lucky.

"He could have punched your nose."

I just wondered why.

In the sparsely populated mountain country, the culture was quite different from those of the Northeast or the West coast. We traveled on empty Idaho highways. I saw an occasional hunting party in red hats and red vests, with a deer draped over the hood of the car. We saw covered eighteen-wheel trucks carrying Idaho potatoes.

From Idaho Falls to Twin Falls in Idaho, we drove on a highway parallel to the Snake River. We followed the river to the west and saw road signs with colorful names like Blackfoot, Pocatello, Jackpot, American Falls, Shoshone, and Twin Falls. The Snake River became wider as more tributaries merged into it. The river then turned to the north to Oregon and Washington and to the Pacific Ocean, but we headed south to Nevada. After 12 days of traveling on turnpikes and highways through cornfields, open spaces, a Minuteman silo, tall grass prairies, and the Rocky Mountains, we finally arrived in Palo Alto.

WILLIAM'S GRADUATE STUDIES AT STANFORD UNIVERSITY

William invited Rahn and me to visit him at Stanford University. During our visit, he showed us to his laboratory in the Durand Building, where he and his team were developing a small satellite. William was a member of the team building a satellite on a low budget; they were planning to send it into low-Earth orbit. When William was an undergraduate at Cornell, he and his

Cornell team made a model radio-controlled aircraft. But did you hear about a student-built spacecraft? I was impressed. William explained that the satellite payload was part of the satellite design and development project at Stanford University. One of the team leaders for this project was a graduate student, Christopher Kitts, and the satellite was called Stanford Audio Phonic Photographic Infrared Experiment (SAPPHIRE). The team designed the spacecraft payload and later built the actual small satellite at Stanford Satellite Systems Development Laboratory (SSDL). Their payload consists of an infrared sensor package, a digital camera, and a voice synthesizer; the satellite bus consisted of a 9-inch tall, 16-inch in diameter hexagonal structure with a communications device, a power unit, a CPU, and a sensors subsystem.

SAPPHIRE was the first of several Satellite Quick Research Testbed (SQUIRT)-class spacecraft. In 1999, Professor Bob Twiggs joined Stanford University facility to start a spacecraft design program in the Aero/Astro department. He came up with the SQUIRT concept. At that time, the trend was toward increasingly smaller and lower-cost spacecraft. Prof. Twiggs later went on to develop the "CubeSat" standards, that is widely adopted today (hundreds of the CubeSat have been put into orbit). The work he did on SAPPHIRE/SQUIRT helped the Smallsat community eventually enter into the CubeSat era, which had a transforming effect in the aerospace industry.[44]

"What is a CubeSat?

"A CubeSat (also known as the U-class spacecraft) is a unit of a small satellite for space technology."

"A CubeSat unit is a standardized structure composed of commercial off-the-shelf (COTS) components and electronics and is a cube of 10 cm with a maximum weight of 1.33 K-grams per unit.

"The program started with low-budget university space technology.

"When a launch vehicle is scheduled to take off, there may be small, unoccupied space of 1,000 cubic cm or more available.

"The NASA CubeSat Launch Initiative provided opportunities for universities to launch small satellite payloads developed by universities.

"The SAPPHIRE/SQUIRT team continued its hands-on space technology experiment, and the NASA provided a launch vehicle in 2015, 16 years later.

In 1993, Stanford University conceived a program to build a satellite with encouragement from the Industry Affiliates Board. Christopher Kitts and Wil-

liam Kim were members of the first student team, which would design and build a small spacecraft, including a working payload. The following year, they presented a paper on the SAPPHIRE satellite, at Eighth Annual American Institute of Aeronautics and Astronautics Conference. The conference was held at Utah State University Conference on Small Satellites in Logan, Utah.[45] Christopher Kitts and William Kim received an Honorable Mention at the Conference.

After completing his Master's degree, William returned to Orbital Sciences Corporation and continued to work on several rocket projects such as Pegasus, which was a rocket launched from a Lockheed L-1011 carrier aircraft. William also worked on a new launch vehicle, the X-34, which was a Reusable Launch Vehicle (RLV) technology demonstrator.[46] The X-34 technology demonstrator was envisioned to be a flying laboratory for techniques and operations applicable to future low-cost, reusable launch vehicles. He presented the results of his project at the 35th Aerospace Mechanisms Symposium, held at the NASA Ames Research Center in Mountain View, California.[47]

PALOMAR OBSERVATORY

One day in 1995, as I was driving uphill through San Diego County Road S-6 to Palomar Observatory, I saw a dozen people resting at a roadside table. To my surprise, I recognized two individuals in that crowd. One was Priscilla Guthrie, and the other was Hank Beebe. I stopped my car and greeted them.

"Priscilla.

"Fancy meeting you here."

"Hi, John, what are you doing in this neck of the woods?"

"I am visiting Palomar Observatory. I am going to check out their charge-coupled-diode (CCD) devices on their telescope."

"What are you doing?"

"Oh, we are attending a week-long TRW executive training course.

"Right now, we are doing a team building activity by climbing the Mt. Palomar road on bicycles."

"I wish there was an easier way to build a team than doing Jinriksha."

"We've already ridden to the top. Now we are heading down to the training headquarters in the hotel."

I bid farewell to Priscilla and Hank and drove to the Palomar Observatory. The observatory belonged to the California Institute of Technology, which operated the research program with the Jet Propulsion Laboratory and Cornell University.

19

Travels through Western Europe

HEIDELBERG, OCTOBER 6, 1992

The high point of 1992 for Rahn and me was traveling through Germany, France, and Italy by train at our own pace on flexible schedule. We began our trip at Dulles Airport on United Airlines flights and then traveled to Heidelberg.

In the afternoon, we visited Heidelberg University. I asked our pension concierge to recommend a beer hall in Heidelburg. He told me we should go to Vette's Alte Heidelberger Brauhaus. In the evening, we went to Brauhaus; from our table, we could see the Alte Bridge over the Neckar River. In this beer hall, Students used to duel with swords, a legacy of the Junkers and the romanticism in German universities. That evening the atmosphere of Vette's Brauhaus was just like what I had imagined, mostly students drinking beer in "gemutlich-keit," like a scene in the Sigmund Romberg's operetta *Student Prince*.

PARIS

The next day, we jumped on the high-speed TGV train at the Frankfurt station. Our train sped through hills of the Alsace-Lorraine. Vineyards covered the hillsides of the valleys with Burgundy grapes. Dijon mustard plants covered fields with yellow flowers. I could almost smell them through the train windows.

When we arrived at Paris-Gare Lyon station in the afternoon, the station hall was busy with travelers, including pesky pickpockets. Inside the station, I saw the famous restaurant Le Train Bleu, where a scene from an Agatha Chris-

tie movie, *Le Train Bleu,* was staged. We went into the restaurant and found fantastic décor.

We checked into the Hotel de Blois, in Montparnasse. In the afternoon, we walked along Champs Élysées Avenue from the Arc de Triomphe. In the middle of the ten-lane avenue, a police car was racing along, wailing its siren, with the rhythmic, "*NEE-eu NEE-eu.*" Shady trees lined the boulevard, where street performers showed their talents on the sidewalk. One acrobat did several cartwheels continuously for 10 yards. Yes, another street acrobat balanced his body horizontally on one arm while rhythmically bounced along the sidewalk. It was fascinating.

We visited the Louvre Museum, passing through the pyramid-like entrance designed by I. M. Pei. When we entered the main hall of the museum, we saw two dozen South Asian monks. They wore bright orange garments. They came up the escalator in a single file. The scene was a piece of living art.

Next, we visited the Museé d'Orsay and saw many 19th century French paintings. We climbed to the top floor, where a huge clock sat in a circular window. We looked through the window to the north and saw the Basilica de Sacré Coeur in Montmartre. The clock used to tell time for passengers at the Gare d'Orsay railroad station, which is now a museum. We climbed Montmartre hill and saw the once-famous cabaret, the Moulin Rouge. I was disappointed to see the old neighborhood, which was not what I had imagined as the place of bohemian life as shown in paintings of Henri de Toulouse-Lautrec.

Instead of visiting the Montmartre district, I wanted to see the Montparnasse district. In the 1950s, when I studied French at L'Etude Français in Pusan, our teacher, Professor Hui-young Lee, often mentioned about Montparnasse, where painters, writers, poets, and composers flourished. I heard from him the names like Chagall, Cocteau, Hemingway, Modigliani, Dali, and Poulenc. Montparnasse was an artist's colony of penniless upstarts from all over Europe and the United States. They often lived in rat-infested, damp, and unheated studios, but became the avant-garde art and literature. What I found in Montparnasse of the 1990s was a far cry from what my professor described. It was an affluent, modern district, where we saw galleries displaying artworks in the show windows. The artwork was very pricey, with asking prices in millions of francs.

Then, we sat on a stone bench in a leafy cemetery, Montparnasse Cemetery,

not far from the city center. There, we found tombs of great Frenchmen, some of the intellectual and artistic elites of France. We passed by the graves of Guy de Maupassant, the writer, and Henri Poincaré, the mathematician, marked with their Ci-gît (meaning "Here Lies") tombstones.

FLORENCE

From Paris, we traveled to Florence in a sleeping train car, which had very uncomfortable couchette. But we were too tired to notice it. Next morning, we checked into a pension near the Duomo (Il Duomo di Firenze). Then, we trekked "the Renaissance Walk." At the Duomo, we met Matthias, a young Austrian man in his early thirties; he had a guitar slung over his shoulder. We shared a conversation with him, and he turned out to be a well-informed student of the Renaissance history.

"Johannes (he called me in German), there is also an Austrian 'Duomo.' It is called Stephansdom, (the Dome of St. Stephens), which comes from a Greek word 'doma' or house."

"You knew the Florentine Duomo was the birthplace of the Renaissance."

"Yes, I knew, but how did it start?"

"In the 14th century, town elders of Florence decided to build a cathedral larger than other cities in Northern Italy. But when they decided to build a new cathedral, the Duomo, they wanted to build a cathedral in Roman architecture, not in the Gothic style.

"Stephansdom in Vienna is a half-Gothic and a half-Romanesque cathedral but is a tall structure.

"Romanesque architecture means a style of medieval Europe characterized by semi-circular arches like the one you see in the Pantheon in Rome.

"But the dome designed and planned for Florence was much bigger than the Pantheon.

"In 1450, they completed everything except the dome.

"The dome builders had run into problems, as the Pantheon was built many centuries ago, and the technical know-how was all but forgotten.

"Eventually, an architect named Brunelleschi completed the dome with his new civil engineering technology, and the city of Florence heralded in the

resurgence of Mediterranean architecture, therefore, the Renaissance."

After Matthias's explanation, Rahn, Matthias, and I settled into a roadside table with a drink and rested.

ROME

After two days of sightseeing in Florence, we went to Rome. We found a pension called Soggiorno at the tourist office. It was part of a residential apartment house with an inner court. Our room was on the second floor, which gave us a taste of Italian urban living. Our pension owner had a family of six, including a young boy, named Angelo, and his grandfather. Grandfather must have been in charge of Angelo. Occasionally, grandfather would look for Angelo outside the courtyard,

"Angelo.

"Dove sei, Angelo?

"Devi entrare, Angelo."

After eleven o'clock, quiet hours prevailed.

The first day, Rahn and I set out for the ancient Roman ruins, the Forum, the Coliseum, the Circus Maximus, and the Palatine Hill. In the late afternoon, we crossed the Tiber River to Trastevere district to find a restaurant. We were too early to dine. Romans do not start their supper before eight o'clock in the evening. But we found a small family restaurant, which appeared to be not for tourist, but for locals. We asked the signora if she could serve us an early supper. She said she could only serve us a lasagna dish with baked eggplant parmesan. The meal was homemade, and the signora served us by saying *"Tu mangi, Abondante et delizioso."*

We visited the Pantheon, which had a rotunda dome with a portico of granite Corinthian columns like the ones I have seen in Paris and Ephesus in Turkey. The Roman Pantheon is a well-preserved building and has been in continuous use for 2,000 years. We went to Vatican City and visited the Sistine Chapel where we looked up at the ceiling on which Michelangelo painted the Creation of Adam. We stood in the middle of St. Peter's Square surrounded by tall colonnades, a scene, which was familiar to me, as I've seen Easter gathering in St. Peter's Square on TV newscasts. St. Peter's statue stands in front of the

51

Enjoying a family gathering at my father-in-law's house in Sajik Precinct, Seoul in 1971. (From left) Me, Yo-Han Chu, and my two brothers-in-law, Tong-Sul Chu, and Tong-Suk Chu.

52

I took this photograph of Yo-Han Chu and my mother-in-law, Sun-Bok Choe, when I visited his office in 1972. He was the president of Korean Shipping Corporation at age seventy-two, with a ship's wheel. He was also the president of the Dae-Han Daily Newspaper Company. He contributed two editorials each week.

53

I helped the Naval Electronic Systems Command to develop this High-Frequency Secure Transmission of Acoustic Data (HF SETAD), also known as AN/USC-32 transceiver. The HF SETAD was a digital HF transceiver, and a vocoder, a precursor of today's secure digital HF communication technology. (From top) the HF radio, the HF modem, the voice digitizer, and the encryption device.

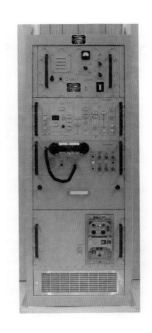

54

I was ready to board a P-3C Orion ASW Patrol Aircraft at NAS Patuxent River, Maryland in March 1976. The destination was NAS Oceana, Virginia. I conducted in-flight tests of the HF SETAD transceiver and the CV-3332 vocoder.

55

Commander Earl Eckert, U.S. Navy, and I enjoying the Bermuda weather at the Pompano Beach Hotel. We were on TDY at NAVFAC Bermuda in 1976.

56

I developed the Shipboard Network Front-End Processor (SNFEP), which was supported by the TRW In-house Research and Development project fund, 1988.

57

Phillip Myong and the family. (from left) Phillip Myong (DDS), Anne-Marie Myong, Susan Myong, Rahn, and I, c. 1977. In 1951, during the refugee years in Pusan, South Korea, Phillip and I were longshoremen in Pusan Pier No. 2, unloading military supplies from American freighter ships.

58

The family toured the National Gallery of Art, c. 1984. (From left) William, Janet, Doug, and Rahn. In the background on the wall was Joan Miro's wool and cotton tapestry Donna *(Woman), and Rahn and the children were wearing their garment in matching colors of red, blue, white, and brown. Miro'* Donna *was woven by Josep Royo. In October 2018, I went to see the tapestry, but it was not displayed as it was being reconditioned in the gallery warehouse.*

59

Rahn, my mother-in-law, Sun-Bok Choe, and I boating in our Winner power boat near Columbia Island in the Potomac River, c. 1980.

Sailing in the Potomac River, c. 1999. The building in the background was NRL, Bldg 43, which is the headquarters of NRL. On the rooftop of the building was the NRL's 50-foot diameter radio astronomy telescope, which was used for Project Moon Bounce, the first "satellite" communication circuit known was E-M-E (Earth-Moon-Earth), c. 1951. It was also known as the Moonbounce, which sent and received the first human voice transmission to be bounced back to Earth from the Moon.

61

I was the Scoutmaster of Boyscout Troop 865, McLean. Scouts made a wooden catapult, which competed in the Patawomack District Camporee, Ft. Belvoir, c.1988. (From left to right): William Kim, Marcus Scheidt, Kevin O'Hara, David Kildee, and I.

The photo of the special people in my life c. 1987 at our McLean house. (From left to right): William, Janet, Doug, Rahn, and I.

Running in the Fair Lakes 10K race, c. 1988. I used to run three miles every day for many years, but switched to walking three miles daily to save my knees.

64

I visited my brother-in-law, Jik T. Chu's house in Cleveland, Ohio, c. 1981. He returned to Seoul, and managed a prosperous electronic company, Song-A Electronics Company.

65

My brother-in-law Dr. Bill Chu visiting our McLean house, c. 2001. One of his accomplishments was the development of medical instrumentation applied to the hadron cancer treatment at Lawrence Berkeley National Laboratory. In May of 2000, he received the Federal Laboratory Consortium (FLC) award for his work on the hadron therapy.

66

Judge Earl Larson of the U.S. District Court of Minnesota and Mrs. Cecill Larson visiting our McLean house, c.1990. In 1962, when Rahn was a graduate student at the University of Minnesota, she was a boarder at Larson's house. In 1973, there was a court case on the ownership of the patent rights on electronic digital computers between Honeywell and Sperry. Judge Earl Larson presided over this court case. Judge Larson ruled that Sperry Rand Corporation and the legal inventor Professor John Atanasoff did not own the digital electronic computer patent. Sperry Rand would not collect any royalties derived from the patent. Unfortunately, John Atanasoff never made a dime from his invention of the digital computer! (From left to right): Earl Larson, I, Cecill Larson, William, Doug, and Janet.

67

Receiving the Meritorious Award from the National Security Industry Association, Amphibious Warfare Committee, c. 1990. (Front left to right): Me, Dick Klein of Unisys,

and Jack Dreyfus of TRW. In the 1980s and 1990s, TRW had significant business in the Amphibious and Sealift ship acquisitions of the U.S. Navy. The ship class included LCAC, LSD-32, and LHD-1.

68

Four sons-in-law of Yo-Han Chu were gathered in Chicago c. 1985 for the first and the last time. We called the gathering as a team building meeting of Yo-Han Chu's sons-in-law, and enjoyed the company. (Front row, from left): Dr. Soon-Deok Koh, and Byung-Lim Roh, MD. (Second row, from left): Me and Jong-Hyeon Choe, MD.

69

William and I attending the Inter-college Model Airplane Competition at Wright Patterson AFB, Dayton, April 29-30, 1991. Operation Desert Shield started on Jan. 17, 1991 and the ceasefire took effect on April 11, 1991. The security of the base was tight, and no spectators were allowed in the base. Only members of the participating college students and support teams were allowed.

70

William adjusting the control system of a Cornell University model airplane. The model airplane was an aircraft that flies in sight with radio control at low speed. Model airplanes were a precursor of now-ubiquitous Unmanned Aerial Vehicles (UAVs), which perform differently. UAVs can fly autonomously beyond the horizon.

At our company holiday party. John Stenbit, Group Vice-President, and his wife Albertine hosted the holiday party. (From left to right): Me, Laura Felder, Dr. Wilson Felder, and Rahn, at Ritz Carlton Hotel, McLean, Virginia in 1997.

72

(From left to right): Dr. Phil Girardi, Sally Girardi, Rahn, and I attended the conference banquet of the 1988 IEEE MILCOM Conference, Monterey. In 1987, Phil and I proposed the Open Systems Critical Item (OSCI) project for the NSSN submarine radar subsystems and presented at the conference. In 1999, Phil and I spent several months in the NRL RF anechoic chamber to measured microwave radiation effects to GPS chips. The chamber was cold in the winter and hot in the summer. During my tenure as the ONR program officer, Phil was my principal T&E agents, and conducted acceptance tests and took care of contract deliverables.

73

Johnny Johnson and I visiting the U.K. to explore procuring NATO's business, c. Feb. 1991. We were touring the Buckingham Palace. It was in the middle of Operation Desert Storm, and security was tight everywhere we went. The clothes we  *wore gave security folks the impression that we were military, as I wore an Army green jacket and Johnny wore his Navy Mil Spec G-1 leather jacket. We did not blend in with the background.*

74

The Kim house at 8006 Snowpine Way, McLean, where our three children grew up. In the spring, c. 1979.

75

My study in the McLean house. I called the study my Sans Souci.

76

At Janet's wedding at Trinity United Methodist Church. (From left) William Kim, I, Janet Lee, Tony Lee, Rahn, and Doug, 1996.

77

My nameplate, the British Telephone Co. telegraph keyer, and the telegraph relay were admired by visitors to my office. I bought the BT telegraph keyer and the relay at an antique store in Portobello Road, in the Nottingham

Hill district, London in 1998. The name plate was at my office door at Systems Research Laboratories, Dayton. I asked a carpenter at Ballston in Arlington, to decorate the nameplate base in the British Museum finishes.

78

Rahn and John Kim were ready to attend a TRW company banquet in 1999.

79

William and I were standing next to the Continental Divide sign, at Yellowstone National Park in 1993. We were on our way to Palo Alto, California, on the northern trans-continental route. We drove 2,920 miles in twelve days in Williams 1987

Acura Integra. When William graduated from Stanford, Doug helped him to drive the same Acura Integra on the southern route through the deep South.

80

I am waiting at Centroid Heliport in NAS Fallen to board a rented helicopter from Ely Helicopter Services, Nevada in 1993. The U.S. Navy invited representatives from prospective bidders of the Naval Tactical Combat Training System to join a site survey to obtain first-hand knowledge of the training range and new TIS networks at Job Peak, located 15 miles due east of NAS Fallon. The mountains were covered with deep snow.

81

I took the photo of another accompanying chopper, while flying in the first chopper to Job Peak (the elevation of 12,400 feet.

I photographed a view of Toledo. I captured the Alcazar (right) and the Primate Cathedral (left) from the south bank of the Tagus River in October 1994. El Greco painted View of Toledo *with more blue and greener sky, while my photograph captured grayish cumulus clouds that day. That was best I could after waiting to capture those clouds for an hour. When I returned home, I compared the locations of certain building, and discovered that some were rearranged by El Greco. The Toledo Alcazar was accurately placed on the right.*

83

I was standing near the Alcantara Bridge over the Tagus River, Toledo in 1994.

84

I found many signs of the Caminho de Santiago in Portugal on the way to Santiago di Compostela in 1994.

85

Rahn owns an Asian watercolor on rice paper painting, Autumn Flowers-Four Noble Ones *by Sang-Beom Lee, c. 1962. I found another Asian water color on rice paper painting on the spring by the same painter. It was* The Spring Landscape, *which was listed in Sotheby's Catalog of Auction,* Korean Art from the Estate of Marcus W. Scherbacher, *Sotheby's New York, 1997. After Marcus Scherbacher's death, Sotheby's of New York auctioned the Scherbacher estate on Sept. 20-26, 1997. The list price of* The Spring Landscape *was $2,000.*

Basilica; he holds the key to the kingdom of heaven in his hand.

We stumbled into a huge market in a neighborhood near Vatican City. It was Mercato Trionfale, which had several hundred stalls selling fish, dry goods, meat, and produce. Rahn and I wished to buy sandwiches, bottles of water, and cheese with red hot pepper added in it. After much hand gesturing and yelling in broken Italian, we were successful in buying them.

During our trip to Italy, I grew fond of Italy and the Italian people. I found similarities between Korea and Italy and their peoples, although some similarities could be superficial. Both countries are on a peninsula stretching along a north-south axis. The length of the peninsula tends to encourage different customs in different geographic areas, such as the spoken language developed into several dialects. Both countries are in the temperate zone. I think both peoples are romantic in nature and are quick to express their emotions. I saw street brawls in Rome just like the ones I've seen in Seoul. Italians and Koreans both express their feelings through music, and are family oriented. Catholicism could have encouraged this trait in Italy; Confucianism fostered a love of the family in Korea. Outsiders have invaded both peninsulas throughout history. Koreans experienced foreign domination by Mongols, Japanese, and Chinese; Phoenicians, Greeks, Goths, Vandals, and Teutons invaded the Italian (or Appenine) Peninsula. The food is also similar, with plenty of garlic and hot peppers. I felt at home when I tasted garlic in spaghetti sauce.

TRAVEL THROUGH THE IBERIAN PENINSULA

James Michener's book *Iberia* gave me an idea to travel to Spain and Portugal. In 1996, Rahn and I travelled through Spanish regions of La Mancha, Andalucia, Aragon, Castile, Extremadura, and Galicia, and Lisbon and Sintra in Portugal. Later, in 2010, we went to Catalonia.

MADRID

We started our Iberian Peninsula trip from Madrid. The air was dry and dusty as we drove from Madrid Airport to the town of Alcala de Henares, an eastern suburb of Madrid. As I entered a traffic circle in the town, I saw a man on the far side of the traffic circle urinating in public. In the town plaza, we found our hotel, the El Torero Hotel; it was easy to park the car in the round driveway. After we had refreshed ourselves, we went down to the lobby and asked the concierge to recommend one or two authentic La Mancha restaurants. His choice was "La Taberna de Rusty." The La Taberna de Rusty restaurant was quiet and comfortable. We asked the waiter to bring us a La Mancha dish. He suggested two Spanish dishes, pan-baked cheese (*queso* in Spanish) and a platter of cured ham (*Jamon Serrano* in Spanish). Cheese was delicious, but cured ham I did not care for because it was too salty and uncooked. We were not impressed by these two La Mancha dishes.

The next day, we rode a suburban train to downtown Madrid. We visited the Prado Museum, which had many masterpieces. My favorite was Velázquez's *Las Meninas* (the Maid of Honor). It was an oil painting on a huge canvas that measured ten feet by ten feet.

"Why did I like *Las Meninas*?

"It was complex and was full of enigmas.

"They say that *Las Meninas* had been one of the most analyzed works in European paintings.

"I had seen Picasso's synthesis of *Las Meninas*, which was featured in the Picasso Museum in Barcelona."

Madrid is a flat, featureless, treeless, and grassless urban metropolis. It was a disappointment as a metropolitan capital, without friendliness to its citizens and tourists alike. For me, the only attraction of Madrid was the Prado Museum, and we soon wished to escape the congested traffic and faceless people. We were anxious to move on to Provinces.

Aranjuez

Aranjuez reminded me of music composed by Joaquin Rodrigo (1901-1999), the *Concierto de Aranjuez,* which was the quintessential Spanish music full of the flamenco dance rhythm. This song reminded me of my travel from Princeton University to McLean in 1994. As one of his extracurricular activities, our son Doug was a disc jockey at the Princeton University radio station, WPRB. In 1994, on our way home from Princeton, we tuned in WPRB and heard Doug and his fellow disc jockey Doug Alexander on air. They played the *Concierto de Aranjuez*, and talked about the composer and music and speculated where Aranjuez was. Of course, I did not know the exact location of Aranjuez either, then.

Toledo

The following day, we drove to Toledo through the rolling hills of La Mancha and saw the barren landscape with occasional olive groves and vineyards. The Tagus River surrounded Toledo forming a three-sided promontory. I took photographs of Toledo from across the Tagus River to capture an image similar to El Greco's *View of Toledo*, which was a landscape painting with the sky and the hill around Toledo with blue and green colors. The spot, in which I stood across the Tagus River, might have been where El Greco sat to sketch his *View of Toledo*. After two hours of waiting, I finally captured a dark cloud over Toledo, similar to his painting. The cloud I captured was tropical cumulus, not exactly like the dark cloud in his paintings. I found that El Greco's painting did not seem to place notable buildings in the right places. The Toledo Alcazar and the Toledo Cathedral were at a different locations in his painting. I was standing north of Toledo looking at the eastern part of Toledo. I did not see the Alcazar, nor the Alcantara Bridge, nor the Castle of San Servando. After I had returned home, I studied the geography of Toledo, and indeed, El Greco moved these prominent structures around in his painting. Maybe El Greco painted Toledo landscape from different angle to mine. (see photos 82 and 83)

GRANADA

When I was a Resident Assistant at Armstrong Hall in MSU, I occasionally enjoyed listening to a student playing Agustin Lara's *Granada* on the piano in the hall.

"Granada, I'm falling under your spell,

"And if you could speak, what a fascinating tale you would tell……"

Ever since I first heard this beautiful music, I wished to visit Granada someday. Indeed, in the summer of 1996, I drove to Granada through olive groves in the Andalusia. We arrived at our destination, the Washington Irving Hotel, which stood across the street from the Alhambra Palace. In 1826, Washington Irving was the American Minister in Spain and excavated the Alhambra using his own private resources. In 1832 he then wrote a book called the *Tales of the Alhambra*. I rested on a bed supported by heavy wooden frames like the Alcazar across the street. But the Washington Irving Hotel had seen better days.

I asked the concierge at the hotel where I could find a hat shop. He gave me directions to a *sombreria* (a hat shop). At the hat shop, we found a saleslady dozing off in the hot afternoon. We asked her to show us a few "*boinas*," and we bought five of them, one for each member of the family. I remember I had started to wear a beret when SNU adopted it as the school cap. Before the 1940s, the SNU school cap was a square cap, a legacy from the tradition of the Japanese Imperial University. The square cap was like the one worn by Polish soldiers, known as the "Rogatywka" cap.

We visited Casa Museo Manuel de Falla. De Falla was a renowned Spanish composer of the 20th century. I liked his music in the opera *The Three-Cornered Hat*. The quiet museum house was high up in the foothills of the Sierra Nevada, overlooking the city of Granada. There were two other tourists besides us in the house, but the museum attendant kept her watchful eyes on the visitors for any walk off with de Falla's memorabilia.

EXTREMADURA

We often hear about regions of Spain like Catalonia, Andalusia, and Castile, but seldom about Extremadura. I first read about the province in James Michener's *Iberia,* which described Spanish Conquistadors from the impoverished Province of Extremadura. In the sixteenth century, many of its ambitious young men sought their fortunes elsewhere as mercenaries, and these young men made their odysseys to the Americas for conquest in the 16th century in the name of God and the king. Notables were Herman Cortes, Francisco Pizarro, Hernando de Soto, and Vasco Nunez de Balboa.

Rahn and I drove to Extremadura and arrived in the town of Merida. When I looked around the Sierras in Extremadura, I had an illusion that I might be standing in Santa Fe or Albuquerque in New Mexico. When Spaniards came to what is now known as Southwestern America, they might have felt at home as far as the terrain and the weather were concerned. I saw adobes built of clay. I heard borrowed words like pantaloons and sombreros. I saw tacos, salsa, and chili con carne on a local restaurant menu. It was all there in Extremadura. No wonder the Conquistadors settled in the American southwest and built their Spanish missions and settlements.

LISBON AND SINTRA

From Extremadura, we traveled to Portugal, and to the hillside town of Sintra facing the Atlantic Ocean. The tourist office suggested an accommodation at a pension by the name of Patio de Soloio. When the tourist office called the pension, the daughter of the proprietor came with a Jeep to the office, and we followed her up the hilly road. A Flemish family operated the pension. The husband, Dieter Deceuninck, prepared meals, his wife Anne ran the business, and their daughter Louise was in charge of transportation. All of them spoke many languages. Each time Anne brought our meal, she said, "*Good appetite!*", not "Bon Appetite."

In the afternoon, we rode on suburban trains, which ran every 15 minutes between Sintra and Lisbon city center. In the harbor at the mouth of the Tagus River, the tall white granite statue of Prince Henry the Navigator stood on the

bow of a Portuguese ocean-going galleon. Prince Henry established a navigation and mapmaking school in the 1500s. I worked with the Navigator of the Navy, whose duty was to oversee navigation, electronic charts, maps, and accurate timekeeping. The modern-day Navigator of the U.S. Navy and the sixteenth century Prince Henry the Navigator both endeavored to advance the science of navigating the Seven Seas of the world. In the Ancient Art Museum in Lisbon, we were surprised to find a collection of 16th Century Japanese artworks. The collection included silk screens (*biombo* in Japanese), swords, kimonos, and samurai armors.

Lisbon had a cosmopolitan air, with a mixture of cultures of the former Portuguese colonies of Brazil, Uruguay, Mozambique, and Angola. Today, the former colonial people have immigrated to Lisbon. Although Portugal's fortunes steadily waned over the course of the past 400 years, it still maintains ties with her former colonies.

When I attended NATO navigation meetings representing the U.S. Navy, at the NATO Research and Technology Agency (RTA). I met Lt. Commander (Comandante de Fragata) Eduardo Soares de Araujo of the Royal Portuguese Navy (RPN), in Paris, Barcelona, and Izmir, Turkey. At one of the RTA meetings at, I asked Soares:

"Eduardo, what is the mission of the Royal Portuguese Navy (RPN)?"

"John, we are a founding member of NATO, although we joined EU belatedly in 1986.

"RPN have two missions.

"The first is naval maritime missions to assure Portugal's sovereignty and international commitments, assumed by Portugal (mainly within NATO).

"The second is coast guard operations in our territorial water and areas of influence with former colonies of Portugal."

"How many commissioned ships are in the fleet?"

"John, RPN has 42 ships, with 12 surface combatants and two attack submarines."

"What is the relationship between the Portuguese Navy and the Navies of former colonies?"

"We maintain a close relationship with the Brazilian Navy.

"I can make an analogy of the relationship between the U.S. Navy and the Royal Navy.

"The Royal Navy and the Royal Portuguese Navy are smaller and older, while the U.S. Navy and the Brazilian Navy are a larger and younger. They sail on the opposite sides of the Atlantic, speaking the same language, Portuguese .

Santiago di Compostela

After two days of sightseeing in Lisbon, we headed north to Santiago di Compostela via the southern approach of Camino de Santiago (St. James Way). The legend had it that St. James was martyred in Jerusalem, and his remains were returned to Spain, where he had earlier spread the Gospel. During the voyage, the ship was wrecked in a storm, and his remains were lost. Miraculously, his remains were washed ashore and were found covered with shells. The seashell became the symbol of St. James Way.

About 50 miles from the Spanish frontier, we approached the town of Pontevedra, where a bridge crosses over the Lerez River. There was a long traffic backup over the bridge. When I consulted my map, it showed an alternate road going inland to the east, and we might avoid the traffic backup on Camino de Santiago. But the side road we took turned out to be a mountainous byway, and I got lost. I saw farmers working in the field, whom I asked for directions to Camino. They did not understand me. However, we saw the picturesque scenery of countryside. Every house had grapevine trellises in the backyard. After two hours of driving, we came to a small village, where I met a middle-aged man.

I asked him:

"Excuse me.

"Can you speak English?"

"Yes, a little bit."

"Where is Camino de Santiago?"

"The Autobahn is fifteen kilometers on this road to the west."

"You know the Autobahn. But Autobahn is in Germany."

"I have been in Germany as a guest worker for five years."

We finally got back on track after the three-hour detour. Nevertheless, I was pleased that I made the detour through hilly country roads of Galicia. "Well, we lose some, we win some in an adventure." If we stayed on the Camino de Santiago, we would not have seen picturesque sceneries. In the late evening, we arrived at Santiago di Compostela.

In the morning, we visited the cathedral, where they were celebrating the Mass. We sat in the back pew, while a young priest swung a massive metal incense-burner (thurible) like a pendulum. White smoke spewed out the burner and filled the sanctuary. Smoke indeed got rid of the sweaty smell. Rahn reacted to the smoke severely and made her cough. We had to leave the sanctuary for fresh air.

As modern-day pilgrims, two of us traveled to Santiago di Compostela by car, but we thought about those medieval pilgrims, who traveled thousands of miles on foot. Some of them were exhausted on the way and could not finish their pilgrimage. We decided to search for the ancient pilgrim's road. Overgrown bushes covered gravel roads, and trees lined both sides of the road and formed a shady canopy from the hot Spanish Sun. In the village of Rua, we asked an elderly farmer,

"Where is the old Camino de Santiago?"

"You are on it, the Camino Antiqua."

Indeed, I found scarred cobblestones marked by ox cart wheels under thick bushes.

The Saint James Way has many names. Germans call it Heilige Jacobus Weg, Spanish Camino de Santiago, and French Chemin de St-Jacques. Along the Saint James Way, we saw scallop shell signs. In the evening, we had a dish of Galician fish called hake and a Spanish omelet for dinner. I wrote a poem about a scallop shell with the radial lines of Saint James Way. (see photo 84)

A Scallop Shell

I began my pilgrimage,
With no awareness and no preparedness,
Of what laid ahead of me on the Saint James Way,
I dragged my weary feet on the cobblestone roads.

I sought salvation in my pilgrimage,
And received the joy of spiritual diet in a scallop shell,
I walked on the Ancient Road of the Saint James Way,
And my staff guided to my faith.

By John Kim
December 3, 1994

Rahn and I continued our travel to the countryside of Galicia. Next to those Galician houses we saw strange stone structures, which were about 6 feet wide, 10 feet long, and 10 feet high.

I told Rahn,

"They could be tombs.

"They look spooky."

We stopped at a store for refreshments and asked:

"Excuse me, what are these stone structures for?

"They could not be living quarters.

"Are they some sort of tombs?"

"No, they are not tombs.

"It is a hórreo.

"It is a granary, where we keep threshed grains and vegetables."

"He solved our puzzle."

SALAMANCA

We left Galicia and headed for the historical region of Castile y Leon, and stopped at Salamanca. I had heard about Salamanca from my friend Davidson Hepburn when we both were students at Michigan State University. Davidson had studied Miguel de Unamuno, who was a 20th-century Spanish novelist and a philosopher. In the 1930s, he was a member of the faculty at the University of Salamanca. In the early Renaissance period, the university was the center of learning in medicine, chemistry, mathematics, and theology. Thanks to Islamic culture and knowledge, which sustained learning in Islamic Spain, whereas Europe was still in the Dark Ages. Davidson told me, during the Franco

regime, Unamuno represented the conscience of the intelligentsia of Spain. We saw the statue of Unamuno, jutting out his strong and defiant chin, which appear to be his protest against the oppression of the Franco regime.

ESCORIAL

The next day, we drove to San Lorenzo de El Escorial, a royal residence, and a monastery near Madrid. The architecture of this massive complex was in the style of a typical Spanish Alcazar. It also contains pantheons of princes and princesses of the Hapsburg and Bourbon dynasties.

In the afternoon, we took a commuter train to Madrid for shopping. Rahn bought a fine linen damask tablecloth at El Corte Ingles department store. In the Middle Ages, Damask weaving began in the Middle East and was a legacy of Islamic culture in Spain. During Iberian travels, I began to understand that Spain was a vast mosaic of different cultures and religions, Christian, Islamic, and Judaic.

In one evening, I mistakenly drove into the wrong way on a one-way street in Escorial. I ran into a squad car of a Guardia Civil sergeant whose attitude was less than friendly. I think police officers in America and England are more polite and civilized than the Guardia Civil.

20

Book Publication, Technical Fellow, and Satellite Communications

BOOK PUBLICATION

In 1990, I discussed with Eugen Muehldorf about writing a book on Naval communications systems. We felt that there could be a need for such a book for engineers and naval officers who need to understand Navy communications practices and technologies. Eugen and I drafted an outline and a proposal for the book, the title of which was *Naval Shipboard Communication Systems*. Our thought at that time was: "Let's run it up on the flagpole and see if anyone salutes it."

We sent the book proposal to Prentice-Hall Publishing Company, which had already published two of Eugen's communications technology books: *Space Communications Systems* and *Space Communications Techniques*. As Eugen was an established author with Prentice-Hall, we thought we had a good chance of getting the book accepted. Sure enough, three weeks after the submission, Tim Bozik, the executive editor, informed us that Prentice-Hall was interested in the book.

We obtained approval for the public release of DoD information, signed by the Information and Security Officer of the Chief of Naval Operations, the Department of the Navy (CNO OP-09N). In November 1994, I met with Bernard Goodwin, Prentice-Hall Editor-in-Chief, to discuss the publication of the book. At the end of the meeting, he said, "John, we just hatched a new book."

The publisher assigned Harriet Tellem as the editor of the book. Bernard Goodwin told us about the pricing scheme of the book. In Europe, where it was expected to sell well, the price should be set higher than in the U.S. In Asia, the price of the book should be set lower than in the U.S. Bestsellers and expensive

books in Asia often become a target for piracy, according to Bernard Goodwin.

For the next five years, Eugen and I wrote the manuscript. During that time, Eugen kept telling me that we had to keep it short, and the total number of pages must be less than 500. When Eugen and Richard Filipowsky prepared their satellite communication book, it was big enough to be divided into two books of 575 and 333 pages, respectively. In addition to the text, our book also had more than 250 photos and figures. At last in April 1995, Prentice-Hall published the book.[48] Here is a review of the book, written by Lt. Commander Thomas J. Cutler, USN (retired) of the U.S. Naval Institute, which appeared in the *Proceedings of the Naval Institute* in the September 1995 issue.[49]

> "Intended as a reference textbook for engineers who under-stand communications and need to become familiar with Navy communications methods and procedure, this com-prehensive work should be useful for serious shipboard com-munication officers, as well. Not for the armchair reader, this book delves deeply into the technology and procedures of naval communications through the use of mathematical for-mulae, revealing photographs, fact-filled tables, and detailed diagrams to cover the many technical aspects of modern ship-board communications."

Another book review appeared in the TRW Journal *Spectrum*[50]

"Keeping Up with Naval Communications Systems"

While naval communications are constantly evolving and adopting modern technology, even the most advanced system has little value if it cannot be operated and maintained effec-tively. To meet this concern, John Kim and Eugen Muehldorf have written a book called Naval Shipboard Communica-tions Systems. The book is intended for engineers who are unfamiliar with naval communications engineering, entry-level engineers who need to understand the background and application of shipboard communications engineering, and

naval officers assigned to related technical areas. For example, when engineers think of satellite communications, they usually envision broadband and high-speed transmission. "This is not so in naval satellite communications. Naval satellites use narrow-band dedicated circuits, and in many cases are protected against jamming," says John. "We hope to bridge these gaps of perception without touching on sensitive military aspects," he added.

The development of communications and data processing technology is fostering significant changes in the way the Navy communicates from-ship-to-ship and from-ship-to-shore. TRW uses the extensive naval communications experience of these two to gain a technological edge, helping the Navy to carry out its mission effectively. Writing this book was by no means an overnight adventure. It grew from a five-year-old briefing about one shipboard communications system to a product that explains all engineering aspects of shipboard communications. "We emphasized the shipboard segment, making it more specialized and useful as a technical reference," said Eugen. "In that way our book is unique." In addition to the state-side appeal, the two expect the book to draw international attention. NATO and United States' standards in naval communications are interoperable, and most Pacific Rim countries have adopted American standards, as well.

John and Eugen have worked together for 15 years on a variety of naval projects. They pooled their experiences to create a finished product stimulated by their work at TRW. "We reached a plateau after one year, and I have to admit that I had doubts at one point as to whether we would finish this book," said John. "But our work at TRW provided the stimulus we needed to complete the project," added Eugen. John has 25 years' experience in naval communications at TRW. He is currently a leading communications systems designer of

Naval and Air Force combat training systems. Eugen's career began in computer and communications system design and analysis. He joined TRW in1978 and is now a senior technical staff member on Systems Division's FAA project. He has contributed to the development of naval communications system for over ten years. Though they differ in their writing methods and personalities, you can almost visualize the synergy between them. "We continually learned from our research, in this book," says Eugen. "Even though we both hold doctoral degrees, it doesn't mean we have stopped learning."

The first printing of the book was sold out. (see photo 90) The publisher printed a softcover edition. Books have a shelf-life depending on the currency of the subject matter. Our book had a longer than usual shelf-life because the U.S. Navy replaces equipment at a slower pace than nonmilitary hardware. The shipboard equipment does not keep pace with technology advances because the U.S. Navy's procurement process is slow for military equipment. For example, the Ultra-High Frequency Satellite Communication Terminal AN/WSC-3s installed in the U.S. Navy in the early 1980s were still in use in 2000 as a primary warfighting communications equipment aboard U.S. Navy ships.

DR. EUGEN I. MUEHLDORF

I met Eugen for the first time when he came to TRW for a job interview. John Bryant, my Laboratory Manager, asked me to interview him for a position in the WWMCSS project. We talked about two WWMCSS-related communication projects. Eugen had extensive experience in communications systems, and he came with a recommendation from Dr. Al Babbitt, the Director of the WWMCCS program office in DISA. Eugen received a doctorate from Vienna Technical University.

Every October, Eugen and his wife Erni held an Oktoberfest party at their home in Potomac, Maryland. For this annual party, Eugen made a big batch of sauerkraut. He fermented shredded cabbage to make half-sour sauerkraut; it was not like the sauerkraut, which was sold in a supermarket. This sauer-

kraut was not sour at all. He called his sauerkraut an Austrian "kimchee." He sprinkled sauerkraut with cooked bacon, herbs, and olive oil. For the party, he would grill bratwursts and sausages, and serve them with his sauerkraut. His wife, Erni, would prepare German potato salad and Austrian strudels.

Eugen lived in Ukraine until 1925, when the country was part of the Austro-Hungarian Empire. In 2003, he visited Ukraine and told me about his travel:

"John, the country villa house in this old photo was our home where I was born.

"I took several photos of the villa from the same angle.

"Not much has changed on the outside.

"I also visited the family cemetery."

"Eugen, was the cemetery crowded?"

"No, not much.

"There were many graves with the Muehldorf name.

"I found familiar names of my grandparents' generation.

"But what surprised me was that many of the names were strangers to me."

"Eugen, that is what I was afraid to hear from you.

"I wonder what I would find on gravestones of my family in Yongbyon in North Korea if I ever get there.

"God forbid, I hope the graves are still there, not disappeared.

"John, what can I say?"

Operational Incentive Plan (OIP)

One day in 1988, Jack Dreyfus, the Vice-President of the Systems Division, asked me to come by to his office. I went to his office, wondering what he had in mind.

"John, come in.

"I have good news for you.

"The division management decided to award you the Operational Incentive Plan (OIP), effective immediately."

"Well, what a pleasant surprise.

"Thank you."

"You earned it.

"The management wishes to recognize you for acquiring the Navy Communication business last year, and all the good work you have been doing for over twenty years."

"John, the recognition came a little bit late."

"I knew you wanted to become the Manager of the Navy Communications Project.

"The company was never wrong but was a bit weak in being right in that decision."

OIP stands for the Operational Incentive Plan, a bonus payment system. I received 20% of my salary as a bonus under the OIP Level 4. I felt a sense of poetic justice. What did I do with the bonus? It was the time when our three children were going to private colleges, Northwestern, Cornell, and Princeton. I paid most of their tuitions with my bonus each year.

I Become a TRW Technical Fellow

In 1996, another recognition came my way. This time, Priscilla Guthrie, the Manager of the Navy System Business Area, announced that the Systems Division appointed me as a Technical Fellow of the Systems Integration Group. She told me:

"The Systems Division management appointed you to the Technical Fellow.

"The company must encourage technical persons like you to climb technical ladder instead of management ladder."

"Priscilla, thank you."

There was an article in TRW's *SIG Bulletin*, titled "Five Honored as Technical Fellows for Achievement.[51]

"The rank of Technical Fellows within TRW Systems Integration Group now includes five new members. Honored with the designation of Technical Fellow in November 1996 were Ken

Aull, John Kim, Richard Langley, Bill Noah, and John Walsh. John Kim, a senior staff engineer in TRW Government Information Services Division, is a leading expert on Navy telecommunications. Kim co-authored a book on Naval Shipboard Communications Systems published by Prentice-Hall in 1995. Named to the IR&D Honor Roll in 1989, he has led communication projects across TRW's space and defense groups and several IR&D projects in communication technologies. The extensive modeling and simulation capability he developed for communications and computer systems has been applied on projects for the Department of Defense and the Federal Aviation Administration. On a recent proposal, Kim led a multi-company team in designing a high-performance communication system for joint force training that required low latency air-to-surface capability and long-haul satellite links. He also introduced an application of Asynchronous Transfer Mode switching to achieve a survivable network for new attack submarines. Kim earned a bachelor's degree in electrical engineering from Trine University and a master's and doctorate at Michigan State University. Contributions to his profession have included leading the Washington chapter of IEEE Cybernetics and System Group and organizing the 1991 IEEE Military Communication Conference. He is a member of the Task Force 2 Study Group for the Radio Technical Commission for Aeronautics and serves on the board of the Fairfax County Volunteer Center. Kim is cited in the 1996 editions of Who's Who in America."

"TRW peers nominate top technologists who are selected by rigorous criteria to become technical fellows. A TRW Technical Fellow is an appointed position at TRW by the Chief Executive Officer (CEO). Typically, only four to six Technical Fellows are elected each year. It is the highest honor an engineer and scientist at TRW can achieve. TRW founded the Technical Fellows program, in 1994, to build a cadre of

technologists of various scientific disciplines. TRW management selects about three percent of the technical personnel in the company, who have shown past accomplishment and demonstrated future potential. The selected TRW Technical Fellows are encouraged to pursue technology that is supported by the company discretionary resources."

I held the Technical Fellow position until I retired from the company in 2001. The position allowed me to pursue the technical subjects of my interest.

When I became a Technical Fellow, Dr. Al Babbitt gave me some advice. Al Babbit had been a technical person as well as a corporate executive in TRW, IBM, and later the Director in the DoD WWMCCS Systems Engineering Organization.

"John, a technical person like you, has the choice of two career ladders to climb.

"One is technical ladder, and the other is management ladder.

"My advice to you is to think twice before climbing on one of these two career ladders. "You have been a first-line supervisor, a project manager, as well as a functional department manager in TRW.

"I know you are an excellent technologist, but could you excel as a manager?

"I know managers get paid more and have the prestige and perks, but you must think long and hard about your business aptitude and ability in "people" skills.

"You know what a people skill is, such as the ability to communicate effectively with people, especially in business.

"You will sometimes run into the ruthless competition and politics if you were on the management ladder."

I resisted the temptation of climbing management ladder and chose to climb technical ladder. I think I fared better than my colleagues who chose the management path . Looking back more than half a century, I think I chose the right career path in TRW and later in ONR.

1991 IEEE MILITARY COMMUNICATIONS CONFERENCE (MILCOM-91)

In 1990, Al Babbitt asked me if I could help him organize an IEEE conference. The IEEE Board of Directors asked him to be the chairman of the 1991 IEEE Military Communications Conference (MILCOM-91). He could not accept the chairmanship of MILCOM without my help. I told him I would help him and suggested that Eugen Muehldorf also join us. Dr. Bob Lawrence of MITRE would be in charge of the classified sessions. Eugen's and my task was to evaluate 650 abstracts submitted in response to the call for papers. There were 49 sessions, including 7 classified sessions in the conference. We found and solicited chairperson for each session and asked him or her to read and evaluate each abstract. After each abstract was reviewed and edited, the technical committee assembled three-volume, 1,320-page proceedings and sent them to the IEEE headquarters for publication. Finally, on Nov. 4-7, 1991, we held the unclassified sessions at the Sheraton Premier-Tyson Corner Hotel and the classified sessions in the MITRE building in McLean. More than 1,000 people attended, and it was a great success. Three weeks later, Al Babbitt called me to come to his office:

"John, thank you for managing the MILCOM conference successfully.

"I could not have pulled it off without your and Eugen's help."

"Al, I thank you for giving me the opportunity."

"Now, I want to talk about another matter. It is about the Global Positioning System (GPS)."

"O.K. What about GPS?"

"John Stenbit plans to spend Division resources on GPS for the aviation automation business."

"Al, I am also interested in GPS.

"I will be glad to help you out."

"I will tell the business office to send you an IR&D request package later this week."

"Thanks, Al."

"John, you earned it. GPS is going to be important technology for our business in Air Traffic Control and Air Combat Training. John Stenbit is keen on pursuing GPS technology."

GPS Augmentation Projects

As GPS was becoming one of the key sensors for aviation navigation, I conducted a company IR&D project on GPS. I performed research on mitigating multipath interference. It turned out that my interest in GPS would open the door to the next phase of my career in navigation technology. After I left TRW, I joined the Office of Naval Research (ONR) and pursued GPS technology for 12 years.

The GPS LAAS interference project was my first study on GPS.[52] I used a simulation tool called the Signal Processing Workstation (SPW). The study result showed that the performance of combined space diversity antennas was better than that of a single-element antenna. GSP LAAS provided navigation corrections to aircraft flying within 30 nautical miles of an airport runway in near real-time via the Air-to-Ground VHF data link.

Shipboard Network Front-end Processing (SNFEP) project

In 1988, I invited Commander Earl Eckert of NAVELEX to my laboratory and explained my SNFEP IR&D project.

"Earl, welcome to the SNFEP Testbed Facility. (see photo 56)

"By the way, SNFEP stands for Shipboard Network Front End Professor."

"Alright, but what kind of shipboard network are you talking about?"

"That is an excellent question.

"A network may be a Link-11, Link-16, or FLTSATCOM IXS (Information Exchange Subsystem), like CUDIX, ASWIXS, SSIXS, etc."

"Then, what is the front-end processor?"

"A ship's RF transceivers connect to the outside world via RF links.

"User networks of Naval ships interface to the combat systems, voice equipment, and computers.

"The front-end processor is a kind of switchboard, which connects RF equipment to user networks."

"I see. The front-end processor is sandwiched between RF equipment and user networks."

"That's right.

"As you know, the original design of RF equipment was stove-piped to a dedicated network.

"That does not allow the efficient use of spectrum."

"So, you think that SNFEP will overcome that issue."

"That is the objective of my IR&D project."

Each year the company set aside 3% of company budgets as discretionary funds to conduct IR&D projects. The company would invest in various research and development efforts that could be of potential interest to DoD. TRW performed IR&D projects without the direct DoD control and guidance. At the end of each year, the IR&D funds were reimbursed by DoD as the allowable cost of doing business.

My testbed included a microcomputer with the VMEbus for developing a communications processor and an electronic switch matrix. A VMEbus is a computer bus standard to connect the printed circuit boards to the back of the computer processor. The ship-to-shore communications media were HF, UHF FLTSATCOM, and Link-16 radio to demonstrate the concept. After the peer review of my project, I received kudos for my SNFEP IR&D project.

LOW-ELEVATION ANGLE SATELLITE COMMUNICATIONS SYSTEM

In 1997, Dave Schall and I conducted research on the mitigation of performance impairment of C- and Ku-band[53] satellite communications links due to the tropospheric effect when the elevation angle of the ground station to a satellite was small (less than five degrees).

"When the Sun sets in the west, it looks a lot bigger and redder than at noon because light bends when it passes through the troposphere.

"Just like the Sunlight, satellite signals also bend when they go through the troposphere in the evening."

"We studied two topics in this project.

"The first was data communications from a high latitude ground station.

"The station of the interest was at Spitsbergen, Norway, and Gilmore Creek, Alaska.

"These stations communicate with lower latitude stations via geosynchro-

nous satellites such as INTELSAT and the National Oceanic and Atmospheric Administration's (NOAA's) Weather Satellite DOMSAT."

"The second was data communications from Low Earth Orbit (LEO) and Medium Earth Orbit (MEO) satellites.

"What are LEO and MEO satellites?"

"O.K. I will explain what they are.

"A man-made satellite goes around the Earth on an elliptical orbit.

"The orbit of a LEO is lower in altitude (approximately 99 miles) than that of MEO satellites (1,200 miles).

"The time required to complete an orbit by an LEO is about 110 minutes, while that of a MEO is about 12 hours."

"Yes, but what do these orbital properties mean to users.

"O.K. It is an excellent question.

"LEO is the simplest and the cheapest for the satellite placement.

"Functionally, LEO satellites provide high bandwidth and low latency. That means there is a significantly smaller transmission time lag.

"Also, LEO satellites can observe objects on the surface of the Earth better than MEO, such that they are suitable for spy satellites.

"The launch cost of a MEO satellite is more than that of a LEO satellite.

"But MEO satellites have a larger footprint. Therefore, they provide a greater coverage on the surface of the Earth.

"Therefore, one may need fewer satellites."

In conclusion, experimental data showed that satellite communication signals experience fading in high latitude ground stations. Fading causes errors in the communications system, but the performance gets worse during the summer months. We proposed two improvement techniques, one of which was the use of adaptive error-correcting codes[54] and the other was the use of antenna beamforming methods.[55]

Dave Schall and I published the results of the study "On the Improvement of Low Elevation Angle Satellite Communications Impaired by Tropospheric Fading Effect" in *the IEEE 1999 MILCOM Conference Proceedings*[56], Atlantic City, New Jersey.

21

Travels to the Czech Republic, the Netherlands, and Germany

PRAGUE AND BENESOV IN THE CZECH REPUBLIC

Rahn and I went to Prague to attend the 1997 Air Traffic Control Association (ATCA) Conference. The first evening, we attended the conference banquet held at the Czech Aviation Museum. The museum displayed some of the past technological achievements of the Czech aviation industry. Czech had a significant history of aircraft production. Czech helped Germans build fighter airplanes, the Messerschmitt 262, during the World War II, and Czech helped Russians build spacecraft during the Cold War. One of the items displayed in the museum was a Russian cosmonaut's spacesuit. The Russian spacecraft and spacesuit were very similar to American spacecraft and spacesuit that I had seen in the Smithsonian Air and Space Museum. Indeed, they were congruent except that the Russian spacesuit was slightly bulkier in size than the American version. Come to think of it, most Russian military airplanes resembled American counterparts. Were they the optimum designs and therefore they arrived independently at the similar profiles? Or, did one copy the other's design of two countries? I often wondered about the congruency of these machines and devices of two countries.

In Washington, before I traveled to Prague, I arranged a meeting with Jan Gregor, the manager of the TRW plant in the Czech Republic. When I arrived in Prague, I invited him to breakfast. When he sat down at the breakfast table, he looked at the menu and saw that the breakfast buffet was €20.

"John, I cannot afford to treat you in this restaurant."

"Jan, I invited you. I am traveling on an expense account."

"Thank you."

"John, by the way, why did you choose this hotel?"

"The ATCA Conference organizer must have made a deal. They offered an excellent group rate for us in this hotel.

"Why do you ask?"

"I heard that Libyans own this four-star hotel."

"Ouch. There were many Arabs in their white "thobe" garments in the hotel. That explains it."

"John, that's O.K. ATCA must know what they are doing. Tomorrow I will see you at my plant."

"I am looking forward to visiting your plant."

In the following day, we drove to the TRW plant in Benesov, 20 miles south of Prague. The Benesov facility was the easternmost TRW plant then. When I drove in the company compound, I noticed three national flags of the Czech Republic, Germany, and the U.S. flying at the entrance of the facility. (see photos 100 and 101)

"John and Rahn, welcome to Benesov."

"Thank you, Jan. I am glad to see the building with the familiar company logo."

"Yes, we got the company logo one year ago from Cleveland Headquarters."

"I see you have Czech, German, and American flags hoisted at the entrance.

"We do the same thing.

"We fly the national flag whenever foreign visitors come to TRW in Washington."

"John, I told my people to hoist the American flag in your honor, following the TRW company protocol of flag display."

"Thank you.

"Tell me, what are the main products of your plant?"

"We manufacture mostly automobile electronic parts like switches and control circuits.

"John, in this town, we have two automotive electronics factories."

"The Czech Ministry of Industry used to run both plants."

"When did TRW buy this plant?"

"TRW bought the factory in 1993.

"That was five years after the opening of the Czech market to the West.

"The state still runs the other plant. TRW owns 87% of this plant, and the state continues to hold 13%."

"I see."

"The Czech government still owns and operates the other plant.

"I am very proud that our plant is increasing its productivity."

"I see. But how do you measure the productivity."

"I use the metric of annual sales.

"Last year the sales increasedby 15%."

"That is impressive. How is your competition doing?"

"They are losing ground."

"Why is it?"

"In my plant, employees must punch their time card at eight o'clock in the morning.

"I do not allow employees a lengthy coffee break in the plant to read newspapers until nine o'clock."

"Jan, you sound just like one of our American plant managers.

"I am very proud of you."

"Thank you."

Jan Gregor was rapidly becoming a capitalist manager. He gave me a plant tour. TRW designed the automobile electronics in America; Czechs provided low-cost, skilled workers. Wages for workers in Czech were lower than those in America, but Jan said all things were relative. The food and housing were not expensive in the Czech Republic. But, his concern was the influx of Western influence; prices had been increasing steadily since the Berlin Wall came down.

Travel through Amsterdam and the Low Country

I attended the 1999 Vehicular Technology Conference (VTC) in Amsterdam. We arrived at Schiphol Airport in Amsterdam and went to a bed-and-breakfast inn in Badhoevesdorp, a small village just outside the Amsterdam city limit. We made a reservation for two rooms, and it was a convenient base for us to tour the Dutch countryside. An Irishman, Dave Walsh, operated the pension. He told me that he was going on holiday for two weeks.

"I will have a few days of holiday starting from tomorrow," said David Walsh.

"Where are you going?"

"I am going to the holy land."

"Where is the holy land?"

"Ireland!

"Where else could it be?"

The next day, we went to Amsterdam for sightseeing and walked many concentric canal roads in the city. We visited the Anne Frank House and had nice dinner at an Indonesian restaurant. Afterward, William, Doug, Rahn, and I walked on the streets along canals and saw the red-light district. We saw illicit drug dealers on a dark street corner. Several people were gathered doing business. I heard about the liberal attitude of the authorities of Amsterdam, but it was a shock to see open drug peddling with my own eyes.

In the evening, Rahn and I attended the Conference reception, held in the hall of the Rijksmuseum, which displays Rembrandt's famous *The Night Watch*. I then had a bit of luck to meet someone knowledgeable about the painting. He was Luuk van Essen, who was an engineer with KPN Telephone Co. and a graduate of Delft University. He was in charge of the PSRCS (a TRW project in the U.K., which stands for Public Safety Radio Communications System) account of KPN. In 1998, I met him several times during my stay in London. That evening, we agreed to meet again. He told me that he would become a tour guide that evening explaining on *The Night Watch* painting. Here is our conversation in front of *The Night Watch* next afternoon.

"So, you are an expert on this painting."

"Oh, I am not an expert, John.

"Many people know about the painting.

"It is the most famous painting of Rembrandt's."

"I read someplace that a group of wealthy merchants commissioned the painting.

"Were these merchants night watchmen?"

"Ya, I understood that night watchmen were a kind of citizen soldiers of the town in the 17th century.

"Then, in the 18th century, night watchmen just became the honorary civic guild of prosperous merchants."

"In America, we had Minutemen, volunteer soldiers who fought the Revolutionary War against England."

"In England, they have chivalric order like knights. Night watchmen were similar to those orders and ranks."

"Now what has that got to do with the Rembrandt's painting."

"John, I told you they commissioned it to the best painter in the country.

"I understood that each of these night watchmen was an actual person. For example, the man in the middle wearing the Puritan hat was Captain Frans Banninck Cocq."

"So, this was a portrait of a militia company."

"It was a little bit different than a portrait of a person. This painting not only showed the persons, who probably paid to be in this painting but also illustrated their assigned jobs. "Look at the musketeer loading his musket with gunpowder."

"I see a dog and a young girl and a woman. I wonder what they have represented."

"That is why this painting became famous. It makes you think and imagine beyond what you see in the rectangular space."

"I never thought about this painting like that."

"John, that is not all.

"This painting was originally hung in the city hall.

"But when they decided to move it to this museum, they had to cut the size down.

"It was a little bit too big for space in this museum.

"Can you imagine?

"They cut out some gentlemen in the group portrait."

"No kidding.

"Ya, I see some faces are cut out on the right-hand side."

"O.K. John, let's go to the buffet tables and get dinner.

"I saw a fresh salad bar in the next hall.

"Luuk, thank you so much for your commentaries.

"I think you are an expert on Rembrandt."

BELGIUM AND THE NETHERLANDS

The next morning Rahn, William, Doug and I drove to Belgium, but made a short detour to Leiden. The four of us walked through the campus, which crossed many canals. Just outside of the Leiden University campus, I was surprised to see a large outdoor mural (see photo 103) on a house, a famous Japanese Edo period haiku poem by Matsuo Basho (1644-1694).[57] The poem by Basho on the wall described the Milky Way as follows.[58]

"The rough sea,
Extending toward Sado Island,
The Milky Way."

Basho was a famous seventeenth-century Japanese poet. This poem appears in his travelogue *The Narrow Road to the Deep North (Oku no Hosomichi)*. Basho wrote this poem while he traveled the northern coast of Honshu Island of Japan, facing the Sea of Japan. When he followed the main roads along the coast, he saw on the horizon Sado Island and composed this poem. I later found a photograph of the poem by Professor Dr. Vincent Icke of Leiden University.

Leiden, the Netherlands
March 21, 2012

Dear Dr. Kim,

I shall be delighted if you would use a photograph of that poem, which has been so valuable to me (and to many others, I am sure). Although I do not live in that house anymore, I retain fond memories of the occasion when the poem was brushed on the wall.

Yours Sincerely,
Vincent Icke

Vincent Icke sent me this letter. He was a man with several hats, Professor of Theoretical Astrophysics at the University of Leiden, Professor at the Old Leiden Observatory, and Professor of Cosmology at the University of Amsterdam. I could imagine why he painted Basho's poem about the Milky

Way. Vincent Icke told me that the Old Leiden Observatory is the oldest university observatory in the world. Einstein was a frequent visitor here during his Leiden years. Icke also was interested in the activities of USNO and ONR Navigation and Timekeeping Program. I sent some brochures of USNO and ONR.

MUNICH

Aug. 30, 2000: My family and I traveled to Munich, Northern Italy, and Switzerland. We arrived in Munich and checked in the Hotel Gasthof zur Post in Ismaning, a suburb of Munich. Smoking bothered us, as there were no smoking restrictions in public places like subway stations and hotels. This trip was my fourth visit to Munich. I knew from my previous visits to the Siemens office near Ismaning that the town had good public transportation to the Munich city center. We liked this quiet town. A stream ran through the middle of Ismaning and emptied into the Isar River.

On this trip, my nose felt uncomfortable. I had nosebleeds, so Rahn drove me to the University of Munich-Roentgen Hospital. After waiting for an hour, a woman doctor in the ear-nose-throat department examined my nose.

"Mr. Kim, so you are traveling. Where are you from?"

"Yes, I am attending a conference here. I came from Washington."

"What is the problem?"

"My nose bleeds."

"I see. Don't worry. I will fix it. How was the weather in Washington? Was it cold or warm?"

"It was cold and damp for several days in Washington."

"And it was dry in the airplane cabin.

"And it is cold here in Munich.

"It does not help your nose.

"But don't worry.

"I will cauterize the inside membrane of your nose to stop it from bleeding."

The University of Munich named the hospital after Wilhelm Conrad Roentgen, the discoverer of the X-ray. The hospital facility was very modern.

"Okay, your nose is not going to bleed anymore, but when you return home, check with your primary care doctor."

"On the way out, please drop by the business office."

I asked the business officer:

"What is the bill for my visit today?

"My Aetna Insurance card shows that they cover medical fees in the EU countries."

"Mr. Kim, there will be no charge to you for today's treatment.

"You are good to go."

I was puzzled but realized that the European Union countries have an excellent health care system. I guess the system included free services to non-EU travelers. Eugen Muehldorf told me that within the European Union, many former Eastern European country residents come to places like Munich or Berlin for inexpensive medical treatment. He said that it was called "medical tourism."

The next day was Sunday, so we were looking for a place of worship. We found St. Johann Baptist Catholic Church-Ismaning next to the Gasthof zur Post. About 50 people were gathered in the church, which was half empty. The service was being conducted in German, but we knew some hymnals. After the Mass, no one welcomed us. They just stared at us without saying a word. I have encountered a situation like this in European churches. When I was on temporary duty assignment in London, Rahn and I went to St. Paul's Cathedral for Sunday service. An usher stopped us and told us that the service was not for tourists. When we said that we came for the Sunday service, the usher let us in.

The bell of St. John the Baptist Catholic Church chimed every hour on the hour. But for whom the bell tolls?

❃ ❃ ❃

We toured the Munich museum, Neue Pinakothek, which exhibited many modern European paintings and artworks from the 18ᵗʰ and 19ᵗʰ centuries. I liked Edouard Manet's *Luncheon in the Studio*. The painting depicted three persons in a restaurant, an elderly gentleman, a waitress, and a young man wearing a Prussian student cap. The elderly gentleman was admiring the waitress, who in turn was looking at the young man, but he was indifferent to her. These three figures form a triangle on the canvas. They formed a triangular human relationship. I bought a print of it and hung in my office.

William and Doug joined us in Munich. After they had settled into the guest house, William and Rahn went to the BMW Museum that is about three miles north of the Munich city center. William had reserved a ticket to the BMW Museum in advance as he was an aficionado of BMW cars. Later, I went to the museum to meet with them. The Munich traffic was terrible. We saw one of BMW's latest cars, the driverless car. Note that this was in the Year 2000. There were no driverless cars like Tesla, Toyota, or Ford at that time. Just outside of the BMW plant at Am Olympiapark, the Munich traffic chaos was horrendous. I thought perhaps they should spend more of their resources on traffic improvements rather than driverless cars.

A tall, four-cylinder building, like an engine piston, housed the BMW Headquarters; each cylinder looked like 20 disks stacked up. The bowl-shaped museum next to the headquarters complex showed BMW's technical achievements throughout its history. Exhibits included engines and turbines, aircraft, motorcycles, and other vehicles. A spiral path guides museum goers through all exhibitions smoothly in chronological order.

Padua

When I think of Padua, I remember a friend in Systems Research Laboratory in Dayton, Dr. Daniel DeSalvo. He was a physicist educated at the University of Padua. He had told me stories about his alma mater and the Po Valley in Italy. One day in 1963, he asked me:

"John, what are you doing this Saturday?"

"Dan, let's see.

"My calendar is open this Saturday. Why?"

"Oh, my wife Angela and I want to invite you to dinner at our place.

"She will treat you with an Italian home-cooked meal."

I had met Angela two months earlier in 1963 at a company picnic. Dan was a fellow physicist at Systems Research Laboratory. Angela was a charming Italian lady from Padua. The DeSalvos lived in the quiet suburb of Kettering in Dayton, Ohio.

With a bouquet of flowers in my hand, I went to their house.

"Oh. John, you shouldn't have."

"Dan, the flowers are for your wife."

It was the first time I had an Italian home-cooked meal.

"We have some Italian wine.

"How about a glass of Veneto Bardolino? "

"Dan, I will have a glass of it."

"Angela cooked fettuccine with ragu sauce."

Indeed, ragu sauce was full of garlic and herbs.

After dinner, we settled down comfortably in the living room. Angela asked me:

"John, are you from South or North Korea?"

"I came from South Korea, but my parent's hometown was in North Korea."

"Have you any family in the States?"

"No, I have no immediate family in the States."

"How about a girlfriend?"

Dan interrupted.

"Angela, you are playing cupid again."

"I have no one special. Now, I have a question for you. Where did you meet each other?"

"I met Daniel at the University of Padua in 1946 when he was working in my father's laboratory in the Department of Physics and Astronomy. Have you been to Padova or Veneto?"

"No, I have not."

"You should visit Padova, Verona, and Veneto. There is plenty of delicious food in this region. Also, it is rich in history."

I toured the Po Valley with my family in September 2000. We passed through Rosenheim, Bavaria, into Innsbruck, Austria, and then to Bolzano, Italy. When we crossed the Italian border at the Brenner Pass in Austria, many cars and trucks were waiting in a queue. At this border control, all vehicles were required to buy a temporary Italian license plate and a road use tax of 30 Euros.

From Virginia, I made a reservation for a two-bedroom pension in Padua. With a city map of Padua, Doug was navigating our car through the old narrow streets of this medieval town, which was busy with pedestrians and bicycles. In the late afternoon, we arrived at the pension. There were no parking spaces near the pension. I met the rental agent and looked around the place, and I did not like it. I told him we would not stay, and we agreed to cancel the reservation.

When I told my family waiting in the car about the cancellation, they were unhappy. Doug said it was getting late, and it might be difficult to find a place to stay before sundown. But I had remembered several hot-springs resorts were in this area when I was searching for a pension. I told them, "We will drive along the main street to the west of the city." About two miles west of Padua, we found the Piroga Hotel on Via Eugenea in the town of Selvazano. This hotel was for Italian travelers, not for tourists. The accommodations were good and we decided to use it as our temporary home base while touring the Po Valley and exploring the Venetia region.

VENICE

On our way to Venice from Padua, we approached the city from the inland via the causeway, then, we parked near the railroad station. We found the causeway to Venice was dilapidated. Thomas Mann in his novel *Death in Venice* describes the hero Gustav von Aschenbach approaching Venice from east on a ferry from Trieste across the Adriatic Sea. We arrived at Piazza San Marco from the Venice train station parking lot by waterway bus. We wanted to tour St. Mark's Basilica and waited in a line to enter the Basilica. After waiting for 20 minutes, I suggested to the family that we skip the Basilica tour. Doug protested:

"Dad, you must be kidding. We came 6,000 miles to see the Basilica, and you want to skip it?"

After Doug's remark, we decided to wait ina line. Above the entrance to the Basilica were the four Horses of St Mark's, which used to be in Constantinople. (The statue above the entrance were actually a replica; the original one was inside the Basilica.) In the early 13th century during the Fourth Crusade, Constantinople was sacked, and the Four Horses were looted and taken to Venice. Napoleon, in turn, looted Venice and took them to Paris; they were returned to Venice a couple of decades later in 1815.

The famous Campanile di San Marco Bell Tower stood next to the Basilica in the Piazza, which was packed with tourists. The Campanile was over 300 feet tall and stood in the corner of the Square, near the front of the Basilica. It had a simple form, the bulk of which was brick, fluted square shaft. There were many pigeons perched on the roof, and "white bombs" from pigeons would often hit tourists. The Grand Canal and bridges connected great and not-so-great houses. Instead of hiring a gondola, we hopped on a water bus and cruised along the canal. We passed under the Bridge of Sighs, which derives its name from the moans of prisoners. (see photo 102)

In the rotunda of the Basilica, a mosaic façade above the portal depicted the recovery of St. Mark's body in Alexandria, Egypt, in the 9th century. We went to the third floor of the gallery where a statue of the *Lion of San Marco* stood. The architecture of the Basilica was a mixture of Italian, Byzantine, and Gothic styles. I could see the Islamic influence in Venice, as it was once a bridgehead

to the Arab world. Venice had preserved its former glory.

Rahn wanted to go to Murano to see world-famous glass factories. We looked for a waterway bus stop near the Ducal Palace in Piazza San Marco. At the waterfront, we were told there was no boat service available as it was Sunday. But a wooden motor boat appeared out of nowhere, and a guide pushed us to the boat. Then it sped to Murano, which was a cluster of small islands and was about two miles across the water from Venice proper. It turned out that the glass factories provided an unsolicited boat service to attract tourists and to sell their glassware. As we were departing the quay of the Piazza San Marco, I quickly got my camera out of the bag, and I took pictures of Venice from the sea with a view of canals and buildings which appeared to be floating on water. After ten minutes, we arrived at Murano Islands. A guide led us to a glass factory, where the skilled artisan made glassware. Rahn bought a blue glass plate. When we returned to the hotel in the evening, Doug showed us an excerpt from his tour book, which said, "When a boat approaches you to give a free ride to Murano, resist the boatman at all costs."

The transportation might be free, but then one feels obligated to buy glassware in the factory.

VERONA

We then made a trip to Verona, which was about 30 miles west of Padua in the Po Valley. As we passed through a small town, we saw a grocery store. I remembered what Angela DeSalvo had told me about food in the Po Valley many years ago. I consulted an Italian dictionary and told the shopkeeper:

"Per favore dammi due sandwich di tonno e due panini proscuitto e formaggio."

"Avete messo in bottiglia l'acqua?"

He made two tuna sandwiches, two ham and cheese sandwiches, and brought us six bottles of carbonated water. Italians drink carbonated water. I can drink Coke, but carbonated water is something else.

"Avete acqua naturale?"

"Si, una momento."

He went to the back of his store and brought back six bottles of plain water.

In Verona, at the house of Juliet Capulet, we saw a bronze statue of Juliet in the small courtyard. We viewed the balcony above it, where Juliet was supposed to have said,

"Romeo, Romeo, wherefore art thou, Romeo?"

Two young tourist girls shamelessly caressed the bronze breasts.

LAKE COMO

We drove further west into the Po Valley on Autostrada. As we approached the metropolis of Milan, there were heavy truck traffics. The air was full of dense smog, as this was the western end of the Po Valley basin surrounded by the Piedmont Mountains. Smoke and fog and perhaps chemical pollutants got trapped and shrouded the valley. We decided to bypass the city and turned north to Lake Como. In Como, we visited the Volta House, which became a museum of Alessandro Volta, the inventor of the battery. It exhibited some of his original instruments and desiccated frogs, with which he performed electrolytic experiments. The museum contained more than 200 of Volta's scientific artifacts. I enjoyed the beautiful scenery of Lake Como, which was fed by melting snow from the Alps. Doug dropped by a wine store and bought two bottles of Italian wine for his professor, Richard Palmiter. From there, we went to the Tre Rosa Hotel, located on the eastern shore of Bellagio. The view of Lake Como was picturesque. At sunset, we sat at a garden table with a beautiful view of the lake. The lakeshore road was very narrow, with many sharp curves. My small car and other small Italian cars could barely squeeze on this curvy road. I was driving very slowly, which bored William. I finally let him drive, and he drove very well, but too fast for my comfort.

LUZERN AND ZURICH

We headed north to Lucerne, Switzerland. On the way, we stopped at the town of Bellinzona. The weather in the Alps Piedmont region felt like the early winter. We stopped our car in a small village on the Andermatt Pass and had lunch at a picnic table. I asked passing schoolboys by if the language in this region of Switzerland were Italian. The boys emphatically told me it was German. I sensed from their tone that they had a sense of belonging to the German culture and language. The highway from Lake Como to the Andermatt Pass was in a valley. This pass was in the middle section of the Alpine Mountains, with an elevation of 6,900 feet. Occasionally there were fogs and even clouds below us in the valley. Then, we passed through the six-mile-long Seelisberg Tunnel.

In the afternoon we checked into Guesthouse Schweizerheim in Ebikon, a suburb of Lucerne. The guesthouse was in rural surroundings, and there was a dairy farm nearby. The pride of the guesthouse was an antique 17th-century clock which the owner had restored and placed in the corner of the dining room. The Swiss have the reputation of making the best clock in the world.

Later, we walked on the covered wooden Chapel Bridge over the Reuss River. The four of us drove to Zurich for sightseeing. Our first stop was the Zurich Museum of Art. The gallery included Van Gogh's *Sunflowers* and Claude Monet's *Hay Stacks*. I knew of a cozy faculty restaurant in the Zurich Institute of Technology. We relaxed and had an early dinner there.

Munich

In three weeks, Rahn, William, Doug and I toured by car four nations, that is, Germany, Austria, Italy, and Switzerland. Our last stop was the Dachau Concentration Camp Memorial Site. Nazi Germany opened its first concentration camp in Dachau, which was 10 miles northwest of the Munich city center. At the Memorial Site, the concentration camp had been rebuilt as a place of remembrance and history. When I entered Dachau, I had an eerie feeling. I was left with a somber feeling by what I saw.

We returned to the Hotel Gasthof zur Post in Ishmaning. Later in the evening, we went to the city center, where things were in a pre-Oktoberfest mood in the Victual Market. We caught the atmosphere of "*Gemutlchkeit*," and had a good time at a hofbrauhaus with mugs of beer. The next day we returned to America.

22

TRW Project - U.K. Public Safety Radio Communications Project

In 1998, I had a temporary assignment in London to work on the development of the U.K. Public Safety Radio Communications System (PSRCS). Two months earlier, I had received a phone call from Earl Williams, who then managed the Systems Integration Group (SIG) Public Sector Solutions Business Area; he asked me if I was interested in working on the PSRCS project in London. PSRCS was the police radio communications network of the U.K. Home Office.

Earl Williams proposed to apply TRW SIG's experience on public safety radio systems to those of the U.K. The public safety forces in various jurisdictions were equipped with different kind of radios, which caused interoperability issues. British Telecom (BT) was the prime contractor, and TRW became BT's subcontractor for the system integration. The PSRCS service included voice, data, and computers. The system must be able to access the computerized database and transmit and receive information such as maps, documents, and photographs. The system included mobile and fixed radios in the public safety stations and vehicles. Earl told me he needed an independent reviewer who would stay for an extended period in London, working with on-site TRW personnel in BT. He asked me to be that independent reviewer, and I accepted the assignment. Here is my first e-mail about my London trip to my family.

London
Jan. 18, 1998

Dear Family,

My company management assigned me a TDY to work in London starting the next week. I will be in London for two months until March 29. Rahn plans to leave DC on Feb. 12 and stay with me for one month. When I arrive in London, I will stay at the Holiday Inn near Victoria Station until TRW finds me a "flat to let." My office will be in the BT Building on Rochester Row near Buckingham Palace. You can contact me by email or telephone. I requested to lease a laptop computer and will carry it to London. I will let you know more about our travel plan as soon as we find out more.

Cheers,
John Kim

My second email letter:

London
Jan. 29, 1998

Hello, Family,

I arrived at Heathrow Airport early on Friday morning. The flights were uneventful, and I had empty seats on both sides of me, which made the six and one-half hour flights comfortable. The immigration officer asked me whether this was a business trip. I said "yes," and he let me go.

I took a shuttle van from the airport to Holiday Inn-Victoria. After that, I went to see our company colleagues. I reported to Gary Good, our company manager and met with Harry Hodges, a fellow TRW employee from Albuquerque and Art

Garrison, another TRW employee from Redondo Beach. I also met with Guy Kenyon, an English engineer. Tomorrow I will move into a flat at No. 25, 1 Ambrosden Avenue, London SW1, which will be rented by our company's London Office. The flat is quiet, although it is two blocks from the downtown business street and is facing the Westminster Cathedral.

Cheers,
Dad/John

My third e-mail letter:

London
January 30, 1998

Hello, Family,

The BT office is about three blocks from my flat. The flat is a small townhouse, much smaller than the ones in America. It has a bedroom, a living room, a kitchen (with a dishwasher, a refrigerator, a washer-dryer, etc.). I will move into the flat tomorrow morning. It is on the second floor, but the building has a lift.

My address is:

No. 25, 1 Ambrosden Avenue, London SW1, U.K.
Telephone: (0171) 828-xxxx
BT office address is 17 Rochester Row, London SW1,
U.K. Telephone: (0171) 932-xxxx

Cheers,
John Kim

Across Grey Coat Street, there is an old girls' school, the Grey Coat Hospital School. Students all wear grey tweed blazers and pleated skirts; they pass Rochester Row in front of our office. The New Scotland Yard is across Victoria Street. My flat is in a prime location in the heart of London, from where I could walk to Buckingham Palace, St James Park, Westminster Abbey, and Whitehall.

London
January 31, 1998

Hi, Family,

It is my second day in London. On Saturday I had a hearty breakfast (with seven-minute boiled eggs, a piece of ham, grapefruit, and a pot of tea, etc.) at the Holiday Inn restaurant. I paid £10.50 for breakfast (about $18), which is rather steep. Since I am on an expense account, it does not matter, but I am still apprehensive. So I decided to go local with meals.

Today I did some sightseeing. I went to Buckingham Palace, watched the ceremony of Changing of the Guard (Queen's Own Regiment). Then, I went to Trafalgar Square. In the Square, I found a church called St. Martin-in-the-Fields. Of course, I have heard about this church, which was famous for its chamber music and choir. This church is a place of worship, but churchgoers are mostly non-Londoners. There are many churches in London, but I heard that only one out of ten Londoners were churchgoers. The church like the St. Martin-in-the-Fields does not attract many parishioners; therefore, these stately inner-city churches have found other roles to fill, such as social service, missions, or music venues.

All the best,
Dad/John

My e-mail letter of February 2 to the family:

London
February 2, 1998

Dear Family,

It is my third day in London. On Saturday afternoon, I bought a bag of food from a grocery nearby. I had a ham sandwich with pickles and carrots, which is my usual lunch staple in Washington. I also bought a carton of non-dairy soybean milk. For supper, I cooked a pot of rice and heated ready-made, roasted chicken drumsticks with a quarter of iceberg lettuce. I have been drinking hot tea (Twinning's English Breakfast) several times daily as fellow BT engineers do.

This afternoon I made an excursion to the Bloomsbury area, where I also found the British Museum and London University. It used to be the English literary and art enclave, where famous intellectuals like Dylan Thomas, Maynard Keynes, Leonard and Virginia Woolf, Lytton Strachey, and Clyde Bell used to live. I read several Bloomsbury books in the past, but these notables were all gone from the District.

On Sunday, I attended a service at St. Paul's Cathedral. The service was a sung Eucharist (or Communion) using the music of Mozart's Missa Brevis; there were about sixty choir members. It is an expanded version of the Trinity UMC's communion services, but it only took 1 hour and 15 minutes, including the sermon. The sermon was excellent. By the way, the ushers all wore a tail with a medal of the Usher Guild membership hung on their neck, which was all very grand. Otherwise, at the office, I have been reading and reviewing all the stuff that our company project members have been doing so far in London.

The weather is what I have expected. I was here in January 1991 with Johnny Johnson and Tom Baird. It was not cold, but it was not warm either. It is not severe, but damp weather which chills your bones after a while. Just about everyone is coughing. I am trying my best not to catch cold. I put on my long underwear, which keeps me warm and comfortable. People on the street are all subdued and very polite. I guess the weather makes people behave like that.

Right now I am at the BT office, working on an analysis of message traffic. My laptop is working, but I have to convert the paper size to A4 when I print it to the European paper size. It is not an 8-1/2 by 11 inches but is a slightly elongated paper.

I also hear everyone saying 'quite right, quite right.' These English engineers are speaking King's English so I can understand what they are saying, but in stores and marketplace, they speak with the Cockney accent, which is hard on my ears.

Love,
Dad/John

My e-mail letter of February 6, 1998:

London
February 6, 1998

Dear Family,

I walk to the office carrying my laptop and briefcase. It is only about a five-minute walk. There is a cafeteria in the building in which they serve hot food to employees at a reasonable price. Today, I missed lunch because I had a visitor during the lunch hour, so I went around the corner to a bustling marketplace,

which is like the East Gate Market in Seoul. I got "fish and chips" lunch for £2.5 (about $4.50).

Wednesday night, I went to a London Philharmonic Orchestra concert at the Royal Festival Hall on the south bank of the Thames River. The guest conductor was Kurt Mazur of the New York Philharmonic Orchestra. The program included Schubert's Unfinished Symphony and Gustav Mahler's *Das Lied von der Erde (The Song of the Earth)*. Chinese poems of the Tang Era were the lyrics of *Das Lied von der Erde*. A soprano and tenor sang the poems of Li Tai Po and Wang Wei. An Austrian poet translated these works into German in 1905, and these Chinese poems inspired Mahler.

One of Wang Wei's famous poems, the Farewell, was inserted into the program. It was one of my favorites.

"The Farewell"

"He dismounted and gave him the parting cup. He asked him where he was going, and also why it must be.
He spoke, and his tones were veiled: O my friend, fortune was not kind to me in this world! When I am going, I shall wander in the mountains,
And, I am seeking rest for my lonely heart,
I shall wander to my native land, to my home. I shall never roam abroad. Still, in my heart, it is awaiting its hour.
Everywhere the lovely earth blossoms forth in spring and grows green anew!
Everywhere, forever, horizons are blue and bright! Forever and ever…"[59]

The Li Tai Po and Wang Wei poems remind me of Cen Shen's *The coming winter as birds fly south.* When I returned home from London, I found Wang Wei's *The Farewell* in a *Tang Poem Anthology.*[60]

> I am reading the International Herald Tribune quite often. The paper contains about 20 pages with news, sports, and financial articles from the New York Times and the Washington Post of that day and some well-written articles by the Herald-Tribune staff. The New York Times and the Washington Post own this newspaper, and it is known as the newspaper for Americans abroad. I like it, and it helps me keep abreast of the stateside news.

Love,
Dad/John

❀ ❀ ❀

My e-mail letter of February 8, 1998, to Rahn:

London
February 8, 1998

Dear Rahn,

I will make an arrangment for you to pick up a laptop battery pack from SIG Fairlakes. The engineer who is trying to find a backup battery for me is Dave Snell of the Computer Service Center. His number is 968-xxxx. He is looking for the right one from his inventory. I will let you know when I hear from him.

I expect to see you at Heathrow Airport on Friday morning. Did you locate the Mathcad software? When you find it, please bring only the floppy disks, not the manual. Please bring 3 or 4 blank floppies (1.44 MB size). You can find them

in the computer desk in the basement. They are in a small floppy disc box on the floor. Bring a blue CD holder, which is right next to the computer.

Cheers,
John

In February, Rahn took one-month leave from her Fairfax County job and joined me in London. When Rahn landed at Heathrow Airport, she followed the queue line at the passport control. When I first came to the U.K., the company instructed me that I should avoid telling the passport control officer about my work in the U.K., which sometimes may alert the officer to the work permit issue. I asked Rahn not to say anything about me working in the U.K. At Heathrow Airport, the passport officer asked her:

"Ms. Kim, what is the purpose of your travel to the U.K.?"

"I am a tourist."

"How long are you going to stay?"

"One month."

"It is unusual to stay for one month as a tourist. Are you going to seek any work in the U.K.? You have no work permit."

Rahn sensed that the passport officer might not approve her entrance to the U.K., so she decided to tell him that she came to stay with me for a month.

"Officer, my husband has a temporary assignment from his company TRW in the U.S.

"If you must know, he works for a project of the Home Office, and here is his office phone number."

"Well, Ms. Kim, why didn't you tell me about his work before.

"Enjoy your stay in the U.K."

Rahn passed the border control at Heathrow Airport.

❋ ❋ ❋

After she had recovered from her jet lag, Rahn and I went to the Royal Observatory Greenwich and stood on the prime meridian that marks longitude of zero degree. When I visited the Greenwich Observatory, my first impression was that the observatory hill and surroundings looked very familiar. Then I realized that this impression came from the U.S. Naval Observatory, which also stands at the top of a hill in Northwest Washington.

We saw John Harrison's famous marine chronometers, which were the clocks used to determine the longitude of ocean-going ships in the 18th century. In 1998, when I visited the Royal Observatory, I saw an oversized red ball on the rooftop. This red ball drops at noon to enable navigators aboard ships in Greenwich harbor to set their marine chronometers. In this case, there is no delay in synchronizing the time. This ball dropping was the method of time transfer in the old days. Today, radio signals are used for time transfer.

Travel Through the English Countryside

One weekend, Rahn and I made an excursion trip to Blenheim. Following was my letter to the family on March 4, 1998, about our tour.

London
March 4, 1998

Hello, Family,

Last weekend Rahn and I explored the vicinity of London. First, we rented a car from Europcar, which was a small Italian Fiat Punto with a 1.2-liter engine. We had been walking on foot for several weeks in London streets. It is comfortable traveling in a car. I thought two of us would be crammed in this peanut-sized car. A rental car and gasoline costs are high in the U.K. even with the corporate discount. To my surprise, my Fiat Punto rental car was speedy on narrow roads. But I

found it difficult to drive on the left side of the road. I kept saying "left, left, left" whenever I approached a crossroad, reminding me to stay on the left-hand side of the road. At first, I got confused. It did not take me long to get used to it. Next were all those traffic circles (roundabouts) which I have to negotiate. In the U.K., most intersections of secondary roads are traffic circles.

BLENHEIM

We drove to Blenheim Palace, the palace of the Duke of Marlborough, who was the seven-generation grandfather of Winston Churchill; Churchill was born there. After we saw the grandiose Blenheim Palace, I sensed part of the class society in the U.K. Almost everything was small and crowded in England; the smallness applies to everything, roads, apartments, even office desks, but English aristocrats live in spacious houses with huge gardens.

Then, we returned to drab and smog-filled but busy and bustling London. In the country, everything was green, the field, the hills, and the garden. One of my English colleagues works in London; he has a flat in the West End, but his family, his wife, and children live in Bath, 110 miles west of London. He commutes every weekend.

Cheers,
John

My Telegraph Key and Relay Name Plate

Tom Curry, my boss at Raytheon (Melpar Division), had a vintage World War II U.S. Army Signal Corps telegraph keyer to which he had mounted his nameplate. I wanted to have a nameplate like the one Tom had, but I could not find an old telegraph keyer. When we stayed in London, Rahn and I visited the large antique shop district on Portobello Road. At an antique store called Scientific and Medical Antiques Shop of Desmond & Elizabeth, Squire, I found an old British Telephone Co. telegraph keyer. As soon as we saw the device, Rahn said to me, "John, here is a telegraph keyer you have been looking for."

The store owner overheard that, and his ears perked up. Indeed, this was the the kind of telegraph keyer I wanted. The price tag showed £200. I could not bargain the price down, so I paid full price and became the owner of the telegraph keyer and the relay. They had BT nameplates. So one day, I called the BT Archive Division in Holborn, London, and asked if I could visit to do some research on old BT telegraph equipment. The associate curator of the Archive Division told me that Archive Division was not open to the public. I explained that I was an engineer working at the BT Wireless Radio Division, looking for the history of an old BT relay device. That opened the door to the museum. I went to the Archive Division. But I could not find any telegraph keyer and relay in the catalog section.

I was disappointed and asked the staff person if I could browse through books, catalogs, and equipment on the shelves. He gave me permission to do so. Then I found an old handbook on telegraphy, published in 1890, in which I found a picture of the telegraph equipment similar to my keyer and relay.

"Excuse me. I found a photo of the same telegraph relay as mine in this handbook. This relay is what I am looking for."

"Oh, very well.

"But I thought what you are looking for was a computer relay, not a telegraph relay.

He searched the catalog box again and found a card that described the type and the description of the telegraph keyer and the relay device.

"It is a Single-Current-Telegraph Keyer,[61] and the telegraph relay is a Standard Relay "B" type.[62]

When I had returned to Washington, I found a carpenter, Peter Alvin, in Ballston, Virginia. He made a nameplate like the one Tom Curry had. He designed my nameplate with the British Museum décor finish. I received many compliments from visitors to my office on my telegraph keyer and relay nameplate. (see photo 77)

ENERGY SAVING MEASURES IN LONDON

One evening at our flat, suddenly the lights went out. The rental property manager sent a technician, who told me that the main power switch in our flat had a meter similar to a parking meter. He inserted several tokens to restore the electricity. He told me that I could buy the token at a drugstore. Obviously, we must have used more electricity than what they expected us to use because we warmed ourselves after returning to the flat by taking a hot shower. The London weather in the winter was damp and bone-chilling. Around the middle of the following month, sure enough, the lights went out again, and we had to buy tokens to restore electricity. We learned energy-saving measures in London the hard way.

Following was my letter to William Kim on March 2, 1998,

London
March 2, 1998

Hi, William,

So, you are back from Salt Lake City. I hope your trip was successful. Yes, please bring the following items for me. First, I need my maroon duffel bag, which is in Janet's bedroom closet. I need to bring back all the stuff we bought in London. Next, I need my *Michelin Tourist Guide to Paris*. Mom wants the three of us to go to Paris on Sunday (March 8) by train

through the Chunnel, which connects England to France under the English Channel. It will be a three-hour trip one way. We will catch the Eurotrains at Waterloo Station at around seven o'clock in the morning and will arrive at Gare Nord (North Station) in Paris at 11 a.m. We will return on the eight o'clock train in the evening and come back to Waterloo Station at around eleven o'clock at night. We will see the main attractions of Paris as much as we can. There are some Paris books and maps in the house. Can you bring them with you?

Please make sure you bring an overcoat. The weather suddenly became cold last weekend. Warm weather was in the forecast for the next week, but just in case, be prepared. Mom is suffering from hay fever because London is really in the early spring and cherry blossoms already come and gone. Mom suggests that you bring hay fever medicine. Did you read Susan Allen Toth's book, *My Love Affair with England: A Traveler's Memoir*? I recommend it.

Cheers,
Dad

This was another email I sent to the family:

London
March 4, 1998

Dear Family,

Last week, the temperature nose-dived. This morning it was warming up a little bit. A TRW engineer came from Fairfax as a courier; he came to deliver a proposal to the International Maritime Satellite (INMARSAT) Consortium in London. The proposal was on the Intermediate Circular Orbit (ICO) System Integration.[63] TRW also sent two

copies of the same proposal via FedEx to the INMARSAT Corporation and the other redundant set by the courier. The manager of the proposal operations instructed us to hand-carry it to INMARSAT. We made it with about five hours to spare. What an expensive way to deliver a document! After the delivery, I bought him a pint of beer at a pub near Victoria Station.

Yesterday, Rahn and I went shopping in London's famous Bond Street. First, we dropped by an art gallery, where they were having a silent auction of two dozen paintings. I entered the gallery wearing my usual beret, which gave the staff an idea that I might be an art collector. There was one painting I liked. It was called *"Fred's Fleet in the Harbor."* In the painting, there are two small wooden boats in a river. The painting looked like a birthday card Doug gave me some years ago. The auctioneer listed prices in ascending order for each painting; A prospective bidder stuck a red dot with his or her bid price. This particular painting started at £350. I saw the bidding had already gone up to £600. I could not afford it. Oh, well.

Meantime, Rahn bought a Paris-made jacket by a designer named Gerard Darell at Fenwick Store, and she was happy with that. Bond Street was about four blocks long, and there were many luxury brand stores like Versace, Gucci, and Hermes. The Tyson's Corner shopping mall has only a few of these name brand stores. The number of luxury brands does not tell the whole story. I believe that these upscale stores cater to wealthy upper-class clients, and the middle class here is less affluent than their American counterpart. They say that the gap between social classes was widening steadily. When you go to the tube station, the public announcement says, "mind the gap," meaning "mind the gap between the train and the platform." "Mind the gap, is a very mournful sound. Also, they

should mind the gap between the wealthy and poor classes. I guess this goes for American society as well as in the U.K.

Cheers,
Dad

ELLY AMELING AND HER MASTER CLASS

One evening, Rahn and I braved the chilly London weather and went to Wigmore Hall to hear Elly Ameling, a renowned Dutch soprano singer, conducting a master class. I had bought her cassette tapes in the 1960s, in which she recorded Schubert's lied. I was surprised by the recital on the stage. It was a musical concert called a master class, in which she taught six post-graduate singers. They sang German lied (Schubert's and Brahms's) and French songs (Poulenc's and Faure's). She kept commenting on the singers' techniques, mostly enunciation. She would tell a student how she or he should clearly pronounce German words, especially guttural sounds. She also instructed students on how they should pronounce French vowels at the front end of their mouths. She also corrected students' breathing techniques. It was very tedious to listen to her instructional comments but was interesting. These singers were graduates of the Royal School of Music, but Ameling grilled them hard.

Here was my another letter to the family.

London
March 8, 1998

Dear Family,

Today, we spent two hours in the London Science Museum, where one could see the glorious accomplishments of the U.K. Exploring the museum, I got the feeling that up until the end of the 19th century, the U.K. was the leading technology innovator in the world. Notable displays were the Watts' steam engine and the Babbage's computer engine. They called

the Babbage's digital computer an engine in the 1860s. One display boasted that not only was J.J. Thomson of Cambridge University a Nobel laureate in physics, but also his seven former assistants and students were Nobel laureates as well. Across from the museum, the Imperial College campus had a dozen massive stone, neoclassical and Victorian red brick buildings. The buildings were much bigger than those at the MIT, UC Berkeley, or Stanford buildings on campuses. The museum also displayed exhibits about a very robust aviation industry that was active until WWII. Then, exhibits of science and technology stopped after the war period. The museum really had nothing to show in space technology. One notable exhibit was the discovery of the double helix in biology in 1953. I observed the decline of the British Empire in one afternoon in the museum. But I guess that is the nature of history. As Arnold Toynbee said, history is like a wheel. I just wondered what it will be like for America in 100 years.

Cheers,
John Kim

To Paris via the Chunnel

The following letter was my e-mail to the family about our Paris trip.

Paris
March 10, 1998

Hi, Family,

This letter is my travelogue for Paris. William came here for a short visit. The first day, he needed to recover from jet lag. After about a three-hour nap, he woke up and the three of us toured London on foot, by bus, and by tube. We went to Greenwich and visited the Royal Observatory. After the tour

of the Observatory, we stopped at the Tower Bridge. They have already started the construction of Millennium Park for Y2K (the Year 2000).

The next day, the three of us went to Paris for sightseeing. We could not purchase second-class train tickets, which were all sold out for the weekend. The only available tickets were first class for £120 per person, round trip, including dinner. The Queen opened the Chunnel two weeks ago, which caused the sell-out. The three of us boarded Eurostar express trains to Paris at Waterloo Station at seven o'clock in the morning, and we went to Paris through the Chunnel. The train was clean, and the service was excellent. On the train, they served us good English breakfast of omelet and sausage.

At Gare du Nord (North Station) in Paris, we bought "un jour" (one-day) metro tickets and "un jour" museum tickets. Then we started our "Around-Paris-in-eight-hours" tour. There were long ticket lines at the Louvre Museum and just about all main Paris attractions, but since we had bought one-day tickets at the train station, we did not wait at all at any museum. I highly recommend it when you want to tour Paris.

As usual in the cold weather, I wore my favorite beret. I wore my Granada beret in Paris to cover my head in the rain. I was surprised that nobody wore a beret in Paris. It seemed that I was the only one wearing a beret that day. A few people stared at me, maybe, thinking, "who is this guy wearing our national headgear?" I enjoyed my dubious distinction in Paris by wearing Spanish "boinia."

In 8 hours, we saw the major attractions of Paris: the Louvre Museum, Notre Dame Cathedral, D'Orsay Museum, Les Invalides, La Tour Eiffel, L'Arc de Triomphe, Avenue des Champs-Élysées, Sorbonne Université, Panthéon, and the banks of the Seine River. I am putting the definite article for

some French words here. Some years ago, I went to Paris and was looking for a hotel (it was L'Hotel Bourgogne et Montana). I asked kids who were playing on the street, "Ou est Hotel Bourgogne et Montana?" One of the kids corrected my French. Do you know what he said to me? L'Hotel! Since then I have been pretty good with L'Hotel and any other articles in French, except I get confused with " le, la and les." Meantime, William carried his full complements of camera equipment in his backpack. He took pictures all over the place. We did not want to miss the train for our return trip around seven o'clock in the evening. They served us dinner with wine on the train (mine was porc, meaning pork. I thought pork is jambon, but jambon is ham). It took about three hours by the Eurostar train under the English Channel from Paris to London. We enjoyed our dinner and wine and the good company. By the time we returned to Waterloo Station, it was a quarter past eleven o'clock in the evening. We caught the last train to Victoria station, just as the underground station was closing, so we had to run through the closing gates of the station. I have never run so fast.

The next day, we went all around London by bus. We also rode a double-decker bus and the underground tube. The three of us went to the Royal Festival Hall on the Thames River on foot and attended the Mozart Festival.

Cheers,
John Kim

I returned to my Washington office and spent several days, reporting on the progress of the project to Earl Williams and submitting travel expenses to the TRW business office. Then, I flew back to London and continued my work at the BT office. This was another letter of mine to the family.

London
March 18, 1998

Hi, Family,

I am back in London on Thursday and moved into a new flat. The new flat is in the Pimlico area of London, not far from Victoria Station. Rahn, this flat has a lift, and everything is working in the kitchen including the washer-dryer this time. It is a 15-minute walk from the office, but I found the route-24 bus, which stops about two blocks from the office. It goes to Pimlico Tube Station, then to Victoria Station and St. James Station, where I get off. So, it takes 25 minutes by bus, but the bus ride is more convenient with a laptop and a briefcase.

Cheers,
John Kim

This was another letter I sent to my family.

London
March 21, 1998

Dear Family,

Saturday night I went to the Alberg Theater in the West End to see a play called "An Ideal Husband" by Oscar Wilde. The theater production was excellent. The plot of "An Ideal Husband" is similar to Wilde's "Importance of Being Earnest," which we saw at the Olney Theater in Maryland, last summer. One cannot compare the quality of the performance at a West End theater to that of a provincial theater in America. Before I bought the ticket for this play, I called around to several box offices of the top five plays recommended by the *Times*. All of them were sold out all the way to April. Fortunately,

there were many popular plays (I think there are around 30 legitimate theaters) just in the West End.

Four engineers came from Fairfax this week, and we have been very busy.

Cheers,
Dad

On March 27, 1998, I returned home, and the next day I went to my office on School Street in the Federal Triangle. During my three-month absence, my inbox was full. It was a welcome change from the damp and cold London weather to the springtime weather in Washington. The TRW engineers in London had made excellent progress, and the project was well on its way to the successful completion. I enjoyed my three-month TDY in London.

23

My 60th Birthday and the Retirement after 32 years at TRW

In the summer of 1999, I heard rumors about mergers and acquisitions of TRW by another company. No one could have imagined that well-established companies like TRW, Bell Laboratories, and Hughes Aircraft were merged, be acquired, and disappeared. In the 1990s TRW gradually became a marginal player in the defense, space, and electronics sectors in America. A few years earlier, the TRW Automotive Group had decided to merge and acquire the British automotive parts manufacturer, Lucas Varity. This merger weakened the company's financial position due to the significant amount of debt. I left TRW in 2001 to join the Office of Naval Research (ONR). The next year, Northrop Grumman acquired TRW. Some blame the takeover of TRW on too many MBAs with the "bottom-line mentality." Throughout its short history, TRW executives were all engineers, like Simon Ramo and Dean Wooldridge. In the late 1990s, the need for near-term profits had driven corporate strategy. The technology base was the strength and resilience of TRW as a corporation. In the end, these business executives were so engrossed with their near-term strategy such that "one day they wake and find themselves dead," as the existentialist philosopher, Soren Kierkegaard said.[64]

As the old Sage, Confucius said, "At 60, as I struggled with my moral sense, whatever I heard, my ears were an obedient organ for the reception of truth, and my ears heard no evil even if my adversary may have uttered foul words."

I know I had yet reached at such a refined state as a human being, maybe, never.

My family gave me my 60th birthday party at the Hilton Hotel, in McLean. Family members and friends came to the party. I have a photograph of me cutting the birthday cake with the family and friends. (see photo 99)

MY RETIREMENT PARTY

In January 2001, TRW held a retirement party for me at TRW in Fairlakes, Virginia. (see photos 95, 96, 97, and 98) Many colleagues came to bid farewell. They were Dr. Eugen Muehldorf, Dr. Wilson Felder, and his wife Laura, Dr. Eugene Kaiser, Dr. Tom Curry, Dr. Phil Girardi, Steve Hertz, Johnny Johnson, Jack Dreyfus, Dr. John Gormally, Dave Schall, Tamas Gyorik di Slansky, and Commander Earl Eckert. Also, attending were Peder Hildre, Sue Markle, Ginnie Brosseau, Maxine Chiavetta, Hank Beebe, Jim Hartz, John Phillips, Alex Gillies, Dr. Al Schuler, and others. My farewell speech was:

"Thank you,

"Let me introduce my family members who are here this evening. First, my wife, Rahn. Rahn supported me all these years and kept me on an even keel. (I presented and pinned an orchid corsage on her lapel.)

"My son William is here also, with his fiancée, Juli Ro.

"I want to introduce a few guests of mine from outside of TRW this evening.

"Dr. Tom Curry is here.

"Tom was my boss at Raytheon-Melpar Division twenty years ago.

"Tom later became the Assistant Deputy Secretary of the Navy for Command, Control, and Communications (DASN-C3), from 1980 to 1983, in the Reagan Administration. "Two other colleagues from my Melpar days are here.

"The first is Dr. Gene Kaiser, now with the Defense Information Systems Agency (DISA), and Dr. Al Schuler of Aerospace Corporation.

"Dr. Kaiser, Dr. Schuler, and I worked at Melpar in the 1960s.

"Dr. Kaiser was Project Manager of the mobile command center program in DoD and now manages the Pentagon Renovation Project.

"Also, I am glad to see Dr. George Donohue, who was the Associate Administrator of the FAA, and now the Visiting FAA Professor at George Mason University.

"I also wish to recognize Jack Dreyfus and Dr. John Gormally for appoint-

ing me to an Operational Incentive Plan position in 1985.

"It is an incentive plan with a handsome amount of the bonus.

"With that bonus every year, my wife and I were able to finance our three children's private college education.

"Our daughter Janet went to Northwestern, our eldest son William to Cornell, and our youngest son Doug to Princeton.

"Thank you, Jack and John.

"For the last seven years, I was a TRW Systems Integration Group (SIG) Technical Fellow. "It was one of the highlights of my career at TRW. This appointment allowed me to do research of my choosing, which resulted in publishing several papers and opening new technology areas for TRW.

"I would like to thank Dr. Wilson Felder, Dr. Al Babbitt, Priscilla Guthrie, and Ray Godman, for nominating me to be a Technical Fellow in 1996.

"Later, in 1999, Wilson and Steve Hertz nominated me again for another three years.

"I wish to recognize my co-authors

"Eugen Muehldorf and I co-authored a book in 1995. I also co-authored several technical papers with Phil Girardi, Juanita Ford, Dave Schall, Angelo Toutsi, and Herb Graham.

"I thank them for their collaboration and help.

"I must thank both John Dadiani and Rosalind Stanson for arranging this party, and John for accommodating my request to give me a gift certificate.

"I always wanted to get a table saw.

"Carpentry is my hobby, and I want to do serious carpentry work when I retire. Thank you very much.

"My last farewell remark is from General Douglas McArthur, quoted from his farewell speech to the Congress, from the 19th-century barrack ballad, on April 19, 1951, "The Old Soldiers Never Die. They just fade away."

"In my case, the old sailor never dies. He just re-enlists as a sailor at ONR."
"Thank you."

After the speech, Bill Demain, who was an ex-Navy chief and a long-time friend of mine, came to me and said:

"John, keep the flag flying on the pole at ONR!"

My tenure at TRW was 32 years. It was by far the longest of my several positions in my 50-year career.

PART FOUR

THE ONR YEARS

(2001–2013)

24

Office of Naval Research (ONR)

THE PROGRAM OFFICER OF THE NAVIGATION
AND TIMEKEEPING PROGRAM

In February 2001, I retired from TRW after 32 years. I was 65 years old but felt that there were a few more years of professional life left in me.

A friend of mine in ONR told me that Dr. Bobby Junker and Dr. Neal Gerr had openings in the Communications and the Navigation Programs. I sent an application to Neal Gerr, who told me:

"John, I received your application

"I am glad that you are interested in the positions Bobby and I have advertised."

"Yes, I am very much interested in the positions."

"I think you are well qualified for both positions."

Two weeks later, Bobby Junker interviewed me at his office:

"John, I have a copy of your book Naval Shipboard Communications Systems. Certainly, we can use your talent in the Communications Program, but I need a strong program officer in the Navigation Program."

"Bobby, thank you. I think I could support you in communications technology. But, maybe it is time for me to move on to a new area."

"Navigation technology is not a new area for you.

"Joe Lawrence told me what you have been working on GPS at the Naval Research Laboratory (NRL)."(see photo 94)

During the interview, Bobby gave me a brief history of the Office of Naval Research.

"John, did you know, during the World War I, Thomas Edison established two important divisions in NRL?"

"I did not know Thomas Edison had his fingers in the pot at NRL."

"Yes, during the war, he apparently advised the U.S. Navy to establish two divisions, Radio and Sound Divisions in NRL.

"Have you seen his bust standing near the main gate of NRL?"

"Yes, I have seen it whenever I passed through the NRL main gate."

"Much later, after the World War II, the Congress enacted a law to establish ONR.

"ONR is a prototype of the research funding organization in the Federal Government like the Defense Advanced Research Project Agency (DARPA).

"Within three city blocks in Arlington, there are four federal research funding organizations: ONR, DARPA, the National Science Foundation (NSF), and the Air Force Office of Scientific Research (AFOSR).

"You heard about the relocation of DARPA by the General Services Administration."

"Yes, I heard about the proposed move of DARPA outside of the beltway." [1]

"Within three city blocks in Ballston, there are four Federal research funding agencies with a total annual budget of over $12 billion. The ONR budget is $2 billion, DARPA $3 billion, AFOSR $2.4 billion, and NSF $5 billion."

At the end of the day, DARPA never moved from Ballston. DARPA built its new headquarters one block from ONR.

My employment at ONR opened a new chapter of the professional career. I asked myself a question, "What does fate have in store for me after I left TRW?" My life was like a voyage on a river. I was afloat, this time being carried by the current of the U.S. Navy. Months later, I received a phone call from Bobby Junker, extending a job offer as the Navigation Program Officer in ONR, with a pay grade of GS-15, Step 10. That meant my pay grade would be at the top of the GS scale, and I would not get a pay raise each year unless the Congress raised the pay grade ceiling.

I had only ten days of break between the retirement from TRW and the start my ONR job. Rahn told me,

"John, you flunked your retirement from TRW miserably. It was not a retirement, but a change of employment."

When I reported to ONR, Bernadette Sterling, the administrative officer of the department, greeted me in the lobby and walked me through corridors of the department on the ninth floor of the old ONR building. Sheila Richardson,

the Program Analyst showied me how to access the ONR financial and technical management systems that were essential for carrying out the day-to-day task of my program.

ONR Organization

When I entered the ONR building in Ballston on my first day, I found it more like a high-tech research institution, not a typical Navy command. In 2001, the leadership of ONR was the Chief of Naval Research, Rear Admiral Jacob Cohen, and Technical Director Dr. Fred Saalfeld. There were six departments of Naval science and technology: aviation, surface sea, undersea, space, C4ISR, and expeditionary warfare for the U.S. Marine Corps. C4ISR stands for Command, Control, Communications, Computers, Intelligence, Surveillance, and Reconnaissance. Bobby Junker's department performed research and development on C4ISR. Before that assignment, Bobby Junker served as the Manager of the Atomic Physics Program at ONR. He initiated the program in laser cooling and trapping of atoms, and interferometric astrometry. (see photo 136)[2]

Bose-Einstein Condensate (BEC) and Laser Cooling

In 1976, one of the principal investigators, whom Bobby Junker sponsored, was Dr. William Phillips of the National Institute of Science and Technology (NIST). Bill Phillips' pioneering work on laser cooling of atoms and BEC earned him the Nobel Prize in 1997, based on the project which Bobby Junker sponsored. The last time Bobby, Bill and I met in a meeting was in August 2012 at the U.S. Naval Observatory (USNO) ceremony to celebrate the Final Operational Capability of the USNO Rb Fountain Atomic Clock.

I mentioned laser cooling and BEC in the previous paragraph. What are they? In 2004, Bill Phillips explained these two physics phenomena at the ONR Distinguished Lectures on "Time, Einstein and the Coolest Stuff." Bobby Junker introduced Bill Phillips at the lecture:

"In 1975, Bill Phillips was a graduate student at MIT working on his doctorate under Professor Dan Kleppner. One day Bill came to ONR and told me that he did not want to become a postdoctoral fellow, but wanted to go directly into research at NIST. At that time, there were a few big electro-optical physics projects in which many researchers were trying to manipulate atoms with light. They were not successful because atoms travel so fast and a laser changes their color accordingly. Bill told me he knew how to manipulate atoms with photons. He would try it the other way around, by trying to change the frequency of light which atoms absorbed and would keep the laser source constant. I thought it was such a neat idea. He did research on it and "Voila," he later won the 1999 Nobel Prize for his work."[3]

Bill Phillips explained laser cooling[4] and BEC. He made an analogy by inflating several balloons with air and then dunking them one by one in liquid nitrogen. As the air inside the balloons cooled, they became smaller, until they became flat, pancake-shaped sheets of rubber. He brought a six-inch diameter Dewar bottle. The bottle was a vacuum flask, which held liquid air for scientific experiments. Each balloon was about six inches across (just under the width of the Dewar bottle), and was collapsed down to be immersed in liquid nitrogen.

Bill Phillips explained that,

"In thermodynamics, there is a relationship between the temperature of molecules and the speed of atoms agitated in a container.

"The temperature of liquid nitrogen, which he used with the balloons, is about 70 degrees-Kelvin.

"By the way, the temperature of atoms by laser cooling is 240 micro-degrees Kelvin, nearly absolute zero, but not quite."

What is BEC?

"Gaseous atoms become liquid, and the corresponding temperature is 70 nano-degrees Kelvin.

"When photons, emanated from the laser, collide with an atom, it emits a particle with its characteristic frequency.

"The frequency shift creates Doppler (or laser) cooling."

What is Doppler cooling?

"Let me tell you a story about "Running a red light signal in the quantum world."

"Let's say you are driving a car and run a red light signal.

"A police officer stops you to tell that you ran the red light at 450 Terra-Hz."

"Officer, there was a Doppler shift in the process. What I saw was a green signal at the frequency of 560 Terra-Hz!"

"Of course, I want to remind readers that the speed of the automobile was fast.

"This imaginary car was traveling at about two-tenths of the speed of light.

"Again, I remind you, this happened in the quantum world.

"Elementary particles become condensates in quantum states when atoms reach extremely cold temperature.

"Satyendra Bose and Albert Einstein theoretically predicted this phenomenon in 1925." Seventy years later, two physicists, Eric Cornell and Carl Wieman, experimentally created this state of matter.

"ONR sponsored Eric Cornell and Carl Wieman, who in 1995 used trapping techniques by optics and magnetism.

"Trapped atoms got packed closer together, and laser-cooled Rubidium (Rb) atoms into condensates, called BEC.

"Another ONR-sponsored physicist was Wolfgang Ketterle, who also experimentally created a large BEC state of matter using sodium atoms."

What is laser cooling?

"It is a techniqueb y which laser beams cool atoms down to near absolute zero, or 10^{-9} (number with nine decimals digits) degrees Kelvin.

"One method invented by Bill Phillips was based on a scientific apparatus called the Zeeman slower, which slows an atom beam from an initial speed on the order of 1,000 meters per second to a final speed of 10 meters per second.

"The corresponding temperature of the initial speed is 300 degrees, Kelvin.

"The temperature of the final speed is 10^{-9} degree-Kelvin.
It is cold physics.

Ultra-Miniature Rb Atomic Clock

During my tenure at ONR, I worked on the development of several atomic clocks using quantum physics. A wall clock uses a pendulum as the time reference, while an atomic clock uses the characteristic resonance frequency of atoms. Each atom absorbs and emits electromagnetic energy at its resonance frequency. The resonance frequency of Rb atoms is 5.6 GHz, which can be harnessed to control the frequency of an atomic clock. Using this physical phenomenon, Kernco developed the Ultra-Miniature Rb Coherent Population Trapping (CPT) Atomic Clock, and Symmetricom developed the Tactical Grade Atomic Clock (TGAC).

Rb Fountain Atomic Clock

A Rb Fountain Atomic Clock uses the motion of a cloud of cold Rb atoms, which resembles that of the water in a pulsed fountain. Hence, it is known as the fountain clock. A popular science demonstration by Bill Phillips was with a balloon as an analogy to the fountain clock. He used a vacuum cleaner with the reversed airflow to exhale air to a balloon; the balloon would shoot up and then begin to descend. The Rb Fountain Atomic Clock uses a similar phenomenon with these BEC atoms.

A cloud of cold Rb atoms is trapped by beams. On the way up and on the way down the cloud passes through a microwave cavity. During the passage of Rb clouds, a microwave detection mechanism is switched on, and the resonance frequency is derived. This resonance frequency is hundred-fold more accurate than that of the Rb CPT Atomic Clock.

Dr. Chris Ekstrom of USNO designed and built the Rb Fountain Atomic Clock, the most accurate operational clock, in 2013. In photograph 105, I was standing next to the Rb Fountain Atomic Clock, which physicists in USNO nicknamed "the Beer Can" Atomic Clock.

GAS-1: MOTHER OF ALL GPS ANTI-JAM ANTENNA

Saddam Hussein called the Gulf War in 1991 the "Mother of all Battles," although it did not go as far as Saddam Hussein envisioned. During the early 1990s, the navigation community called one particular GPS Antenna System-1 (GAS-1) as the "Mother of all GPS Anti-jam antennas," which implied that GAS-1 could mitigate all types of jamming threats. But they laid it on thick. The GAS-1 array antenna was a 14-inch disk-like device. It housed, at most, seven array elements and could null up to six jammers. It turned out that the maximum number of jammers, which could be handled by an array, was the number of the array elements minus one.

What is the reason that one cannot increase the number of array elements?

"The wavelength of a GPS signal is approximately 7.5 inches.

"The separation distance from one array element to the next must be equal to or less than a quarter of the wavelength (1.875 inches).

"Therefore, the 14-inch disk can only hold seven array elements or less.

"If the placement area on a host system is smaller than 14 inches, even fewer elements can be placed." This was one of the technical challenges of the Anti-jam (AJ) antenna design.

"What would happen if more array elements were added to a GAS-1 antenna?

"Such an antenna results in the mutual coupling of signals, which reduces the effectiveness of the anti-jam capability."

GPS EXCOM

In 2001, the Department of the Navy established the Navy GPS Executive Committee (EXCOM) to address emerging electronic threats to GPS. GPS EXCOM gave ONR responsibility to manage the GPS anti-jam program. Dr. Dale Uhler, the Deputy Assistant Secretary of the Navy for Command, Control, Communications, Computers, and Intelligence, chaired GPS EXCOM. He agreed with Rear Admiral Jacob Cohen, CNR, that the Navigation and Timekeeping Program would annually be funded by the Navy budget of $10 million.

ONR committed a block of funds to Navy Warfare Centers, which in turn farmed out their navigation tasks to contractors. In June 2001, I presented to GPS EXCOM an overview of the ONR Navigation and Timekeeping Program, and my plan to undo the block funding of the Navigation and Timekeeping Program from Navy Warfare Centers. Instead of managing projects in two layers, the ONR Program Office would directly manage all navigation programs. Dale Uhler understood our position to evaluate all proposals with the competitive process from the fiscal year 2002.

PROGRAM REVIEW MEETING AT SPAWAR SYSTEMS CENTER (SSC) - SAN DIEGO

I have been to SSC-San Diego a dozen times over the last 30 years. SSC-San Diego is located in Point Loma, on a hilly peninsula that juts out into the Pacific Ocean. In the late afternoon, ocean mist slowly rolls over the mesa and cool the air of the peninsula. In the 1970s, I visited the old Naval Electronics Laboratory, where I worked on SOSUS, the tactical communications network, and the shipboard satellite communications terminal.

In 2001, I went to SSC-San Diego to review ONR-funded projects. The projects were Dean Nathans' High-dielectric Mini-array Anti-jam Antenna task and Dr. Thomas Jones' Ultra-sensitive Electro-optical Accelerometer task. SSC-San Diego's Navigation Department and PMW-156 arranged the meeting for me. Also to this meeting I invited Eddy Emile, the Manager of the GPS User Equipment Branch, the USAF GPS Joint Program Office.

High-dielectric Mini-array Anti-jam Antenna

When I dip a pencil into a cup of water, I see that the image of the pencil bends as the light goes through the media from water to air. When an RF signal passes through the media from ceramic to air, it bends like the image of the pencil. Dean Nathan was working on a *High-dielectric Mini-array Anti-jam Antenna* project. He planned to design, simulate, and build an antenna that had two layers of the ceramic dielectric lens. One lens was placed above antenna elements to bend GPS signal. This technology could be applied to antennas with limited space and thus reduced the footprint of the antenna.

Antenna designers used ceramic lenses to shape RF signal. The lens could focus RF signal, or it could defocus to split energy in different directions. Such lenses could be implemented to shape the three-dimensional propagation of RF signal.

The issuesDean Nathan discussed during the review meeting were the schedule delay and the cost. I recommended he withdraw his task from the SSC-San Diego Simulation Center and hand it over to Dr. Hung Ly of NRL Advanced EW Division. Ly completed the project and published the results in the *Proceedings of the Institute of Navigation Conference – GPS 2002*, Portland, Oregon, in September 2002.[5]

Electro-optical Accelerometer

Dr. Thomas Jones and Dr. Richard Waters of SSC-San Diego developed the Ultra-sensitive Electro-optical Accelerometer using laser and electro-optics technology. At the completion of the project, they brought the equipment to ONR for a demonstration in November 2005. ONR published the following press release on this Optical Accelerometer.[6]

> "This technology project is funded by ONR Code 313 (Dr. John Kim) and is a new approach to measuring the displacement of Micro-Electro-Mechanical Systems (MEMS). The research effort integrated a monolithic optical resonant cavity and a silicon photodiode. This technique was a patent-pending

universal MEMS integrated dual-spring fabrication process. MEMS is the technology of small mechanical devices embedded in an electronic device. The size of MEMS devices is between 0.02 mm and 0.1 mm."

"What Thomas Jones and Richard Waters are trying to do," Kim said, "is to build a smaller Inertial Measurement Unit (IMU) more accurately and more cheaply." One of the key applications of this technology, Kim said, is integrating an inertial navigation system with GPS in such a way that a missile, for example, that has its GPS guidance system jammed in flight could still continue to its target once the inertial system takes effect. A lot of munitions programs rely on IMU for the final targeting if they have lost GPS signal. What has been found is that munitions can miss their targets because the quality of the small units is not very good. So, what we hope to do is bring higher-grade navigation to a smaller package." This technology has been under development for three years by ONR, and it is ready for Advanced Development and Technology insertion."

Program Review Meeting at NAVAIR Warfare Center at Pax River

The Naval aviation community has its warfare center at NAS PAX River, located 50 miles southeast of Washington at Cedar Point, adjacent to the waters of the Chesapeake Bay.

In the 1970's I was in NAS PAX River to conduct calibration of the CV-3332 vocoder onboard P-3C Orion ASW Patrol Aircraft. Dr. Bill Richter and I went to the ASW Patrol Wing Hangar in NAS PAX River to ride a P-3C to NAS Oceana in Norfolk. A vocoder is a device to digitize voice communication. Today, almost all voice communication uses vocoders or voice digitizers.

It was always a pleasure driving in the Southern Maryland countryside, which had many farms, some of which featured a red barn for curing burley tobacco. Today, many of the farms and barns are things of the past, and instead

one finds clusters of vacation homes. The Cedar Point community became the town of Lexington Park, Maryland.

When E-Systems, Inc., finished the first article of the AN/USC-32 SETAD HF radio and the CV-3332 vocoder, I tested the radio and the vocoder with the help of Bill Richter. The vocoder was sensitive to the pitch of propellers and engine noise. We measured noise on both the port and the starboard sides, and the bow and the stern of the P3-C aircraft cabin. To perform the test during the flight, Bill Richter and I went to ASW Patrol Wing at NAS Patuxent River and boarded a P3-C aircraft. (see photo 54) We took off and flew the route following the Patuxent River, along Cedar Point and the western shore of the Chesapeake Bay, then along the Atlantic coast. At various speeds and altitudes, we measured the acoustic response of the vocoder. The radioman on board the aircraft operated the HF radio for us. HF radio intermittently dropped out, and the radio link was interrupted. When this happened, the radioman would pick up a mallet and hit the rack-mounted transmitter-receiver to restore the HF radio. I asked him, "What are you doing?"

"I'm trying to loosen off the rusty bolts."

"All these rusted connections, corroded by salt spray and humid air block the electrical current. I can usually fix them by banging the radio and loosening the joints."

So much for high-tech, I thought, but it worked. After the two-hour flight, we landed at NAS Oceana in Norfolk. Our flight was provided only one-way transportation on P3-C patrol aircraft, and we returned to NAS PAX River, the distance of 200 miles, by taxi in the evening.

In 2002, I went to NAS PAX River to review the GPS Miniature Controlled Radiation Pattern Antenna (M-CRPA) project. Dennis DeCarlo of NAVAIR was managing the ONR project. During my visit, DeCarlo showed me his well-equipped "Facilities for Antenna and RCS Measurements (FARM)," including a full-scale F/A-18 aircraft model, and an anechoic chamber, which provided capabilities for measuring electromagnetic signals without reflection. He could place an F/A-18 aircraft model on a platform, adjustable to any pitch, yaw, or roll. He demonstrated measured and calculated antenna patterns. M-CRPA may have an application to F/A-18 aircraft as a low-observable conformal antenna.[7]

Program Review at the Naval Underwater Warfare Center (NUWC)

The U.S. Navy submarine community also has a warfare center NUWC in Middleton, Rhode Island on Aquidneck Island in Narragansett Bay. The Claiborne Pell Bridge connects the city to the neighboring Conanicut Island across the East Passage of the Narragansett. Ten miles south, there is a New England summer resort, where one can find the famous Newport Mansions.

In 2003, I received a NUWC proposal on GPS anti-jam antenna design for submarines. I received an NUWC proposal to testa nd evaluate a submarine mast-mounted GPS anti-jam antenna. They would study the placement of the selected antenna array in a small space and the cabling of signal and control cables in the mast.

They worked on two types of submarine masts. The first one was the Type 18(I) submarine mast and the second one was the OE-538 multi-function communications mast. The Type 18(I) submarine mast was one of the first hull-penetrating submarine periscopes. OE-538 was a collection of antennas on the submarine mast. One of the antennas on these masts was for the GPS receiver. One must place the GPS antenna of a 4.7-inch diameter on the submarine mast. One could hardly find enough real estate on these masts.

NUWC would use the Submarine Sensor Test Platform (SSTP) Facility in Fisher Island, four miles south of New London, Connecticut in the middle of Long Island Sound. The project was not completed due to a funding shortage.

"Publish or Perish" versus the International Traffic in Arms Regulations (ITAR)

Occasionally, I had to deal with the public release of DoD information generated by the contract work of the Navigation and Timekeeping Program. On the one hand, academic researchers wished for broad dissemination of technical knowledge of their research results as academic researchers must "publish or perish." For technical information developed by universities and industry for basic science research, I recommended to the ONR security department that

the research results be published with minimal restrictions. However, results obtained by applied research and advanced technology development had to pass the test of two government regulations before its publication. One was ITAR, and the other was the Military Critical Technologies List (MCTL). As for the private corporations, they wanted to protect their proprietary information as much as they could.

In 2002, BAE Systems Inc., Green Lawn, Long Island, submitted a proposal to build a GPS Controlled Radiation Pattern Antenna (CRPA). However, ONR raised the issue of ITAR and MCTL as its parent company, BAE Systems PLC, was a U.K. corporation. BAE clarified that BAE Systems, Inc. was an American corporation, and could do business with the Department of Defense through a Special Security Agreement although BAE Systems, Inc. was owned by a foreign entity.

ADVANCED GPS ANTI-JAM ANTENNA PROJECTS

The first time I worked with a GPS receiver was 1985. I received AN/WRN-6 as a government furnished equipment (GFE) from the NAVSEA LCAC Program Office for application to LCAC. Rockwell-Collins built this equipment, with only one channel. Therefore the receiver needed four consecutive signal readings from GPS satellites to determine position and time.

Today, all GPS receivers are able to receive four or more GPS signals simultaneously. Four channels allow the position and time determination much faster than a single-channel receiver. Civilian and military platforms rely on the GPS system to provide accurate position, navigation, and time information. Unfortunately, GPS is susceptible to interference due to its weak signal strength, as GPS signal travels from space to the Earth, the distance of 12,550 miles. Therefore, the Navigation and Timekeeping Program Office performed research on interference mitigation.

In 1992, Bob Van Wechel of L3-Interstate Electric Co. supported my GPS range improvement projects for air combat training at NAS Fallon and Nellis AFB. I knew Bob and his team were well-versed in GPS technology. In 2005, he submitted to ONR a proposal to develop the "Space-Time Adaptive Processing (STAP) for GPS Anti-jam Antennas."

What is STAP for GPS Anti-jam antennas?

"STAP is an antenna electronics algorithm, which could increase the number of jammers.

"For example, if the antenna array is N, it could detect at most (N-1) jammers. "N-1" became known as the constraint length.

"Bob Van Wechel came up with an algorithm on how to increase the constraint length of a GPS anti-jam antenna.

"Until then, the jamming mitigation method was accomplished with spatial antenna arrays.

"He designed an antenna system by adding the temporal information to the GPS antenna." With this antenna arrangement, one can receive signals in two dimensions using an array of spatial antennas and a set of time taps.

"For example, if the number of array elements is 7, the maximum number of jammers detectable by the antenna array is 6.

"By adding three time-taps the maximum number of jammers detectable increases to twenty (or twenty-one minus one). STAP increases the capability to handle more jammers.

"This algorithm was called STAP.

"However, STAP required additional computations to increase the array antenna constraint."

TACTICAL GRADE ATOMIC CLOCKS (TGACs): KERNCO AND SYMMETRICOM ATOMIC CLOCKS

One key research area of my Navigation and Timekeeping Program was the atomic clock. The Navy needed to embeda tactical-grade atomic clock into tactical platforms such as aircraft, ships, weapons, and sonar.

First, I awarded a contract to Kernco to develop a miniature atomic clock. This atomic clock derived the reference frequency from Rb atoms as it changed its states and generated the transition frequency at 5.6 GHz. The light source used in the Rb CPT atomic clock was the vertical-cavity surface-emitting laser (VCSEL), which enabled the miniaturization of atomic clock technology, reducing the form factor of a Rb CPT Atomic Clock down to the volume of 5 cc's.

Next, I awarded another contract to Symmetricom Co. to develop the Tactical Grade Atomic Clock (TGAC), which was designed and built with stringent size, weight, and power (SWaP) requirements. The SWaP for the ONR TGAC was 5 cc's, 50 grams, and 100 milliwatts. To give you an idea of how small TGAC is, SWaP for the Symmetricom 8040C Atomic Clock are 5,000 cubic centimeters, 2,700 grams, and 45 watts. The volume and weight of TGAC must be smaller than the space available in small-diameter munitions, an aircraft cockpit, or a cruise missile. TGAC must meet the power consumption requirements of autonomous underwater vehicles and is also subject to environmental, mechanical, and electrical tests in compliance with military standards. For example, TGAC undergoes "shake-and-bake" (vibration and heat) and five-pound hammer (shock) tests.

PRECISE TIME AND TIME INTERVAL (PTTI)

My interest in timekeeping technology was not only in the atomic clock development, but also in the Precision Time and Time Interval (PTTI). PTTI is one of the DoD scientific disciplines: (1) time transfer, (2) time scaling, and (3) GPS time monitoring.

THE TIME TRANSFER

What is the time transfer?
"I have already mentioned the red wooden ball dropping at noon each day at the Royal Greenwich Observatory.
"That enabled navigators aboard ships in the Greenwich harbor to set their marine chronometers.
"The accuracy of this time transfer was on the order of a tenth of a second.
"Similar to the red ball in Greenwich, there once was a time ball at USNO. It was the first systems enabling USNO to transfer time to ships in the Potomac River.
"In 1844, USNO was located at Twenty-third and E Streets,

NW, near the Foggy Bottom neighborhood, from where the timekeepers on ships in the Potomac River could see the time ball by line-of-sight.

"In 1893, USNO moved to its present location at 3450 Massachusetts Ave., NW. From then on, radio communication replaced the visual transfer.

"You've heard: 'At the tone, the time will be eleven forty and 40 seconds – beep.'

"This is a time service provided by the telephone company.

"Today, NIST sends time information from its WWV radio station to users via audio tones at several HF bands to allow for clock synchronization with the accuracy of 10^{-5} second.

"However, with the advent of GPS technology, USNO transferred its DoD Master Clock time to the GPS Control Segment at the USNO Detachment in Colorado Springs.

"With GPS, the time transfer requirement is more stringent than those I have mentioned above.

"Today, the satellite communications system called Two-Way Satellite Time Transfer (TWSTT) provides the highest accuracy in time dissemination using the C-band geosynchronous satellite connectivity.

"It is not an easy task to transfer time from a clock to another when the accuracy of the master clocks itself is on the order of 10^{-14}."

ONR had two PTTI issues. The first issue was a transfer of time between two fixed locations, which is between USNO and the GPS Control Station; the second issue was a transfer of time between two mobile, tactical platforms like aircraft and ships. TWSTT is a fixed-location, point-to-point time transfer system. GPS sends Universal Coordinated Time (UTC) one pulse-per-second, which is the primary source of time for most tactical platforms. GPS jamming could deny timing information. But tactical platforms need to get timing information from other sources. Son Dinh and Ilya Stevens of SSC-San Diego

proposed an idea to solve this problem. They proposed a capability of transferring GPS-provided one pulse-per-second UTC via an RF link, called the Joint Tactical Information Distribution System (JTIDS) Link-16.

TIME SCALING

The second PTTI issue was time scaling.

What is time scaling?

"I measure the weight of an object by using a scale.

"Likewise, I can measure the time by using the time scale.

"That scale is the U.S. DoD master clock at USNO.

"The DoD master clock consists of an ensemble of atomic clocks, one Hydrogen maser clock, twenty Rb-atomic clocks, and sixty Cesium (Cs) atomic clocks.

"The Hydrogen maser clock provides short-term stability while Rb and Cs atomic clock ensembles provides long-term stability.

"This DoD master clock becomes the time scale."

"Dr. Paul Koppang was in charge of the DOD master clock Enhancement Project at USNO."

GPS TIME MONITORING

There was another team of PTTI researchers, Dr. Ed Powers and Blair Fonville at USNO. ONR tasked them to work on another technical problem in timekeeping of the next generation GPS. DoD would modernize the GPS system, known as GPS Block III Upgrade. The GPS Block III system would include a new atomic clock, which needed occasional monitoring and calibration. Powers and Fonville developed the GPS Block III Timing Monitoring Receiver, which would measure accuracy of the GPS III time signal. Theyd etermined the amount of the correction required to the GPS Block III clock and incorporated this correction data into the GPS Block III Operational Control Segment.

VERTICAL-CAVITY SURFACE-EMITTING LASER (VCSEL)

One morning my telephone lost its tone. A day later, a phone company technician came to repair the line. I was curious about the latest phone technology, which needed fiber optics. First, he found a buried box at the corner of our lawn. There were several optical fiber connections in our neighborhood. He then checked the optical cable connectivity by using light source. He saw no light and confirmed the outage. I asked him, pointing to his light source,

"Is your light source VCSEL?"

"Yes, it is VCSEL. How did you know that it is VCSEL?"

"I also use VCSEL in my job.'

"What is that?"

"Oh, I use it for an atomic clock, not in telecom."

"I see."

What is VCSEL?

"VCSEL is a type of semiconductor lasers.

"You own a computer mouse with a laser; on the bottom side of your mouse, you can see a red light.

"The light is a laser, generated by a VCSEL.

"A laser device is applied to many things, such as a barcode scanner, laser cutting, and laser printing, to name a few.

Why is the laser so ubiquitous in modern high-tech apparatus?

"A common light source like a flashlight emits light incoherently.

"A laser emits light coherently.

"Coherently emitted light is easy to focus.

"Laser light becomes coherent by the process of optical amplification.

"A laser beam stays narrow over a considerable distance. That is called collimation.

"There are several methods for generating a laser beam.

"There are chemical lasers and a semiconductor laser.

"VCSEL is semiconductor laser; it emits a light beam, vertically from the top of a diode. VCSEL revolutionized fiber optic
communications by improving efficiency and increasing data
transmission speed.
"The advantage of VCSEL is cheaper to manufacture in quantity, easier to test, and more efficient than other lasers.
"Also, VCSEL emits high-power laser light in a solid state,
unlike chemical laser. It interfaces better with fiber optic
cables."

Although it had desirable features, the weakness of VCSEL for Naval applications was in the power requirements. For example, underwater sonar would
have a limited power supply. To overcome this weakness, I initiated a project
to develop VCSEL for an underwater application that drains power at a much
slower rate than currently unavailable VCSELs. Professor Kent Choquette of
the University of Illinois had been working with several chip-level VCSEL
devices, which could meet my requirements for underwater applications. I
announced a Small Business Innovation Research (SBIR) project on VCSEL
for atomic clock applications. ONR awarded Kent Choquette an SBIR grant
to develop a low-power VCSEL device.

What is SBIR?
"SBIR is a program to foster technological innovations in the
small business sector.

25

Astronomical, Astrophysical and Radio Observatories

I visited the U.S. Naval Observatory (USNO) in Washington to review my ONR projects performed there and to brief to the newly appointed Oceanographer of the Navy and the Navigator of the Navy when the change of command occurred.

THE U.S. NAVAL OBSERVATORY

In June 2001, Rear Admiral Richard West became Oceanographer of the Navy. I briefed him on the status of the ONR Navigation and Timekeeping Program. In 2007, Rear Admiral (RADM) David Gove became the twentieth Oceanographer and the sixth Navigator of the Navy briefed him on my program While rear admirals, who have assumed the command of the Oceanographer/Navigator of the Navy, rotated their tour of duty every two or three years, a civilian scientist like Dr. Kenneth Johnston (the Scientific Director of USNO) had a tenure of two decades and sustained and maintained the continuity of USNO.

During a briefing on my program, RADM Gove asked technical questions about GPS navigation, atomic clocks, time transfer, inertial, and bathymetric navigation. He had a good grasp of navigation and timekeeping technology and asked me tough questions. When I returned to my office, RADM Gove sent an email to me and CCed the Chief of Naval Research (CNR) RADM Bill Landay. I received a letter with a "BZ," meaning "Well done," in an email. His email was:

The Office of the Oceanographer/Navigator of the Navy

Washington, D.C.
August 6, 2007

Dr. Kim, thank you for an excellent brief this morning. I appreciated your thorough treatment of the subject and enjoyed our discussion. In addition to GPS, I am gratified to see that CNR has so much ongoing navigation work in other areas. I believe this will be very helpful in the future when we need operational flexibility without undue reliance on GPS. I look forward to a continued strong relationship with CNR (Code 312) as N84 refines our vision for Navigation 2030. Thanks again for coming over to USNO to lay out your work. BZ!

RADM Dave Gove
OPNAV N84

I wished the admiral has sent his "Bravo Zulu" by a naval signal, hoisted on a flagpole.

HARVARD-SMITHSONIAN CENTER FOR ASTROPHYSICS (CFA)

A team of Harvard physicists conducted an experiment in which they "stopped" light. A medium like water or glass can slow light; this lag in the speed of light is due to the bending of light rays. Dr. Ron Walsworth was a physicist at the Harvard-Smithsonian Center for Astrophysics, whose team "slowed" and stopped light in a sodium gas medium. The result was that light became invisible. By exciting the second light through the gas media, the Walsworth team could energize the medium to emit a light beam. Ron Walsworth had made headlines by publishing "The Story Behind Stopped Light," in the May 2002 issue of *Optics and Photonics News*, and drew praise from the scientific community.[8]

In 2000-2004, I funded Ron Walsworth to perform research on a hydrogen maser clock. This hydrogen maser clock was similar to that of USNO's. For many years, the highest-performance, field-operable atomic clocks had been Rb and Cs atomic clocks. In contrast, the most stable field-operable microwave frequency source of any type available was the hydrogen maser. However, hydrogen masers were large, cumbersome devices, not suited to installation in vehicles or aircraft. New atomic clocks, called the Double-Bubble Rb Maser atomic clock, proposed by Ron Walsworth had the potential to provide frequency stability comparable to that of the hydrogen maser but in much smaller, field-operable devices.

KITT PEAK NATIONAL OBSERVATORY (KPNO)

Before the 1950s, only astronomy researchers from well-established major universities had access to the best astronomical instruments, while astronomy researchers from smaller universities had limited access. During the Cold War and especially after the launch of Sputnik, the federal government leveled the playing field for these astronomy researchers. The Russian advances in space technology prompted researchers to share scientific resources. In the 1960s, a group of astronomy researchers petitioned the National Science Foundation (NSF) and DoD to build a national observatory. After the approval of the petition, NSF began the search for a site for the new national observatory. From several candidate sites in California, Arizona, and New Mexico, the final location was Kitt Peak in Arizona.

In February 2004, I toured the astronomical observatory at Kitt Peak, which was about 60 miles southeast of Tucson on the Tohono O'odham Indian Reservation. I drove on Arizona State Highway 86 to the observatory, which was at the elevation of 6,875 feet. As I approached Kitt Peak, I could see a dozen buildings with several antenna dishes and observatory domes.

I was interested in the Observatory's large charge-coupled device (CCD) mosaic plate mounted on a telescope.

What is CCD?

"CCD is the same optical component as in a digital camera, which captures images.

"A CCD image sensor converts light into electrons.

"I was interested in optical sensors, mounted on the ONR celestial navigation device developed by Trex Technologies Inc.

"The CCD camera of Trex Laboratory has the optical components of 6,000 x 6,000 pixels or 36 megapixels

"The Kitt Peak Nicholas Mayall telescope has CCDs of 67 megapixels.

"By the way, the average digital camera sensor contains has CCDs of 2 megapixels."

In the afternoon at KPNO, a staff scientist gave us a guided tour of the observatory. We visited only three telescopes out of twenty-five on the observatory. Walking from one building to another in the elevation of 7,000 feet was not so easy. Rahn also had a slight bout of altitude sickness at Kitt Peak. We visited the four-meter glass lens reflector telescope, one of the largest telescopes in the world, named the Nicholas Mayall telescope; it includes 8,192 x 8,192 CCDs or 67 megapixels.

I had been working on a CCD camera with Dr. Mikhail Belenkii of Trex on the ONR Precision Celestial Navigation System (PCNS).

How are astronomy and celestial navigation related?

"Both are concerned with observing stars in the sky for navigation.

"A staff scientist helped us to understand the optical geometry of the CCD camera.

"Two factors of optics are the focal length of the telescope and the CCD size.

"These two factors determine the field of view (FOV).

"For example, when you look through a telescope at an object in the distance, you see only a small view of an object.

"But when you look through a mobile telephone camera viewer, you see a wide view of the scene.

"The KPNO Mayall Telescope operates with a small FOV to obtain the higher resolution for astronomical observation. "On the other hand, PCNS needed wider FOV to capture known visible stars. How does one determine FOV for CCD sensor and the telescope?

"To determine FOV of an imaging device, one needs to determine two things.

"The first is the size of the CCD sensor (D in millimeters), and the second is the focal length of the telescope (Lin inches).

"FOV (in arc-minutes) for the telescope and imaging device is (135.3x D) / L in degrees.

"For example, a Nightscape 8300 CCD camera has a sensor size of 22.5mm (D).

"If you use this camera with an 11-inch Celestron Edge telescope, which gives you a focal length of 110.24 inches and FOV becomes (135.3 x 22.5)/110.24=21.62 arc-minutes.

"A hole punctured with a needle is about 21.62 arc-minutes.

"Suppose you capture an image on the CCD sensor with a 50-million-pixel camera.

"The telescope would capture a large number of detailed imageries of far-away stars."

National Radio Astronomy Observatory (NRAO) in Green Bank, West Virginia

In the highland meadows of Green Bank, West Virginia, a radio astronomy telescope points its large dish straight up to the sky. The diameter of the antenna dish was 300 feet the length of a football field. I first visited Green Bank in 1987. (see photos 123 and 124) NRAO radio astronomers were interested in searching for signs of life in deep space using radio signals. Over several decades, I had visited a dozen astronomical observatories in and outside the U.S. Most of these visits were job-related as a program officer at ONR. NRAO houses the Robert Byrd Green Bank Telescope (GBT), which was a large land-based structure in the Allegheny Mountains. In photograph 124, I am standing

in front of the 300-foot antenna at the National Radio Astronomical Observatory; it attempted to listen to signals from extraterrestrial beings. This region was designated as the National Radio Quiet Zone for Green Bank for NRAO and Sugar Grove for the US Navy.[9]

In 2011, I had an opportunity to revisit Green Bank. I toured the operations control room of NRAO, where a project engineer explained the Super-Heterodyne Receiver (SHR).

What is SHR?

"SHR is like an ordinary commercial AM radio, except the carrier frequency is not in the medium frequency band of 535 KHz to 1,700 KHz, but in the frequency band of 1 GHz to 10 GHz.

"Green Bank SHR is a one-of-a-kind receiver designed and constructed by NRAO engineers at the observatory. (see photo 113)

"Signals of this type of radio can carry information to galactic space and could convert signals of extraterrestrial beings if, indeed, there are any intelligent creatures in the universe."

Once, my son Doug asked me a question on extraterrestrial beings communicating with us:

"Dad, why did the research team choose frequencies between 1 GHz and 10 GHz?"

"Well, this frequency band is known to be a quiet "microwave window" for deep space radio transmission.

"Below the 1 GHz band, space is flooded with a large amount of background noise. Above the 10 GHz band, the Earth's atmosphere and presumably the atmosphere of other Earth-like planets absorb broad ranges of radio frequencies."

"Dad, humans are trying to listen to extraterrestrial communication. But what messages are we sending to intelligent extraterrestrial beings?"

"Well, two messages were already sent some years ago.

"The first message contained universal facts of physical and biological sciences, which intelligent extraterrestrial beings might understand.

"When I was working at TRW, in 1973, the company built the Pioneer-10 spacecraft for NASA, which was designed to escape the solar system for the first time in human history.

"Professors Frank Drake and Carl Sagan of Cornell University designed the message for Communication with Extraterrestrial Intelligence (CETI) on a plaque known as the Pioneer plaque.[10]

"You probably have seen it. It showed male and female human figures, the profile of the spacecraft, and information about the origin of the spacecraft (the relative positions of the solar system to galactic stars)."

"Yes, I saw it."

"O.K. That was the first message."

"Then, there was the second message.

"In 1974, the Arecibo Observatory in Puerto Rico sent a radio frequency message, also designed by Frank Drake and Carl Sagan. They called it the Arecibo Message.

"The Arecibo message also contained universal facts from the physical and biological sciences.

"In experimenting with CETI, they tried to send heuristic information about the subject of biology.

"The CETI message was concerned mainly information about DNA and its structure, the atomic number of hydrogen, carbon, nitrogen, oxygen, and phosphorus, which make up of DNA, the formula for sugars, the types of nucleotides in DNA, and other DNA-related information.

"From the CETI and Arecibo projects, Carl Sagan told us, 'Somewhere, something incredible is waiting to be known.' Doug, I think the law of probability favors Frank Drake and Carl Sagan to achieve the goals of the CETI- and Arecibo-like project to actually communicate with extraterrestrial intelligent life."

"Dad, why do you think that they may succeed?"

"O.K. The number of stars is incredibly large, as Dave Kornreich of Cornell University used a very rough estimate of 10 trillion galaxies in the universe.

"Multiplying that by 100 billion (the number of stars in the Milky Way's) results in a large number (1 with 24 zeros after it.)

"And so, there are many opportunities for life and intelligence in the universe.

"I think the dice are loaded in favor of Drake and Sagan."

26

Personal Miscellany IV

WILLIAM'S WEDDING

My family went to the 2001 Legg-Mason Tennis tournament in Rock Creek Park in Washington to watch my nephew, Alex Kim, play in the second round of the tournament. Before the match started, we were pleasantly surprised by what William told us. He introduced to us his girlfriend Juli, whom William had met at KUMC in McLean. Juli had come from Los Angeles a year earlier and was a lawyer in the Office of Chief Counsel at the Internal Revenue Service. They were engaged in the following year. (see photo 111)

William and Juli decided to tie the nuptial knot the following spring. One day in the early spring, Rahn and I went to buy a wedding gift chest (*hahm*) in New York City. We drove to Manhattan and went to a Korean wedding gift store at 32nd Street and Fifth Avenue. We found the store but had to pay $30 for parking in midtown Manhattan.

"Hello, I called you yesterday about a Korean *hahm*."

"Yes, I will show it to you. This is the one."

"Well, is this the largest chest in your store?"

"Yes."

"This is more like a jewelry box, not a *hahm*."

"I am sorry. This is the biggest one we have. Maybe you should try Korean gift shops in Flushing."

So, we hopped into our car and crossed the city, and drove through the Queens Midtown Tunnel to Flushing, where we found several Korean gift shops. To our disappointment, they did not have a larger *hahm* either. They suggested another shop in Palisade Park in New Jersey. From Flushing, we crossed the George Washington Bridge, and to Palisade Park.

"Hello, we are looking for a wedding gift chest, *hahm*."

"Yes, we have several of them."

"Rahn, is this the right size?"

"Yes, John, this will do."

It was quite a shopping expedition. We returned to McLean in the late evening.

On May 24, 2002, we held the traditional Korean pre-wedding ceremony (*pae-baek*), at our house with family members and friends. Ted Ahn, Jack Quarles, John Riedy, and Tony Lee performed the ritual of delivering our *hahm* to the Ro family. The next day, on May 25, 2002, Pastors James Sprouse and J. P. Hong conducted the wedding ceremony at Trinity UMC in McLean. We held the reception at the Westfield Marriott Hotel in Chantilly. Jack Quarles delivered his best man's speech:

> "William has had a steady job at Orbital Sciences Corporation since 1980. He still maintains his friendships with his junior and senior high school classmates. I know Will very well as we shared a rented townhouse in Ballston for several years. Often, Will and I had bull sessions about girls and ladies. We advised each other on 'what to do and not.' Last spring, I started to notice he was going to the Korean Methodist Church more often. One day, Will told me he found a girl at the Korean Methodist Church, to whom he might propose marriage. Later, when I have met Juli, I knew she was the right girl for him. Juli, Will is a solid guy, and he is all yours now." (see photo 112)

At the reception, I made the following after-dinner speech.

> "I am honored to have all of you here tonight to celebrate the marriage of Juli and Will. First of all, I would like to express my gratitude to Samuel Ro, the proverbial father of the bride, who made this wonderful party possible. He has the tough job tonight as he is the one who has to foot the bill for this reception. But let me assure you Mr. & Mrs. Ro, it is worth

I own an Asian watercolor on rice paper painting, Painting on the theme of a Tang poem of Cen Shen's - The coming winter as birds fly south, *by No-Soo Park, c. 1963. The celebrated Eighth Century poet, Cen Shen, write his poem on the frontier garrison along the silk road of the China's western region, where he was a magistrate and military commander.*

87

An oil on canvas painting, Cityscape in the snow, *by Ju-Yeong Lee, c. 1970.*

88

An Asian watercolor on rice paper painting, A snow-covered thatched-roof house, *by Hwa-Gyeong Kim, c. 1969. Hwa-Gyeong Kim (1922-1979) taught Asian watercolor painting at Sejong University, Seoul. He painted Korean farmhouse with a thatched roof, using the brush with black and pastel color inks.*

89

I also own an etching print, The Harvest Moon, *by Yoong Bae, c. 1964. This print was a four color (black, blue, cold, and red) etching intaglio, made on zinc plates. I saw another similar etching print of Yoong Bae, titled* Meditation, *exhibited in the Asian Art Museum of San Francisco, in which I saw similar techniques as used in* Autumn Harvest Moon.

90

Dr. Eugen Muehldorf and I were editing the manuscript of Naval Shipboard Communications Systems, *in 1994.*

91

My portrait in McLean, in 1995.

92

I served as a National Judge of the Mathcounts Competition, Shoreham-Americana Hotel, Washington in 2000. Mathcounts is a mathematics version of the spelling bee competition.

Doug and I were standing next to the stately bronze "Princeton tiger" guarding the entrance of the University's landmark Nassau Hall in 1992.

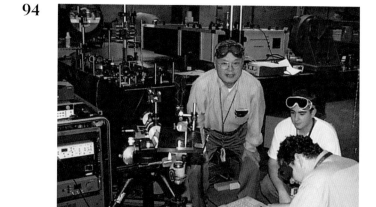

I was working with NRL engineers at the Optics Laboratory of NRL Advanced Electronic Warfare Directorate in 1999. We wore an optical goggle for protecting the eyes from the laser beam.

95

Rahn and I were at my TRW retirement party, held in TRW Fairlakes Building. Many colleagues came. (From left) Jack Dreyfus (2nd), Richard King (3rd), John Gormally (4th), Tom Curry (6th), and Laura Felder (8th), in Feb. 15, 2001.

96

At my retirement party. (From left) Dr. Tom Curry (former Deputy Assistant Secretary of the Navy for Command, Control, and Communications), and (right) Dr. George Donohue (Associate Administrator for Research and Acquisition of the FAA) in Feb. 2001.

97

Commander Earl Eckert, US Navy (ret.) and I at my retirement party in February 2001.

98

At my retirement party. (From left) Dr. Al Schuler of Aerospace Corporation, and Dr. Eugene Kaiser of DISA in Feb. 2001.

Cutting my birthday cake on my 60th birthday at the McLean Hilton Hotel, June 15, 1995. (From left) Rahn, Doug, William, I, and Janet.

Jan Gregor, the Manager of TRW-Benesov Operations, and I were standing in front of the TRW Automotive Electronics Factory in Benesov, the Czech Republic, c. 1997. Jan Gregor told me he hoisted the American flag in my honor, along with the flag of the Czech Republic.

101

Jan Gregor and I were standing in a clean room of the Automotive Electronics Factory of TRW-Benesov Operations, the Czech Republic in 1997.

102

Doug and I were standing on the Bridge of Sighs in Venice in 2000.

103

I found Basho's celebrated poem on the Milky Way *on the wall of a building in Leiden, the Netherlands.*

104

I sang the song Wooden Bell, *and kept the tempo with a wooden bell at the Song-A Literature Meeting. I think I received grades of "F" for my performance and "B-minus" for the effort, at Auditorium of Northern Illinois University, Chicago in 2006.*

105

I was inspecting the USNO Fountain Clock No. 1, designed and developed by Dr. Chris Ekstrom in 2012. This atomic clock was known as the "beer can" fountain clock.

106

Dr. Chris Ekstrom and I were discussing the USNO Fountain Clock No. 1 at the machine shop of the USNO in 2012.

107

I with Dr. Bill Stachnik, who was my senior staff member at ONR. He was Program Officer of Laser/ Optical Science at ONR-Boston in 1988-1995.

Rahn and I attended the Four-Nation Navigation Conference Dinner hosted by the U.K. MoD at the Royal Air Force Club in 2005.

At the Royal Air Force Club, London. (From left) I, Eddy Emile of USAF GPS Wing, and Paul Olson of the U.S. Army Communications and Electronics Command in 2005.

110

Rahn and I at the Royal Air Force Club in 2005.

111

Juli and William's engagement party in Alexandria in 2001. (From left) Pastor James Sprouse, Rahn Kim, William Kim, Juli Ro, and I.

Our family photograph at William and Juli Ro Kim's wedding at Trinity United Methodist Church, McLean in 2002.

This photo was taken during my visit to my brother Moon-Kyu Kim's office at Whitman School of Management, Syracuse University in 2006. He received his MBA in 1971, and Ph.D. in Finance in 1974, both from the University of Illinois at Urbana-Champaign. He became Professor of Finance in 1986 and served as Chairman of the Finance Department, Syracuse University.

We visited my sister, Kyung-sook's house in Tucson, Arizona in 2004. (From left) My brother-in-law Dr. Ted Won, and Kyung-Sook. Ted is a materials science engineer, and Kyung Sook is a registered pharmacist.

115

Rahn at her office in the Fairfax County Government on April 3, 1995. She was a financial analyst in the Public Works Department.

116

I made this deacon's bench using the cherry and ash wood, in 2006. I designed this bench with a long seat like a single span bridge. To support the strain of the single span, I used 23 truss-like back-boards using the ash dowels. Ash is strong and absorbs shocks without splintering.

the effort. Six years ago I was also a father of the bride. Let me tell you the fruits of that effort. We now have two beautiful grandchildren, Keaton and Katie.

"At this time, I would like to introduce my family. The one who traveled farthest is from Hawaii, my nephew, Dr. David Kim, who teaches OB-GYN at the University of Hawaii. From the San Francisco Bay Area, my brother-in-law, Dr. Bill Chu, a physicist, and his wife, In-soo, their daughter Jean and her husband, Doug Dalton. From Chicago, my sister-in-law, Dr. Tong-he Koh, a psychologist. From Boston, my wife's nephew, Pastor Weon-yeol Chu. My brother, Professor Moon-kyu Kim, who teaches Economics at Syracuse University, and his wife, Jung-hi and their son, Peter. From Baltimore, my wife's cousin, Young-sun, and her husband, Dr. Tae-young Lee, an economist, and their two sons, Mike, and Kenny. From Potomac, my brother, Dong-kyu Kim, an architect, and his wife, Ki-nam, and their daughter, Julia, and son Alex Kim.

"And of course, my immediate family, our daughter Dr. Janet Lee, an electrical engineer, my son-in-law Tony Lee, an attorney, and our youngest son, Douglas, a biologist, doing his post-doc work at Harvard Medical School.

"Thank you, and enjoy the party."

DOUG AT PRINCETON UNIVERSITY AND THE UNIVERSITY OF WASHINGTON

Our son Doug enrolled at Princeton University, and during his freshman and sophomore years, he stayed at Rockefeller College-Holder Hall. In the summer of 1993, Doug went to Paris, where he did a two-week long research project on Medieval France in the Cluny Museum in Paris for his French Literature course. Doug submitted his research paper to his professor, Andre Maman, who served as a senator for French citizens living abroad. (see photo 93)

At the end of his sophomore year at Princeton, he applied for a summer research internship at Jackson Laboratory, Bar Harbor, Maine, and he was one of forty interns selected from two-hundred applicants. Dr. John Schimenti was his supervisor at the Jackson Lab. Doug took some biology courses at Princeton University, and his advisor was Lee Silver, Professor of Molecular Biology. Rahn, Doug, and I drove to Bar Harbor. Nearby was Acadia National Park, a beautiful park along the rugged coast of Maine. The Jackson Laboratory was a research institution well-known for its pure strain mice suitable for genetic research. The Laboratory had two million mice, which they distributed to all over the World.

In his junior year, he stayed at Edwards Hall on the fourth floor, to which Rahn and I had to climb up many flights of stairs to get to his room. We were concerned about Doug's health when he became a vegetarian, and prepared all his meals at his dormitory. Doug looked pale. In his senior year, he joined Quadrangle Club, an eating club, where he had a more balanced diet.

When he graduated from Princeton University, Doug entered the University of Washington for his graduate study. During our visit to Seattle, we invited his academic advisor, Professor Richard Palmiter, to dinner at Nishino, a Japanese restaurant in Seattle. "Dad, Richard hates small talk," Doug warned me, and I expected dinner to be not too long. A waitress served us a jug of Japanese rice wine, cooled in a bamboo bottle. The bamboo bottle was wet as it was cooled in ice water. It was raining outside as usual in Seattle. We talked about sonar devices, and their effects on dolphins and whales. Our small talk lasted more than two hours. Later, I asked Doug:

"Why did you tell me that Richard dislikes small talk?"

"Dad, sonar devices, and the environmental protection were not small talk."

Doug's research topic, *Dopamine, and Adenopine Receptor Function in Adult and Developing Dopamine-Deficient Mice,* was about the dopamine and its treatment of Parkinson's diseases. In 2005, Doug received his Ph.D. in Molecular and Cellular Biology and became a post-doctoral fellow at the Harvard Medical Center-Connie Cepko Laboratory. He then became a post-doc fellow at the National Institutes of Health, Bethesda, Maryland. In 2010, he moved to the Howard Hughes Medical Institute (HHMI) at the Janelia Research Campus as a Project Manager. The Cepko Laboratory and the NIH Laboratory both used mice for their experiments. When I entered the Janelia facility, there I saw some flies, which escaped from their container and were flying around in the middle of the room.

One of Doug's research projects was the development of imaging technology for neuronal activity by using ultrasensitive fluorescent proteins. He published the research results in "Ultrasensitive Calcium Sensors Shine New Light on Neuron Activity" in the journal *Nature*.[11] Then in July 2018, after 8 years of employment at HHMI, he moved to NIH, where he became the Health Scientist Administrator/Program Officer, the Office of Technology Development & Coordination at the National Institute of Mental Health, NIH.

27

Travel - Istanbul, Melbourne, and London

PASSAGE TO ISTANBUL

The Istanbul morning started with a call to prayer (Adhan) by the muezzin, chanting mournfully from the minaret using a public announcement system. It broke the tranquility of the Istanbul morning.

"Allahu Akbar – Ash-hadu an-la ilaha illa,"
Or, in English;
"God is greatest - I bear witness that there is no god except God."

After a couple of days, my ears were able to filter the Morning Prayer sound out, and it did not wake me up in the morning. As a Christian, I am accustomed to the liturgic music and hymns of the Church. But I find the Adhan chanting peaceful and beautiful music.

In October 2002, I traveled to Istanbul, Turkey, to attend the navigation symposium, sponsored by the NATO Research and Technology Agency (RTA). Although Istanbul was a safe place to travel, I was still apprehensive about security. As we left the airport by taxi to go to our hotel, a huge crowdof people was demonstrating in the traffic circle of the airport. The taxi driver told me that it was a political demonstration and nothing serious. I checked in to the Akgun Hotel, where all persons entering the hotel must go through a metal detector. The metal detector and the security measures were a comforting thought.

NATO NAVIGATION SYMPOSIUM

Professor Jacques Vanier of the University of Montreal, Dr. Marty Levine of Kernco, and I co-authored a paper, titled "Recent advances in atomic clock development: Rb CPT Atomic Clock research," and we presented it at the symposium.[12] We explained basic physics involved in the implementation of an atomic clock and reported on the progress made in the development of a working unit based on the new CPT approach, as it opened the way in the search for size and weight reduction, and better frequency stability as compared to the existing atomic clock. Our paper drew much attention from conference attendee, especially researchers from France, Germany, and the U.K.

Charles Falchetti and Barry Tanju of the SPAWAR Systems Center in San Diego (SSC-SD) and I presented another paper, "the GPS/Link-16 Integration."[13] We explained how the GPS system could take advantage of Link-16, used widely in the U.S. and NATO tactical data network, thereby improving navigational accuracy. The results showed that the integrated GPS/Link-16 system could provide: (1) high accuracy navigation solutions for platforms in hostile electronic warfare environments, (2) improved situational awareness through the enhanced Link-16 network, and (3) time distribution by the Link-16 network.

THE BLACK SEA, MOSQUES, AND THE BAZAAR

In the evening, the Turkish Ministry of Defense invited the conference officials to a banquet held on the cruise ship *Semiramis*. The cruise ship sailed through the Bosporus Strait toward the Black Sea. Brightly lit mansions lined both shores of the Strait. The distance we cruised was about 20 miles.

During a break at the symposium, Rahn and I toured the Blue Mosque, which was covered with blue tiles. Its domes were made of multiple, cascading domes. Another famous site was the Hagia Sophia,[14] now a museum, and originally a Christian basilica with a mosaic of the Virgin Mary and the Child Jesus. It was converted to a mosque after the Ottoman conquest. The altar of the Basilica faces due south, but the mosque mihrab (a niche indicating the direction of Mecca) faces slightly off to the south. Inside the mosque are a soar-

ing dome, which gave a sense of vast space and a calming effect. (see photo 119)

In the afternoon, we took a bus to the Asian side of Turkey by crossing the Bosporus Strait, to tour the legendary town of Uskudar. During the Korean War, a Turkish regiment was stationed near our high school in Pusan, and the traditional Turkish folk song about Uskudar became popular. That evening, the ONR team went to the Kumkapi district for dinner. The menu consisted of typical Turkish dishes, lamb shish kabobs, fish grilled over an open fire, and Baklava for dessert. During dinner, three musicians approached our table to sing the Turkish song Uskudar. I knew the tune and the lyrics in Korean. When I joined them, they were encouraged by my singing. We all enjoyed the music and food. The next day we toured the Topkapi Palace in Old Istanbul. We saw the museum, where art collections were exhibited; the harem with many apartments where women of the Sultans lived; the divan where viziers met; and the barracks where the Sultan's own guard Janissaries were quartered.

The next morning, the ONR team went to Bursa by Dolmush (a shared minibus). Bursa was the first capital of the Ottoman Empire. Dolmush crossed the Sea of Marmara on the Istanbul-Yalova Ferry. The captain of the ferry allowed us to enter the pilot room to see how the ferry maneuvered the busy waterway in the inland sea. At Bursa, we ate lunch at the Kebab of Alexander the Great. The great name did not translate to great food. Bursa's most famous monument was the Green Mosque, where we washed the dust off our hands and face at the ablution (washing) fountain and sat on the broad stone steps of the mosque.

In the evening, we returned to our hotel and asked the hotel concierge to recommend us a restaurant. He called a free taxi, which dropped us at the Galata Tower. The Galata Tower served us excellent food and showed us Middle Eastern belly dancing for entertainment.

Down Under in Australia

We traveled to Melbourne, Australia, to attend the 2003 International Conference on Satellite Navigation Technology. During the long flight, I saw the Southern Cross through the airplane porthole; it looked like a cross to me, but some sees a woman's face in the Southern Cross.

We had trouble adjusting to the Australian way of the metric system, driving on the left side of the road, the season (the winter in July), the currency rate, and the time difference. I noticed that the solar panels on the roof were facing north.

One morning, Rahn and I drove a rental car to the edge of Australian bush land, where we found a winery. It was open but serving no wine as it was the winter season in July. In the vineyard, I saw large, colorful Australian parrots, called Crimson Rosella, flying around. We saw several buildings with the architectural style of Australian bush land houses. There were tall eucalyptus trees all around a farm. We bought several travel blankets with a red and black Scottish tartan pattern that was made with pure, high-quality Australian wool. As I was driving along a country road, a herd of sheep crossed it. A shepherd with a red flag jumped out of his pickup truck to stop the cars in both directions. His sheepdog was riding in the back of the pickup truck, not nipping at the heels of sheep. Sheep had the right of way.

International Satellite Navigation Technology Symposium

At the session on Integrated Navigation Systems, Dave Lewis of Raytheon and I presented the technical paper on "MEMS IMU and Temperature Controlled Crystal Oscillator (TCXO) Effect on Ultra-Tightly-Coupled (UTC) GPS-IMU Tracking Performance."[15] The idea of using an integrated GSP and IMU receiver was not a new one. In 2001, Tony Abbott of Aerospace Corp. published a technical paper on "GPS and IMU Ultra-Tight Integration."[16] He showed that an ultra-tightly-coupled GPS receiver with IMU would provide a significant improvement to navigate if GPS was disabled due to jamming.

However, Abbot's implementation was impractical, as IMU was cost prohibitive. Dave Lewis and I developed the UTC-GPS Navigation System by

using low-cost MEMS-based IMU and TCXO, which provided an excellent dead reckoning during the absence of GPS signal due to jamming. We proved that such an implementation could deliver anti-jam capability and reduce the cost of IMU augmentation. Our UTC, GPS, and INS could provide valuable weapons guidance in the GPS-denied environment. We applied this technology to Raytheon's Paveway-2 missile, which was one of the preferred weapons for the U.K. during the first Iraq War (the Operation Desert Storm).

In the previous evening, I received a phone call from the conference program chair, Professor Kurt Kubick of the University of Queensland, asking me if I could chair the session on "GPS Integrity & Vulnerability Issues." Conference organizers did not appoint all session chairs ahead of time. Instead, they selected an appropriate person, who was a participating author, to chair the session. Authors of technical papers included in the GPS Integrity & Vulnerability session were mainly from the U.S. DoD and its contractors. The program chair was looking for an official of U.S. DoD as the session chair. I accepted his invitation. There were five papers in the session. They included "Threat flow in the GPS integrity machine" by Professor Per Enge, Stanford University; "Critical considerations in addressing geo-location of interference sources" by Joseph Lortie, Overlook Systems Technologies, Inc.; and "Accuracy augmentation systems for surface vehicles" by Captain Curtis Dubay, Commanding Officer of the U.S. Coast Guard Navigation Center. I introduced Professor Enge:

> "It is my pleasure to introduce Professor Enge. He will discuss two systems of the "Free Flight" program, namely the Local Area Augmentation System and the Wide Area Augmentation System. Professor Enge has studied GPS threats, the flight safety, and overall system efficiency. Pilots want to land and take off their aircraft as quickly as possible at a busy airport to economize fuel. That will be the challenge of the Free Flight program."

In the evening, we went to the conference dinner banquet held at 55-story Rialto Towers. Kurt Kubick invited Rahn and me to the head table. The Rialto Towers banquet hall was a room with a view, as it was the tallest building in Melbourne. After the banquet, we walked back to the hotel in the chilly night

with Dr. Don Sinnot, Chairman of the Australian GNSS Coordinating Committee, and Kurt Kubick and his wife.

The next day we toured the Old Melbourne Observatory, a tour arranged by the Australian GPS Society. The star map of the Southern Hemisphere was compiled in 1887. The observatory was essential to making of the star map. For the first time, the star map project built a revised map of stars using photography, which was new technology. (see photo 125)

LONDON – THE MOD MEETING OF FOUR-NATION NAVIGATION WARFARE

I went to London to attend the 2005 Four-Nation Navigation Warfare (NAVWAR) meeting, held at the Ministry of Defense (MOD) in White Hall, London. The four nations were Australia, Canada, the U.K., and the U.S. The head of each nation's delegation was to be an Army or an Air Force bird colonel, or a Navy, four-striper captain. The country delegations told the NAVWAR committee that their defense forces were much smaller than those of the U.S., so there were not enough colonels and captains to spare, and it was proposed that the head of delegations should be a Lieutenant Colonel or a Navy Commander. The standing defense forces of the four nations were 1,380,000 (U.S.), 152,000 (the U.K.), 64,000 (Canada), and 58,000 (Australia). The annual defense budgets were $611 billion (the U.S.), $152 billion (the U.K.), $24 billion (Australia), and $15 billion (Canada).

I presented an overview, and the current status of the ONR Navigation and Timekeeping Program, which was structured to provide the scientific and technological research and to maintain maritime superiority of the U.S. Navy to rule the waves. I explained the portfolio of the ONR program in GPS anti-jam, atomic clock and time transfer, and non-GPS navigation. I told them that my Navigation and Timekeeping Program's annual budget was $10 million. They commented that my budget was as big as all of their combined R&D budgets. The situation looked like "one giant and three dwarfs," but not really. If you compare their budgets to the percentage to their GDPs, they carry their own weight.

Reception and Dinner at the Royal Air Force Club

The next day, the MoD host invited us to the Royal Air Force Club in the Mayfair District. We were welcomed by the RAF Club staff and served wine at the Churchill Bar. When Eddy Emile and Paul Olson arrived, we looked around the club, which included the Running Horse Tavern. Four of us enjoyed a relaxed pre-banquet drink. At the entrance foyer, we saw photographs of the Duke of York (later King George VI) and Princess Anne. I read a plaque on the entry of the club that the Duke of York and Princess Anne were the patrons and patronesses of the RAF Club. After a glass of sherry in the drawing room, we went into the big boardroom, where they seated us at a round table. Rahn and I sat with colleagues and shared jovial conversations. (see photos 108, 109, and 110)

Cambridge University

On Friday morning, Rahn and I went to King's Cross Railroad Station to catch a train to Cambridge. We were surprised that the train was almost empty on the way to Cambridge, but on the way back the train was jam-packed, with students and Cambridge dons returning to London for the weekend. We wished to visit the Cavendish Laboratory in Free School Lane.[17] On the wall of the building, there was a slate plaque commemorating the first 100 years of the Cavendish Laboratory. In 1874, the founding Professor of Physics was James Clerk Maxwell. We got permission to tour the laboratory and entered the lecture auditorium, where old physics instruments were still on display. An old lift (elevator) was still in use with a scissor gate. We also visited the New Cavendish Laboratory at Mott Building in West Cambridge, built in 1975. Today in this building, scientists in physics, chemistry, biology, and other disciplines meet and solve scientific problems. James Watson and Francis Crick discovered the famous DNA double helix in the Cavendish Laboratory.

28

Non-GPS Navigation Projects

GPS provides navigation to various military and civilian platforms accurately and economically. Or, that was what we thought in the beginning. But GPS became vulnerable to jamming. It became necessary for the Navy navigation community to find backup or alternative navigation methods, instead of relying solely on GPS-based navigation. I solicited the navigation community for ideas based on non-GPS, physics-based navigation technologies such as the bathymetry, gravity, inertial, and celestial.

BATHYMETRIC NAVIGATION

A backup navigation device suitable for submarines could be bathymetric navigation. Marvin May of Penn State University-Applied Research Laboratory (PSU-ARL) proposed to develop the Geophysical Low Observable Bathymetric Enhancement (GLOBE) device, which could become an underwater navigation aid for submarines. He used AN/BQN-17 sonar to make a bathymetric map in an operating area. GLOBE then performed pattern recognition on the bathymetric map.

I occasionally visited the PSU-ARL Navigation Research and Development Center (NRDC) in Warminster, Pennsylvania. The facility was part of the Naval Air Development Center (NADC)-Johnsville. The Navy closed NADC-Johnsville as part of the 1996 Base Relocation and Closure (BRAC) program. PSU-ARL received the ownership of the navigation-related laboratory from the Navy. NRDC was a large concrete, domed building. The12 test piers were attached directly to the bedrock of the Pennsylvania Allegheny Mountains. These test piers were isolated from the domed building to reduce

the vibration.[18] Dr. Terry Roszhart of ARL tested the ONR-sponsored MEMS gyroscope. Herb Seligman, the Director of NRDC, once told me :

> "The NRDC inertial and gyroscope test facility is a national asset. It is the only building of its kind, built from the ground up for the purpose of navigational research and testing." (see photo 134)

Adaptive Bathymetric Estimator

Another bathymetric navigation project I worked on was the Adaptive Bathymetric Estimator (ABE) for submarine navigation. Dr. Dave Cousins of BBN Technologies, Newport, Rhode Island, proposed the ABE project in response the 2003 Navigation BAA, which could improve sonar bathymetry measurements. Sound travels in straight lines in the water if there is no temperature gradient. However, the temperature of the shallow sea water is warmer than that of the deep sea water, which results in the sound traveling on a curved line, the amount of which is called the Sound Velocity Profile (SVP). Dave Cousins developed an algorithm to predict and quantify SVP by using HF sonar.

The Navy Oceanographic Office collects, compiles, and distributes this SVP data to the fleet, as part of the Anti-Submarine Warfare Environment Prediction System. The time required to disseminate the SVP data is in the order of several months. Dave Cousins developed a method to construct SVP in near-real time by using a Kalman filter to predict error and to correct the expected value.

Dave Cousins applied a mapping method called Precision Underwater Mapping (PUMA) to his bathymetric navigation project. The University of Texas Applied Research Laboratory developed PUMA, which made maps of underwater objects like mines by using HF sonar and provided high-resolution imagery. Cousins developed Simultaneous Localization and Mapping (SLAM) using this sonar device.

I have introduced two terminologies, PUMA, and SLAM.

What is PUMA?

> "PUMA is a mapping system mounted on a submarine by using AN/BQQ-10, which is HF sonar.
>
> "PUMA looks forward over the submarine to perform imaging of the ocean bottom in front of the submarine, which identifies the location of mine-like objects."

What is SLAM?

> "SLAM is a method of making the map without previous knowledge and determining its position while map-making is underway.
>
> "ONR SLAM is planned to be applied to submarines and unmanned underwater vehicles."

SONAR-AIDED INERTIAL NAVIGATION TECHNOLOGY (SAINT)

During my 12-year tenure at ONR, I sponsored two doctoral students. They were Dave Cousins and Barry Tanju. Cousins was a doctoral candidate at the University of Rhode Island (URI). He used the results of the SAINT project as partial fulfillment of the doctoral degree requirement in the Ocean Engineering Department of URI. The title of his dissertation was *Model-Based Environmentally Adaptive Sonar for Bathymetry and Obstacle Avoidance*. Dave Cousins received his doctorate in 2006

Dave Cousins applied the Kalman filter method in his SAINT system, based on the ONR-sponsored project.

What is the Kalman filter?

> The dynamic behavior of a natural system is governed by a rule. But the natural system often is subject to a perturbation, or an erratic behavior. A Kalman filter makes prediction about what the system will do next, when perturbed, based on the past behavior. A Kalman filter predicts the immediate future behavior of a dynamic system if the system does not behave

as predicted. The Kalman filter estimates what will happen, and corrects the prediction in the next step.

PRECISE AT-SEA SHIP INDOOR-OUTDOOR NAVIGATION (PASSION) PROJECT

Barry Tanju was a doctoral candidate at George Washington University (GWU). He used the results of the ONR-sponsored project, "the Precise At-Sea Ship Indoor-Outdoor Navigation (PASSION)," as partial fulfillment of his doctoral research at GWU. The PASSION project developed the wireless position tracking system aboard the aircraft carrier George H. W. Bush, CVN-77. The PASSION system was able to locate and track ships' personnel as well as high-value assets.

I worked with Barry Tanju of SPAWAR to develop the PASSION system aboard CVN-77, who told me about the need for personal navigation aboard aircraft carriers. The proposed system could solve the deficiency identified in the 1996 Naval Research Advisory Committee (NRAC) study.[19]

"The ability to remotely and reliably determine the real-time status of the ship and crew must be expanded far beyond the current capability. In virtually any damage control scenario, knowledge of the location and status of crew members is essential." The committee also said, "Electronic dog tags or communication through a wireless sensor telemetry system could quickly provide crew location information and could report a general summary of individual status."

SPAWAR Systems Command (SSC) Portsmouth Activity assembled the PASSION system and successfully tested and demonstrated it aboard CVN-77. I participated in the test conducted at the SSC Portsmouth Activity. This PASSION project is my response to the popular Navy motto, "What have you done for the fleet today?" CVN-77, a Nimitz-class aircraft carrier, was one of the most advanced major combatants in the U.S. Navy. (see photo 135)

During the PASSION test, there was a retirement ceremony for a Navy

Captain in the hangar deck. The ceremony interrupted our test. Many guests came to the retirement ceremony. Whenever an officer came aboard, a bell was peeled a designated number of times according to the time-old Navy tradition. The boatswain's mates, who lined up on the quarterdeck of the ship, blew the whistle to pipe in the guests aboard the carrier.

After the ceremony, we continued our test. At the end of the long day, the commanding officer asked me to drop by Captain's stateroom.

"John, it is a custom to present you with a souvenir. I give you a CVN-77 flight jacket."

"Thank you, captain, for your generosity."

"You're welcome. May I suggest you take this purple flight jacket. On an aircraft carrier, a purple jacket is worn by the aviation fuel handlers."

"Is that right? What task do those with yellow jackets perform?"

"Oh, yellow jackets are for catapult and arresting gear crews. You probably do not want that."

"I like the purple jacket."

"O.K., John. You are now officially the apprentice Aviation boatswain's mate fuel (ABF)."

The purple jacket has a logo "George Bush – CVN-77" on it, and when I returned home, I gave it to Rahn. She is now the proud owner of the purple jacket with a CVN-77 logo on it.

Two weeks later, ONR Public Affairs Office published the following news release.[20]

ONR-Guided Technology Tracks Assets Inside of Ships

"*March 16, 2009, Arlington, VA.* - ONR is funding emerging technology, which will allow wireless surveillance not only of ships but also the tracking of people and high-value assets on board ships.

"To help the Navy keep accurate tabs on its environment, a concept the Navy calls Maritime Domain Awareness, ONR is sponsoring work in advanced electronics that ratchets up

the Navy's ability to do just that. The Precise At-Sea Ship System for Indoor-Outdoor Navigation (PASSION) enables wireless position tracking of both the external and internal environment of naval vessels.

"The concept is the brainchild of Dr. John Kim, Program Officer for Navigation and Timekeeping. PASSION is being developed and reviewed under Kim's oversight by Navy civilian Dr. Barry Tanju and carried out by the Navy's Carrier and Air Integration program office and partners. PASSION meets a need, recommended by a Navy Research Advisory Committee study, for positioning systems aboard aircraft carriers and other vessels to reduce onboard manpower, for damage control and maintenance, and for locating personnel and equipment.

"Based on successful simulations, and integrated indoor hardware tests conducted at George Washington University buildings and onboard USS George H.W. Bush (CVN 77), we are envisioning that the Navy will introduce PASSION technologies in all Nimitz (CVN 68) class ships as a part of their wireless networks," Kim said.

Interferometric Gravity Gradiometer (IGG)

Another physics-based navigation tool was a gravimeter The Navy initiated the development of the Gravity Gradiometer to support the Trident Missile,[21] as a backup to undersea navigation. Bell Aerospace/Lockheed Martin built a gravity measurement device, the Gravimeter (BGM-3).

Professor Mark Kasevich of Yale University came up with an idea to measure the gravity using laser-cooled BEC. The proposed device was called the IGG. He solicited ONR funding to investigate the application of BEC to gravity-based navigation.

What is a gravity gradiometer?

"A gravimeter measures the gravitational field of the Earth, while gravity gradiometer measures the relative value of minute differences in gravity.

"IGG measures gravity and acceleration of cooled atoms and is used to detect land mass or tunnels, which induce gravitational anomalies.

"For example, a sea mound would increase gravity due to a heavier land mass. Therefore, IGG could make a bathymetric map of the ocean bottom.

Mark Kasevich started the IGG project while he was working at Yale University. He appeared to be a lone physicist, surrounded by faculties of literature, economics, law, management, and other non-hard science in Yale University. I was not surprised when he told me he decided to move to Stanford University, where his scientific project could find more sympathetic ears.

ONR Afloat Research Ship YP-679

In 2008, ONR held ship tours of the afloat research ship YP-679, which was docked at Gibb's Pier of NRL on the Potomac River. I invited Rahn and my grandson Keaton to the ship tours. Janet, his mother, asked me to keep my eyes on Keaton, while we were on the ship. The ship had the latest research devices such as torpedoes and unmanned underwater vehicles. Keaton asked a lot of questions to attending sailors. He also went up and down the ship. I followed him from stern to the fore of the ship back and forth, and from the quarter-deck to the topside and the pilot room. I was exhausted after an hour. But he was still going. (see photo 127)

Drug Test

I found "drug test" was the way of life for employees when I joined ONR. Drug testing was more strict and frequent than in the private sector, as ONR scientists and engineers were lumped together with all sailors. One day I got a call from the human resources department:

"You have been selected for a substance screening test. She announced it as though I had won one of those big sweepstakes.

"Please go to the sixth-floor men's room immediately." Then it dawned on me that it was a drug test.

I went to the designated room, where a drug tester gave me a plastic cup. From then on, I received a drug test call two or three times a year. It was my contribution to the "war on drugs." During one particular test, I could not produce a urine sample. As I was unable to provide the sample, the drug tester said:

"Please let the water faucet run, that may help you to make water."

That was a not-so-typical day for me in ONR.

Yearly Annual Review Report

Like any employee in the Navy, I received a Yearly Appraisal Review (YAR) from my supervisor. Following is Dr. Joe Lawrence's appraisal of my performance.[22]

"John Kim has been a Government employee since February 2001 at ONR. At the outset, he was given responsibility for the entirety of Navy Navigation Science and Technology (S&T) Program. This Program is a high impact and very high visibility program having oversight by an EXCOM chaired directly by Deputy Assistant Secretary of the Navy for Command Control Communications Computer and Intelligence. John has critically reviewed the program, culled out projects that did not show significant promise for the payoff; and has conceived and initiated a series of new projects that have

been accepted by EXCOM and that now are beginning to deliver on their anticipated high payoff. He has been successful despite at times unyielding opposition from Navy laboratories who would have preferred block funding. John's success in this reorientation, and in the assertion of ONR S&T leadership, has been enabled by his superb and widely recognized technical expertise. His success also was accomplished by his tenacious approach to technical management, his innovative project conceptualization, and his solid grasp of the issues and requirements facing the Navy in the navigation area (specifically including GPS and inertial guidance on the many smart munitions in the national inventory).

"John is a nationally and internationally recognized technical expert in navigation, he is a tenacious negotiator, he is a gifted and innovative technical manager, and he is a hard-working and trusted member of the ONR S&T team."

GLOBAL POSITIONING SYSTEM (GPS) AND ITS CODES

How does GPS work?

"GPS determines position through triangulation, just like a land surveyor determines the three-dimensional position of points and the distances and angles between them.

"In three-dimensional space, if I know the ranges from the satellites in space, I can calculate the fourth point by using the triangulation method.

"These four points would make a skewed pyramid.

"In other words, a three-dimensional shape that is made up of four triangles is called a tetrahedron.

"The key is the determination of the distance between a known GPS satellite position and my position.

"One determines the distance by a ranging sequence. The GPS code sequence of 1's and 0's, generated by the C/A-code

translates into the distance.

"GPS sends the code to a receiver, which determines the distance by this ranging sequence.

"In addition to the C/A-code, GPS uses several additional codes such as the Precision P(Y)-code, which is encrypted to prevent unauthorized access to GPS."

Since its initial operations in July 1995, the GPS Wing has upgraded the GPS system twice. The first upgrade of the GPS system was known as the Block II. The second upgrade was known as the Block III. The code for the Block III is the Military (M) code, which is designed to improve the security of GPS signals. In 2001, DoD approved the GPS Wing to proceed with the GPS Block III upgrade. I initiated parallel efforts to introduce the next generation GPS M-code receiver to Navy navigation systems. My concern with the GPS Block III receiver was an interoperability issue of the Blocks II and III codes. They were not interoperable, as the code used in the GPS Block III was not designed to be downward-compatible. The two generations of GPS systems would operate together for several years. I asked Dave Lewis of Raytheon in El Segundo to solve this interoperability issue. He developed a system which could interoperate the two generations of GPS receivers, the GPS Block II, and the Block III. I awarded a contract called the M-, Y- and C/A-code (MYCA) project. The GPS Wing recognized the interoperability issue and adopted the concept and designated the modified device as the YMCA project, which became part of the Modernized User Equipment (MUE). The interoperability issue was such an obvious feature of the GPS Block upgrade, but they missed it, and I was pleased with the MYCA development and Raytheon's contribution to the issue.

29

Executive Education Programs at the Brookings Institution

At ONR, I worked on technological aspects of national defense, but not on political and economic aspects. As a Program Officer, I felt the need to understand emerging national security issues, and American policy responses to them. Also, when the ONR Corporate Strategic Communication (CSC) Office announced newly completed Navigation and Timekeeping projects, I met with news media to explain the project. Also, as a Program Officer, I need to understand the U.S. science and technology policy. ONR sent me to take courses in several executive education programs, which address these topics. The executive education program was offered at the Brookings Institution on *National security policy issues, Communicating for success,* and *Science and Technology Issues Facing the U.S.* .

U.S. NATIONAL SECURITY POLICY ISSUES

The first program I have attended lectures and panel discussions on *U.S. National Security Policy Issues* by defense policy experts, some of the country's leading military strategists, and past and present senior policymakers. Several speakers and panel members lectured us on crucial issues, of nuclear nonproliferation, the Arab-Israeli conflict, energy security, the Middle East strategy of the war on terrorism, and homeland security. These lectures were all relevant to my work as a Program Officer. I needed to learn national security policy issues ranging from the Cold War paradigm to the new emerging Global War On Terror (GWOT) to asymmetrical warfare.

We heard a lecture by Kenneth Pollack, Senior Fellow at the Brookings, who was an expert on the politics of the Gulf region. During our lecture, a real-life drama unfolded as we watched on TV news about a Spanish gunboat intercepting in the Arabian Sea a North Korean cargo ship which was carrying a dozen concealed SCUD missiles. A U.S. Navy search party boarded the cargo ship. The news media announced this with the usual media hyperbole, but our lecturer predicted that the intercept of the North Korean ship which was carrying missiles would be a tempest in a teapot. He predicted they would soon release the seized missiles.

Sure enough, the next day, an Associated Press correspondent in Yemen reported that the U.S. Navy team had released the ship carrying North Korea-made SCUD missiles, sending the vessel and its cargo on their way to the original destination of Yemen. Pollack commented that Yemen had first purchased North Korean SCUD missiles a decade ago. Yemen now needed to replace the aging SCUD missiles. Several missiles were in Yemeni's launch sites as a show of force to their neighbors. What concerned America was that these missiles could fall into the wrong hands like Al-Qaeda and Houtis in Yemen. Apparently, the Yemeni Government assured that those missiles were guaranteed to be kept by them. The two-day media hype became a tempest in a teapot. But in 2018, these SCUD missiles were used for harassing Saudi Arabia and neighbors.

The luncheon speaker of that day was Dr. Zbigniew Brzezinski, the National Security Advisor to President Jimmy Carter. I sat at the table nearest to the podium. Unbeknownst to those of us, who sat at that table, one seat was empty. It turned out that the seat was for the luncheon speaker, Dr. Brzezinski. He came to the luncheon meeting late. When he arrived and settled down in his seat with us, he quickly asked five of us at the table what our organizations were to adjust the level of his speech for students. His topic was how to stop the nuclearization of the Korean peninsula, and told us about his recent visit to Tokyo. He said that the production of nuclear weapons by North Korea could trigger the chain reaction of the nuclearization of the Korean peninsula and of East Asia. During his recent visit to Tokyo, Dr. Brzezinski met with Japanese officials. He was sure that Japan was a proto-nuclear nation. Japan

does not have nuclear weapons now, but it is quite capable of manufacturing nuclear weapons in short order once it decided the need to have one. It was a disconcerting statement to many of us.

❊ ❊ ❊

On the second day, we heard a lecture given by the former Secretary of Defense Robert McNamara on the *Role of nuclear weapons in the U.S. strategy: Action to prevent the apocalypse.* McNamara said he was worried about nuclear weapons during the Kennedy administration and advised President Kennedy to take cautious steps in dealing with Russians. We all knew that Robert McNamara was one of the key strategists of the Vietnam War. But he did not go into his role in the Vietnam debacle during his lecture. We were disappointed that he made no mention of the Vietnam War.

COMMUNICATING FOR SUCCESS

I attended another executive education program on *Communicating for success.* During my tenure at ONR, I was interviewed several times by the media. ONR announced newsworthy items related to my program through the ONR CSC Office. I often received a request for an interview from news media covering defense projects.

For example, when I completed the project on the wireless communication system on the aircraft carrier CVN-77, the ONR CSC office released the story. As I knew the subject well, I did not prepare sound bites. That was a mistake. When I met with a reporter, I responded to one question, which led to another but the unrelated topic. Then, the ONR CSC staff person sitting with me in the room gave me signal to finish the interview as the interview went astray to an irrelevant topic. The ONR CSC staff kept me out of trouble of possibly appearing in the front page of the next day's Washington Post. I realized then how important it was to prepare a few sound bites on the topic and stick to the script, whether my response is relevant to questions or not. I could stay out of trouble that way.

In the afternoon, I attended a lecture on *Communicating for Success* delivered

by Bill Connor of Oratorio Media Training & Associates. Connor was a former White House correspondent. He conducted with me an exercise interview in the Brookings media studio. I stood in front of a TV camera. After a quick look at my card, he asked me to describe my job of developing the ONR atomic clock. He then asked me:

"John, why does the Navy spend so much resource on developing atomic clocks?"

"We are developing not just any clock but a clock that is very accurate, small, and requires low battery power.

"Clock accuracy is directly related to the efficiency of weapons delivery.

"Today's weapons like smart bombs are a case in point.

"The bomb needs accurate guidance and control.

"1-nanosecond accuracy (nine zeros after the decimal point) corresponds to one foot of error.

"If the accuracy of an embedded clock were one microsecond, that is six zeros after the decimal point, the weapons delivery error would correspond to one thousand feet.

"Now that would create enormous collateral damages or would require many bombs to neutralize the target. Weapons delivery accuracy for surgical bombing is one of the reasons why the Navy has been developing accurate atomic clocks."

Connor critiqued my TV interview by telling me that I should look straight into the camera and deliver my speech, and stop waving my hands, which distracts the audience.

The next lecture was on crisis communications. We viewed a three-minute speech which former President Bill Clinton delivered on national television in defense of his conduct in the Monica Lewinski scandal. In that short television broadcast, we heard Bill Clinton say the phrase "I did not do it" twenty-three times, and his famous quote: "I did not have sexual relations with that woman, Miss Lewinsky." On January 26, 1998, President Clinton, standing with his wife, spoke at the White House press conference and issued a forceful denial. He was a good spin doctor.

The third lecture on the crisis communications was about using vague and ambiguous words. Connor said that the phrase "Error has been made..." has been used quite often, and it is an example of vague and ambiguous words.

There is no person identified who made the error in question. In contrast, Connor showed us General Dwight Eisenhower's statements on D-Day in June 1944. The first was delivered on June 6, 1944, which itself was not an example of crisis communication.[23]

"Soldiers, Sailors, and Airmen of the Allied Expeditionary Force. You are about to embark upon a great crusade, toward which we have striven these many months. The eyes of the world are upon you. The hopes and prayers of liberty-loving people everywhere march with you. In company with our brave Allies and brothers in arms on other fronts, you will bring about the destruction of the German war machine, the elimination of Nazi tyranny over the oppressed peoples of Europe, and security for us in a free world. Your task will not be an easy one. Your enemy is well trained, well equipped and battle-hardened; he will fight savagely. But this is the year 1944! Much has happened since the Nazi triumphs of 1940-41. The United Nations have inflicted upon the Germans great defeats, in open battle, man to man. Our air offensive has seriously reduced their strength in the air and their capacity to wage war on the ground. Our home fronts have given us an overwhelming superiority in weapons and munitions of war and placed at our disposal great reserves of trained fighting men. The tide has turned! The free men of the world are marching together to victory! I have full confidence in your courage, devotion to duty and skill in battle. We will accept nothing less than full victory! Good Luck! And let us all beseech the blessings of Almighty God upon this great and noble undertaking."

However, we learned that General Eisenhower prepared another message[24] to the world in case the Normandy invasion failed. I saw on the screen a photocopy of General Eisenhower's handwritten message, which said neither "error has been made," nor "I did not do it."

"Our landings have failed, and I have withdrawn the troops. My decision to attack at this time and place was based on the best information available. The Troops, the Air forces, and the Navy did all that bravery could do. If any blame or fault attaches to the attempt, it is mine alone."

This unused statement by General Eisenhower shows that he did not have complete confidence in the success of the Normandy invasion. The good thing is history went in such a way that Eisenhower never used that second speech. It was found by his aide weeks after the initial landing. This undelivered message shows the character of General Eisenhower. The main point of the lecture was that General Eisenhower prepared two speeches in the first person. He was prepared to take all the responsibility for failure. It is "I" who had crushing responsibility of the D-Day invasion. Indeed, General Eisenhower was a statesman. Bill Clinton was no Eisenhower.

SCIENCE AND TECHNOLOGY ISSUES FACING THE U.S.

The Brookings Institution offered another Executive Education Program on *"Science and Technology Issues Facing the U.S."* On the first day, I heard a lecture by Norman Augustine, the retired CEO of Lockheed-Martin Company, on *U.S. leadership in science and technology: Is America slipping?*

He said, "The leadership in science and technology is related to the growth of the national economy."

The outlook for America to compete for quality jobs has further deteriorated over the past five years.

"The Gathering Storm increasingly appeared to be a category 5."[25]

Forecasting one country's science and technology, and its impact to the economy, is a tricky business, as it can rise and fall with alarming regularity. For example, in the late 1980s, Japan's economy was a great success, but that was followed by years of stagnation. In its halcyon days, Japanese bought up real estate in America. Many Americans took it as a sign that Japan could soon control the American economy. But optimists said America should not worry too much about Japanese buying up real estate, as they could not move the land

and the buildings to Japan. Sure enough, that worry had ended when the Japanese economic bubble burst in the early 1990s. It took a long time for Japan's economy to recover and is referred to as the "lost two decades" of stagnation.

After his lecture on American leadership in science and technology, Norm Augustine told us about his personal recollection of the merger of Lockheed Corporation and Martin-Marietta Corporation. That merger created the second largest defense contractor in America. He emphasized that the merger was a good idea for taxpayers as it would lower the cost of doing business by eliminating dual function of the second and third largest defense contractors in America. I never thought about the merger from the national point of view. But Augustine saw the bigger picture on the canvass of national economy.

DARPA and Fostering Creativity

The next day, Dr. Tony Tether, the Technical Director of DARPA, delivered his lecture on *Fostering creativity at DARPA.* DARPA has been an organization with autonomy and freedom from bureaucratic barriers and has focused not on the evolutionary but revolutionary innovation by making high-risk investments. DARPA considers its project completed when a performer could prove the feasibility of scientific and technological principles. I was not a stranger to the modus operandi of the agency as I worked with the DARPA colleagues on navigation and timekeeping technology. While DARPA pursued revolutionary innovation, ONR had a different paradigm, and thus used a different metric for success. ONR valued transitioning from basic science to development of systems which would have utility to warfighters within five or less years, not ten or more years.

When I reviewed proposals on navigation and timekeeping science and technology in the 6.2 (Applied Research) and the 6.3 (Advanced Technology Development) categories, I knew that each idea went through the proof of principle. Feasibility had been already answered. I always emphasized to principal investigators that he or she remembers the 7 Ps, that is, "Prior Proper Planning Prevents Piss Poor Performance." On the other hand, when I reviewed a proposal in the 6.1 (Basic Research) category, I knew it was about discovery and invention. I could not ask the principal investigator planning for basic

science. That is not how revolutionary technology, like GPS, the transistor, or the Internet, was invented.

Both ONR and DARPA performed and competed for research in atomic clocks and inertial navigation systems. One DARPA atomic clock project, known as the Chip-Scale Atomic Clock (CSAC), competed with the ONR Tactical Grade Atomic Clock (TGAC).

The other competing research area was the Inertial Navigation System (INS). DARPA initiated the development of INS, called the Precision Inertial Navigation System (PINS), which was aimed at achieving a drift rate of no more than 1 microdegree per hour. State-of-the-art commercial INS had a drift rate of 1 millidegree per hour. The PINS performance goal was three orders of magnitude smaller than the commercially available INS. It remains to be seen whether PINS could deliver the result as advertised.

In contrast, the objective of my ONR INS projects was to build an INS which the fleet could use within three to five years. Our candidate INSs were the Resonant Fiber Optical INS (RFOG INS) and the Lateral Motion MEMS INS. These INS would deliver a drift rate of no more than ten millidegrees per hour.

National Institutes of Health (NIH) Budgets

Another lecture in the program was about the NIH budgets from 1995 to 2005. The former Congressman Robert Walker, who chaired the House Science and Technology Committee, was the lecturer. The NIH R&D budgets were the second-largest after the DoD R&D budget. During the second term of the Clinton Administration (1997–2001), the NIH R&D budget doubled from $13.6 billion to $27.3 billion in five years. Much of this increase was allocated to big projects such as the human genome project and the cancer research project. Meantime, the cost of hiring staff in university research laboratories had also doubled during this time. This situation resulted in almost no effective budget increase in the research community.

During the first term of the George W. Bush administration (2001-2005), the NIH budgets decreased, and researchers in these communities were hard-hit. We learned that budget cuts affected many NIH-sponsored laboratories

and university researchers. Only a few years before the Bush administration, the budget had doubled in five years. This volatile funding practice hurt the American biomedical and life science community. Some promising researchers were forced to move to the pharmaceutical industry, and some stopped pursuing science and left the field. "Hard landing" is the word used for this pattern of federal funding for biomedical research.

The hard landing of the budget might cause the country falling behind in the competition in science and technology. This was concerns of the S&T community. I read a book, *Falling Behind - Boom, bust and the Global Race for Scientific Talent,* by Michael Teitelbaum of the Alfred P. Sloan Foundation.[26] His primary question in the book was "Is the U.S. falling behind in the global race for scientific and engineering talent?" Like Norm Augustine's *The Gathering Storm* report, his concern that the U.S. industry would face the shortage of scientists and engineers. But the demand and supply of these scientists and engineers are cyclical. His analysis used historical data of the last 70 years. Booms turned to busts, leaving a generation of accomplished scientists, who had been encouraged to pursue biological science, with disheartening career prospects. Their experiences deterred talented students from following in their footsteps, thereby sowing the seeds of the next cycle of boom and bust. What Teitelbaum wrote in his book was the opposite position to Norm Augustine's *Gathering Storm* theme. Teitelbaum pointed that the gathering storm of a category 5, warning about the deficiency in the number of American scientists and engineers, was inconsistent with nearly all the available evidence.

He also told us that the feast or famine funding cycle of science and technology tended to repel bright young talents from Science, Technology, Engineering and Mathematics (STEM) and drive them to other fields like business and law. Teitelbaum said the symptoms and signs of malaise in the American science and engineering workforce are structural and cannot be cured merely by providing additional funding. However, recent efforts of this kind have caused destabilizing effects, and policymakers should be careful of what they intended to do. There is no shortage of trained experts in the life science fields, as too many biologists and related scientists are produced, while there is a lack of trained experts in information technology, electrical engineering, and mechanical engineering.

Energy Policy and Peak Oil

Next on the agenda was the energy policy, an equally important science and technology issue for the nation. Congressman Roscoe Bartlett delivered a lecture on *Peak Oil*, a term that I heard for the first time. I found out that it was the notion and the theory about oil production formulated by M. King Hubbert of Shell Research Laboratory in 1956. Peak oil is the point in time when we reach the maximum rate of extraction of petroleum, and, from then on, the rate of production enters a terminal decline. Hubbert's original prediction of peak oil would be in about 1970 as U.S. average production peaked in 1970 at 9.6 million barrels per day. However, after a decades-long decline, the subsequent successful application of massive hydraulic fracturing to additional tight gas (produced from rocks) reservoirs caused U.S. production to rebound, hitting 9.2 million barrels per day in early 2015. This increased production contributed to bringing down the price of oil by half.[27]

Congressman Bartlett reviewed the Energy Policy Acts, passed in 1992 and 2005, which included many provisions for conservation, energy development, and grants and tax incentives to encourage renewable energy. However, in 2006, less than 8% of the total energy consumed in the U.S. was from renewable energy, and hydroelectric power plants generated two-thirds of that.

Other potential renewable energy sources are the wind, the sun, and the tide. In 1954-1957, during my undergraduate years at SNU, renewable energy was earnestly discussed in South Korea as the country had no fossil energy deposits. One noteworthy renewable-energy we discussed was the tides because the Yellow Sea in East Asia has very high tides of over 10 meters. Such tides could be harnessed to generate a large amount of energy. In fact, in 2011, Sihwa Lake Tidal Power Station was built on the west coast of South Korea. It is the world's largest tidal power electric generating station with a total output capacity of 254 megawatts.

My undergraduate major in SNU was Electrical Engineering, with emphasis on power engineering. The core courses were hydroelectric power generation, steam power generation using coal, power conversion, power transmission, power distribution and electric machineries such as motors, generators, and transformers. The curriculum of SNU was about 10 years behind that of American universities in the 1950s. Later, in my undergraduate and graduate

school programs in America, Electrical Engineering moved more to electronics rather than electrical power engineering.

Roscoe Bartlett told us that something went wrong with the Peak Oil theory. That does not mean that Peak Oil won't occur. The original forecast of Peak Oil was around 2000, but in 2019, there was no Peak Oil but rather an oil glut. What happened to Peak Oil was that America increased oil production by fracking and the demand for oil in China and Europe sagged. The fundamental theory regarding Peak Oil still holds true. The production rate of fossil fuels would reach a maximum level and then decline. But there will be a peak and a decline, although in a different shape. But there will be a decline.

HOWARD HUGHES MEDICAL INSTITUTE (HHMI)

The next day, the Brookings lecture continued at the suburban campus of the Janelia Research Campus of HHMI. Dr. Gerald Rubin, the HHMI Director, briefed us on the operation of the Janelia Research Campus. He said that two renowned research organizations, the Cavendish Laboratory and the Bell Laboratories, were the models for the Janelia Campus. The Cavendish and the Bell laboratories were structured to provide a multi-disciplinary approach to solving scientific problems. During lunch or coffee breaks, the Cavendish and the Bell researchers exchange ideas and find a lead to solutions in "outside the box" thinking. That was how they discovered the concept of the double helix model of DNA in the Cavendish Laboratory. Rosalind Franklin was a biophysicist who was an expert in the X-ray crystallographic method. James Watson and Francis Crick got the idea of the double helix structure of DNA from her crystallography.

At the Bell Laboratories, scientists and engineers interacted with colleagues in corridors and the cafeteria, which resembled a scientific and engineering marketplace, to meet and talk about their problems. Also, the Bell Laboratories was not a place where the only theory was discussed. I visited the Bell Laboratories' ASW project facility in the 1970s. I saw they pursued science on the top floors, while manufacturing factories occupied the first and second floors. The ultimate goal of the Bell Laboratories was transitioning science into practical products. That was the strength of the Bell Laboratories. Much

of today's electronics technology started at the Bell Laboratories, such as the transistor, laser, a charge-coupled device, fiber optics, the cellular telephones, the solar cell, computer operating systems (C and UNIX), communications satellites, and others.

THE INTERNET AND VINTON CERF

The next day, I met a luncheon speaker, Vinton Cerf, who was a legendary computer scientist. He delivered a lecture on *The Internet: How an idea became a reality, and where it's heading.* Cerf is recognized as one of the innovators of the Internet, sharing the title with another computer scientist, Bob Kahn. By the way, what I liked about the Brookings Executive Education Program was that I could meet a dozen notable lecturers and speakers in one place in a classroom environment. Otherwise, I would not have had an opportunity to meet any of them in person.

In the 1970s, Vinton Cerf was a program manager in DARPA, who funded various groups to develop a networked computer system, by using the Transmission Control Protocol/Internet Protocol (TCP/IP) to provide service for many users in a wide area. TCP/IP is a handshaking protocol for two communication nodes to exchange data or messages. All digital communication systems need a pre-arranged transmission protocol. The resulto f such a network became known as ARPANET, and later the Internet. In 1985, Vinton Cerf moved to MCI Communication Corp, where he was the principal developer of the first commercial email system (MCI Mail) connected to the Internet. When the feasibility of the Internet was proven, ARPANET was taken down in February 1990. ARPANET was expanded into "the World Wide Web," which became the Internet.

30

NATO Navigation Meetings: Antalya, Ottawa, Paris, Barcelona, and Izmir

I went to Antalya, Turkey, to attend the 2007 NATO Navigation Symposium on *Military Capabilities Enabled by Advances in Navigation Sensor,* and checked into the Sheraton Hotel. Rahn and I stood on the balcony of the hotel. The hot, dusty, and dry Mediterranean Sirocco winds blew on our faces. The hotel concierge told us the Sirocco winds are unusual in this part of the Mediterranean coast in late September. We found in the back of the hotel a charming Middle Eastern garden with palm trees, date trees, and wisterias on louvered canopies, which provided the cool shades in the hot late summer day. It was the first time I had ever seen dates hanging from a tree.

I invited four Principal Investigators of the Navigation and Timekeeping program, Dr. Dave Cousins of BBN Technologies, Son Dinh and Ilya Stevens of SSC-SD, and Dave Lewis of Raytheon to this symposium. In the evening, we attended the Conference reception hosted by Turkish MoD at the hotel. Next day, I co-chaired a session on *"Sensors and enabling technologies"* with Steven Davison of the U.K.

In the evening, our team dined at a seaside restaurant where the waiter tried to sell us a large fish. We asked the waiter the price of the fish; the waiter quoted the price by the weight. Quickly Rahn calculated and figured the price was to be $320. The price was almost lost in translating kilograms and Turkish Lira. It could have been a big catch for the waiter! Instead, we ordered smaller seafood dishes individually.

We toured the ancient city of Aspendos, where we found many scattered stone structures of Greek and Roman antiquity in the countryside. In the

city of Sidé, there were ruins of Hadrian's gate, fallen capitals and pilasters, columns, pediments, and statues. According to our tour guide, over several hundred thousand items are buried in many ruins in Turkey today. I know any one of those nameless capstones would be a featured exhibit in an American provincial museum. In Sidé town center, I saw the Temples of Apollo and Athena. At the sunset, the marble columns and pediments of the temples were part of a superb scenery of the Gulf of Antalya.

NAVWAR MOU MEETING IN OTTAWA, CANADA

I traveled to Ottawa to attend the 2010 NAVWAR Memorandum of Understanding (MoU) Meeting, held at the Defence Research and Development Canada (DRDC). Rahn and I stayed at the Westin Hotel in Ottawa. Unbeknownst to us, Chinese President Hu Jintao and his entourage were also scheduled to be in the hotel during our stay. The Chinese delegation occupied rooms on several floors of the hotel. Outside the hotel across the street, there was a day-and-night demonstration by followers of the Chinese religious sect, Falun Gong, protesting the oppressive policy on religious freedom in China. They made much noise. In the afternoon we returned to the hotel. We saw Canadian security contingents positioned on the rooftop and outside our room. To top it off, a magnitude 5 earthquake hit the city, the epicenter of which was 35 miles north of Ottawa. I felt a tremor and a jolt at the DRDC facility while I was attending the meeting. During the earthquake, Rahn was at the hotel, where she also felt the room violently shake for few seconds.

At the NAVWAR meeting, we discussed ongoing GPS field tests. The first was Joint GPS Combat Effectiveness (JGPSCE) Tests and the second was NAVFEST.[28] In this meeting, the U.S. Air Force Test Squadron 746 presented the results of JGPSCE Hotel conducted in 2011 at the White Sands Missile Range (WSMR), New Mexico, and presented test planning of JGPSCE India in 2012 at Kauai, Hawaii. Also, the Squadron 746 presented various static and dynamic test results of NAVFEST conducted at WSMR.

In the afternoon session of the MoU meeting, the Canadian Ministry of National Defense Information Technology (IT) group told us that the Chinese security details, which accompanied Hu Jintao, might have searched our rooms

below the floor occupied by the Chinese delegation. Some laptop computers might have been compromised. My laptop was in the safe in the room, and Rahn had stayed in the room that day. We had an earthquake outside and the Hu Jintao quake inside!

THE LAST TIME I SAW PARIS

The NATO Research and Technology Agency (RTA) invited me to the 2010 Organizing Committee meeting held at RTA in Neuilly-sur-Seine, which is a western suburb of Paris. NATO RTA and Turkish MoD sponsored the Symposium in Izmir, Turkey, to be heldi n the fall of 2012. Dr. Murat Eren (Turkey), the chair of the working group, Jeff Bird (Canada National Defence Ministry), Dr. Mikel Miller (USAF), Lt. Col. Elio Vincitorio (Italy), and I discussed the organization of the third symposium, *Navigation Sensors, and Systems in GNSS-Denied Environments.*"

Just like a typical tourist, I had toured central Paris during my previous three visits. But, this time, I stayed in Neuilly-sur-Seine district, which was one of the wealthiest communities in Paris, and I wanted to see how locals live in residential neighborhoods. There were several restaurants in Neuilly-sur-Seine where locals dined. We tried several restaurants, one of which was an Italian restaurant, Trattoria, and the menu included linguini with clams. We liked the linguini with clams, but one evening the chef came out from the kitchen and said they ran out of clams. We must have eaten them all in the last two dinners.

BASTILLE DAY 2010

We had a day off from the NATO Navigation meeting to observe the celebration of the French national holiday. We got up early in the morning and went to the Champs Elysses to see the parade. France was once an empire, and the Bastille Day parade gave us a glimpse of the glory of the former French empire. There were many uniformed soldiers and sailors of former colonies

of France in their colorful uniforms at the parade. The French Armed Forces displayed many weapons and tanks in the parade.

We could not see much at the parade as the crowds stood four or five rows deep on the sidewalk. Then, I saw a ladder in front of a store, which I borrowed from the store owner. I went up the rickety ladder, while Rahn held it. What I saw on the Champs Élysées that day reminded me of a painting of Monet's *The Rue Montorgeuil on Bastille Day*. I took a picture at the spot where Monet might have stood. I saw a platoon of French gendarmes with the quintessential kepi, the boxy cap, with gold braids on their black jackets and their blue pantaloons; and a company of French grenadiers with uniforms similar to George Washington's outfit with a black waistcoat, red inner lining, and white breeches. Some units wore a golden metal helmet with a spire. Soldiers, who wore the metal helmet, were sweating in the hot July sun. I saw a group of horses waiting patiently and ready to join the parade. A military aircraft formation flew overhead, and I saw tank soldiers in smart uniforms in front of their tanks. There was a company of firefighters wearing colorful uniforms standing next to vintage red firefighting carts. We were exhausted and returned to the hotel via Metro subway train. There was no "Storming of the Bastille" that day, but the storm passed on the Champs Élysées and got us wet. We did see fantastic fireworks near the Eiffel Tower that evening.

PALACE OF VERSAILLES

We went on a day trip to the Palace of Versailles by a bus from Pont de Sèvres Station. When our bus crossed the bridge over the Seine, I could see many condominium towers. Here, I saw another face of Paris. These were the Paris suburbs. Along the bus route was a continuum of stores of camera dealers, cafes, laundromats, real-estate agencies, tailors, and others, where ordinary people of the over 20 million residents did their daily trade, shopping, and commerce. They were Parisiennes, but I could spot some minorities by their appearance, garb, and headgear.

There must be height restrictions or building codes in this arrondissement (borough), as many residential apartments were not taller than five stories. I saw many school children standing on a trafficis land in the busy street. Our

bus passed through neighborhoods with interesting names—Marché Saint-Romain, Place Gabriel Péri, Puits Sans Vin, and Pointe de Chaville. I wished to get off from the bus and just walk a few blocks to enjoy the hustle and bustle of the Paris of the working people. As we approached the University de Versailles on Route D10, the bus was passing through the leafy, wide boulevard. A few hundred yards from the university, we got off at the Versailles bus stop, which was near the old palace stables. In front of us was the parade ground, Place de Armes. At the end of the parade ground was the equestrian statue of Louis XIV. The inscription on his statue says, "*L'etat c'est moi.*" (I myself am the nation.) Gravel stones covered the street in the Versailles. D'Artagnan and two musketeers must have ridden their horses here, shouting: "*Un pour tous; tous pour un (One for all; all for one).*"

There was a long line at the gate of the palace. After waiting in line for 20 minutes, we finally entered the Chateau, where the Sun King once ruled the kingdom. I learned that Louis XIV was a hands-on king, who made all decisions of state himself. The motto "*L'état c'est moi*" meant that he was an administrative king instead of a titular king. The 250-foot-long Hall of Mirrors was magnificent; it was where the League of Nations dictated peace terms of the Treaty of Versaillest o defeated Germany. With heavy rain shower and the crowd, the interior of the Chateau was quite humid. From one of the rooms, we found a door ajar and stepped out to the patio. Below we viewed the Palace Garden, which stretched five miles long. The Palace of Versailles was very grand and beautiful, but I liked the busy streets we had traveled more than the palace.

CHARTRES CATHEDRAL

In Washington, I visited and appreciated the magnificent Romanesque Basilica of the National Shrine of the Immaculate Conception. One of my photographs of the Byzantine Basilica of the Hagia Sophia decorates the wall of my study. Also, I think about Saint Mark's Byzantine Basilica in Venice, where we were white-bombed by pigeons. As for a Renaissance structure, I think about the Cathedral of Santa Maria del Fiore (Duomo) in Florence. What I remember about the dark sanctuary of the Baroque Cathedral of Santiago De Compostela in Spain was the incense burner swung almost to the ceiling of the

sanctuary like a pendulum, trying to dispel sweaty smell of pilgrims. Then, of course, I liked the Modernism architecture of the Sagrada Familia Basilica in Barcelona by Antoni Gaudi.

During this trip to France, Rahn and I visited the Chartres Cathedral, which the Baedeker guides suggested as a day-trip excursion. We followed Baedeker's guides and started from Gare Montparnasse and bought second-class train tickets. The train ride to Chartres on the French National Railroad SNCF was pleasant, and the passing landscape of the countryside was idyllic with the green field of wheat and bean. When we got off the train, we saw two towering spires, but not the cathedral. When we finally stood in front of the cathedral, we saw the second spire in the Gothic style with more pointed arches and elaborate decorations. This gothic architecture started 100 years before the Duomo of Florence was built. Many gargoyles decorated the edge of the roofs. Inside the sanctuary there were several stained glass windows. According to the Baedeker guides, one of the special stained glass windows was composed of 10,000 separate glass pieces. Thin colored glass pieces were used to cover plain glass to save the cost of making stained glass. Inside the Cathedral the apse and the nave, there were well-preserved statues of saints from the Renaissance period. Of course, the name of saints I have never heard of. From the spacious porch, we could see a labyrinth garden below.

However, the highlight of the Chartres visit was a Franco-Russian confectioner, which a colleague at RTA told me to visit to get a taste of Menchikoffs, a candy made only in Chartres. We found a candy store "Daumesnil," on Rue de la Pie. Rahn bought a box of Menchikoffs for her grandchildren, which was made with the mixture of chocolate and butter, encased in a fine layer of dried Swiss meringue (whipped egg whites and confectioner's sugar). The candies were as white as the Russian steppes under a blanket of snow.

BARCELONA

Around the cool and large fountain in Catalunya Plaza, well-dressed young men were standing in groups. I asked my friend Santiago Oviedo, who was driving us to his office in Indra Company:

"Why are all these young people huddled together near the fountain?"

"They are unemployed young men. I think they are mostly college graduates by the look of their attires."

"Really."

"They are looking for jobs. The unemployment rate for college graduates is 40% in Catalonia today.

"Our problem in Barcelona is the overproduction of qualified workers, but not enough jobs to hire them.

"Today if you are a college graduate, you compete for a job which does not need a college degree, or you go to France, the U.K., or Germany."

"The situation is the same in almost every city in Spain, like Madrid, Seville, and Valencia."

I had traveled to Barcelona, Spain, to attend an organizing committee meeting of the NATO Navigation Symposium, held at Indra Company. Again, Dr. Murat Eren of Turkey made an arrangement to hold the Symposium in Izmir, Turkey, in Aug. 2012. Indra Company is one of the leading Spanish defense-related information technology company.

BARCELONA OF PICASSO, GAUDÍ, MIRÓ, AND DALÍ

During a break, Rahn and I visited Barcelona museums of Spanish masters Picasso and Miro, and the Sagrada Familia Basilica, designed by Gaudi. In the museum, we saw a huge painting that was Picasso's interpretative analysis of Velazquez's famous painting, *La Meninas (Young Ladies of the Court)*. I saw *La Meninas* in the Prada Museum in Madrid. Picasso was trying to transform three-dimensional people and objects into a flat, two-dimensional surface. He synthesized the *La Meninas* by sixty pieces of individual paintings in a canvass. Picasso reinterpreted the original La Meninas by synthesizing with 60 two-

dimensional pieches into one large three-dimensional La Meninas. Picasso reinterpreted the original La Meninas by synthesizing with 60 two-dimensional pieces into one large three-dimensional La Meninas. Next, we visited the Fundacio Joan Miro Museum in the Montjuic District. His sculpture "*Women*" (Donna) looked familiar to my eyes because I saw a similar tapestry of Miro in the East Wing of the National Gallery of Art in Washington. (see photo 58) We then toured the Sagrada Familia Basilica, in which I saw tell-tale signs of the cubism in Gaudi's face of Christ. I saw the bas-relief face of Christ, put together by different geometric shapes. Maybe I imagined, but I saw a glimpse of the cubism in Antoni Gaudi's work on the front façade of the basilica. This bas-relief of Christ's statue and the disciples' faces were all three-dimensional, but the sculptured head of Christ's was unmistakably cubic. (see photo 130)

We went to the National Museum of Catalonian Arts, which had a collection of artworks by Picasso, Gaudi, and Ramon Casas. At the ticket office of the museum, I saw a sign for a senior citizen's discount. I presented my passport, and the ticket office agent gave us tickets with the senior discount. I saw the picture of two persons riding a tandem bicycle. It was a painting by Ramon Casas. The title of the painting was *Ramon and Pere Romeu on a Tandem Bicycle*.

I found Barcelona and Catalonia Province different from other Spanish provinces such as Andalusia, Galicia, and Extremadura. The spokenla nguage also sounded different; the intonation of speech was nothing like what I heard from Latinos speak Spanish in America. The speech sounded more like French. The next day Doug joined us in Barcelona, and in the evening the three of us dined at the restaurant "Four Cats." From there, we strolled along La Rambla Boulevard. There were many shops decorated with very curvy Art Nouveau style all over La Rambla.

I bought a large, flat beret called a "txapela" at Sombrereria Obach in Fontanella Street. In the evening, we went to see a Flamenco dance show at the Palau de La Música Catalana. A couple performed flamenco dance with music by a singer and a guitarist. Then two Fandango dancers performed a tap dance with clapping castanets, while a female singer sang with deep, guttural sound, a Fado-like song. The female singer was in her sixties with very angular and bird-like face.

The Palau de la Música Catalana was not only a music hall, but also the building was a work of art. It is a UNESCO World Heritage site and a popu-

lar venue for the variety of performance by symphonies and Catalan musical groups. My eyes were unaccustomed to architecture of Barcelona and Gaudi, with many forms of ornament, all curvilinear, lacking any logic or control. A column bulged in the middle to give viewers illusions.

MONTSERRAT MONASTERY

We toured Montserrat Monastery by train. The suburban train passed many apartment buildings in the northern suburbs of Barcelona. At noon, we got off at the Montserrat Monastery station. About a five-minute walk from the station, there was a small town square and a café called Braseria El Raco, where we had brunch. I had an omelet and a piece of thick smoked bacon. The ambiance of the plaza was delightful, I really enjoyed a small town square off the beaten path.

After brunch, we walked ten minutes to the funicular railroad station, located at the foot of Montserrat Mountain. We rode the Santa Cova funicular train to the top of Montserrat Mountain (the elevation of 4,000 feet), where we found a tranquil Benedictine monastery, built with granite stones.

IZMIR, TURKEY

Our bus sped on a forlorn Turkish highway along the coastline of the turquoise Aegean Sea. The wind was blowing inland from the sea. I felt the sea breeze mixed with the hot air rising from rocky hills. High-voltage electric power transmission lines, which followed the asphalt highway were an eyesore. But then it was a rural Turkey, mixing the ancient hills with dusty pine trees, and the modern structure which was optical pollutions of the 21st century. Red-tiled roof houses were scattered along the seafront. Several old Ottoman-era stone houses were clustered at the confluence of the river and the seashore. Salt air had crumbled the yellow plastered walls. I could see Aegean Turkey mingled with modernity, started by Kemal Ataturk. I saw fewer women wearing the hijab (or veil) in Aegean Turkey than in Istanbul. The culture along the Aegean coast was closer to secular Greece. In the inland of Anatolia, some

women would not show their faces at all.

I traveled to Izmir to attend the 2012 NATO Navigation Symposium. I also invited two ONR principal investigators. Dr. Mikhail Belenkii presented his paper on "*Precision Celestial Navigation System*," and Dr. Barry Tanju presented his paper on "*Aircraft Carrier Personal Navigation*."

I co-chaired the "Development of Sensors and Systems" session with Professor Alain Muls of the Royal Military Academy in Brussels. There were five papers in the session. Included in the session were: "*Precision Celestial Navigation System*," by Mikhail Belenkii of Trex Technologies, Inc. and "*Small Diameter GPS-AJ Antenna Systems for Navigation*," by Eddy Emile of the U.S. Air Force GPS Wing. It was the third time in a decade that the Turkish military and industries sponsored NATO RTA symposiums on navigation technology. The first was in Ireland in 2002; the second in Antalya in 2007; the third in Izmir in 2012. Dr. Murat Eren of the Aselan Company was instrumental in organizing and conducting all three symposiums. Turkey became a member of NATO in 1952, but they failed to accede the EU membership. We have seen many wars, chaos, and human suffering in the Middle East for the last several decades. But Turkey provided stability as a modern, secular nation in the Middle East. I do not deny that the Turkish nation has its shortcomings in politics and whatever the western world may criticize them for. As the Ottoman Empire's successor, they could act as a role model for the modernization in the Middle East. I once mentioned to a friend of mine the book *What Went Wrong?- Western Impact and Middle Eastern Response* by Bernard Lewis, which is 188 pages long. My friend responded that it should have filled more than 188 pages.

THE SEVEN CHURCHES IN ASIA MINOR

During a break from the meeting, Rahn and I toured Ephesus and the surrounding area by a private tour bus with a tour guide. The guide stopped at a grocer and bought a watermelon and a postcard, which showed the Seven Churches of Asia Minor, as mentioned in the *Book of Revelation*, and gave the postcard to Rahn. The guide said he could cover three sites, Ephesus, Smyrna, and Pergamon in one day. He could arrange another tour for the remaining four sites at Thyatira, Sardis, Philadelphia, and Laodicea the next day. Ephesus was a center of commerce in Asia Minor in biblical times. The hills of Ephesus were full of ruins of antiquity. In the hot afternoon Sun, I sat down on a stone step below a stone gate, which shaded me. I had stumbled into a fallen remain of an ancient Greek marble capital.

Amidst the ruins, a marble epitaph from the second century features Nike, the goddess of victory, stood tilted in the dusty surroundings, near the Agora of Ephesus. The tour driver climbed a winding dusty road, where, according to the Bible, Jesus's mother, Mary, spent her last years in Izmir. At the House of the Blessed Virgin Mary, several Turkish high school girls asked Rahn to pose with them for their photo ops with her. They giggled and exchanged pleasantries just like school girls in America. Ephesus was a well-preserved archeological site. The dry and hot weather preserved the ancient temple, the library, the Agora, and the amphitheater. The ruins had many cornices and dentils.

Speaking of building structures, I made similar features on the wooden furniture I had built. I think I know why cornices were used in the upper portion of architecture or furniture; the cornice was a projecting horizontal member, which crowns an architectural structure. Functionally it provides a secure base on which one could place additional structures. I made a Canadian cupboard (see photo 117) with similar dentils, cornices, and crowns, which gave the finished piece a balanced look.

I saw signs of opulence in daily Ephesian life in the exhibit of the recently excavated "Terrace Houses," where archeologists found hot and cold water plumbing, stucco wall paintings, and gold and silver accessories. I could understand why Paul's message to the Ephesians in the Bible, was about his concern on material wealth.

I found Ephesus was an active archeological site. The dry weather and the

marble and stone construction have preserved the structure of the famous Library of Celsus. There must have been some wooden shelves and doors in the ancient days, but I saw no trace of wood, only marble stones. When we visited the ruins, Turkish archaeologists were working on the restoration of Ephesus. The archaeologist told me that they have excavated only one-tenth of the site so far.

Ephesus was once a seaport, and the city center was on the coast of the Aegean Sea. However, rubbles and silts carried by the Menderes River from the inland hills through the valley were deposited along the coast. According to arithmetic, the coastline advanced at the rate of ten feet per year. The shoreline had advanced three miles to the west over the course of 2,000 years. Indeed, I could see the Aegean coast several miles away from the Ephesus hilltop.

The tour guide then told his driver to go down the road, and we went to the ruins of Pergamon. On the way to Pergamon, we stopped at a roadside picnic table, and our guide served us the refreshing watermelon, which he carried all morning. This region has very fertile land. I like Turkish kebob, with grilled, skewered meat, supplemented with greens, vegetables, cucumbers, potatoes, and green onions. I thought Pergamon was the place with the library, the altar, and the church. However, I saw only cornerstones of an acropolis on the hilltop and the scattered foundation stones of the altar. German archaeologists had systematically moved the Pergamon Altar to the Berlin Museum.

31

My Job Description at ONR

At ONR, I managed annually a $10 million program on Navigation and Timekeeping Science and Technology. I also organized an annual gathering of stakeholders in the Navy navigation community, researchers, and principal investigators. Also, I participated in the year-long DoD budget process and worked with the contracting department to fund projects.

To manage a $10 million program, I had to receive the Defense Acquisition Level III Certificate. I was responsible for running a good-size enterprise, which included requirements definition, procurement, research and development, manufacturing, marketing, and sales.

After forty years of on-the-job training in business and finances at TRW and Melpar, managing the Navigation and Timekeeping Program seemed like an extension of my previous career. At TRW and Melpar, technology included communication and network systems, undersea surveillance, and aviation systems. I think I am, by temperament and nature, a good businessman. I enjoy administration, business, and dealing with people.

BAA and Annual Gathering

Each morning, holding a cup of coffee, line managers and business development staffs of defense contractors scan the FedBizOps,[29] looking for any interesting business opportunities with the government or DoD. I provided such an opportunity to the prospective bidders. Once a year I posted a BAA for the Navigation and Timekeeping Program in FedBizOps to call for proposals on such topics as GPS anti-jam receivers, atomic clocks, and non-GPS navigation devices. Typically I received 50 proposals in response to my annual BAA. From

those, I selected about ten new projects a year, which brought new ideas to my program. This call for proposals, or BAA, was like a vacuum cleaner for science and technology, receiving new ideas.

The annual gathering of principal investigators was held to review current projects and to plan for the next year's program. The panel from the Navy stakeholders and those of other services reviewed on-going ONR projects in the Navigation and Timekeeping Program.

Interestingly, the proposals I received were not distributed evenly among the 50 states. I once made a map of the proposal origination and discovered that they came from a half-dozen regions of the country. Most of them were from the East Coast (Massachusetts, Connecticut, New York, Virginia, Maryland, and Georgia) and the West Coast (California and Washington). A few were from Colorado, Ohio, Michigan, Illinois, and Iowa. Universities like the University of Washington, Johns Hopkins, the University of Texas, Penn State University, and the University of Hawaii, which were part of the University Affiliated Research Center (UARC) system also responded.

When I asked professors outside of the regions mentioned above why there was a lack of interest in ONR's research opportunities, they responded:

"Well, the first reason is that the emphasis of my university is placed on teaching."

"Of course, my university encourages researchers to seek funds from defense-related applied research.

"The second reason is that we need research publications to obtain research funding, but to produce research publications we need the research funding."

"It is the question of which comes first, the chicken or the egg."

I funded several projects to UARCs.

What is UARCs?
    "They are science and technology research organizations attached to universities.

    "They collaborate with the Department of Defense.

    "The Navy funded five UARCs to ensure that essential engineering and technology capabilities of importance to the Navy were advanced.

"From 2001 to 2013, I sponsored several projects to three UARCs.

"They are the University of Washington Applied Physics Laboratory (Dr. James Pitton), Penn State University Applied Research Laboratory (Dr. Terry Roszhart, Marvin May and Dr. Cale Brownstead), and Johns Hopkins University Applied Physics Laboratory (Dr. Robert Osiander).

"My experience with these UARCs was very positive, as they were willing partners with the Navy and maintained long-term strategic relationships with their Navy sponsors."

Using the BAA vehicle, I received many outstanding science and technology proposals. However, the research opportunities in my program were very competitive, and I was not able to support several excellent proposals responded to the BAA. For those projects selected through this process, then I prepared procurement requests and submitted them to the contracting department.

DEPARTMENT OF DEFENSE BUDGET PROCESS

Each year, I prepared input data for the annual Department of Defense budget process, which my department head initiated by defining my program budget. The budget process had its cycle of activity: the allocation, the appropriation, the authorization, and the execution of the authorized budgets. I prepared and submitted a DoD budget preparation document, known as the R-2 exhibit (RDT&E budget item justification statement), which provides the summary funding data, the program description, and the justification for each RDT&E program element. The GPS projects were part of Program Element (PE) N0602271 (RF Systems Applied Research); the Navigation Technology projects were part of PE N0903271 (RF Systems Advanced Technology). These PE's became the ONR budget allocation and then became part of the President's budget. Next, the Congress would appropriate the budget to DoD, part of which becomes the Department of the Navy, and finally the ONR budgets.

The appropriated budget for my Navigation Program was $10 million. But the budget problem begins when the Congress could not pass the next year's

budget on time, that is, by October 1 of each year. As a stopgap measure, the Congress would provide funding by a Continuing Resolution Authorization (CRA), which allowed the Federal government to spend its budget at the same level as the previous year for the several months. By January of the following year, the Congress should have authorized the rest of the appropriation. But it didn't always work that way. In FY2011, the Congress passed six CRAs from December 2010 to April 2011.[30] There had never been such a protracted appropriation and an authorization process. When the authorization was finally approved for the entire annual appropriation, program officers fell short of their benchmark of budget execution. The comptroller's office pressured program officers to obligate funds although the authorization came much late in the fiscal year. Such was the situation in the budget execution of the programs. Or, the worst case is that the CRA cannot be passed by Congress. Then the government has no budgets and must be shut down. This worst-case scenario happened most recently on December 21, 2018.

ONR CONTRACT ADMINISTRATION

For those proposals selected for contract award, I sent procurement request packages to the contracting officer. During my 12 years at ONR, I processed over 100 contract requisitions. The process usually took three months. However, in 2012, the contract award time stretched out to 180 days, which was 90 days more than the expected time to process a procurement request. This slow award process affected the expenditure of obligated budgets. On the financial side, the comptroller requested that the contractor needed to spend its funds in a timely manner. The comptroller's office, in turn, put pressure on program officers to make sure that contractors spend funds.

In 2012, I found the budget authorization process went from bad to worse, as the Congressional budget sequestration added burdens to the already half-broken process. The protracted CRA process delayed the appropriated budget execution. In previous years, I had workloads to prepare PRs, first in October and next in July of the following year. However, with the sequestration, the Congress released CRAs four times in 2012, which caused an additional contract execution workload. The increased workload and the pay freeze for the

federal employees were backhanded compliments to program officers.

GPS ANTI-SPOOF PROJECT

By 2007, a new kind of threat to the GPS system emerged in the form of spoofing. Spoofing is comparable to a ship of war flying under false colors in the bygone era. I broadened my emphasis in the GPS anti-jam area to find a way to mitigate emerging spoofing threats.

The first anti-spoofing project was a Rockwell-Collins' project (Principal Investigator-Dave Anderson), which was aimed at detecting and isolating false GPS signal, allowing the receiver only to track and perform navigational solutions with real signal. The second was also a Rockwell-Collins anti-spoofer project (Principal Investigator-Karl Ulmer), which was to isolate spoofers through the use of a prototype GPS M-code signal acquisition and tracking receiver. The third was an L3-IEC project, which detected spoofers by measuring the angle difference of arrival of all signals and checking the range rate consistency. The fourth was a Raytheon project which used electronic support measures, using the battlefield situational awareness of both spoofers and GPS signals.

These projects produced useful anti-spoofer devices which were tested and evaluated at the NAVFEST (previously known as JAMFEST) in the White Sands Missile Range (WSMR), Holloman AFB, New Mexico. For more than a decade, the DoD navigation community conducted a series of annual developmental and operational test and evaluation of various GPS systems. The first was the Joint GPS Combat Effectiveness (JGPSCE)[31] series from 1999 through 2004, operated by the Air Force Operational Test Center at Kirtland AFB. The second was the NAVFEST series, conducted by the Joint Navigation Warfare Center (JNWC) and the Air Force 746th Test Squadron at WSMR . The purpose of NAVFEST was to test GPS devices using GPS jamming scenarios.[32] I sponsored several ONR GPS anti-jam and anti-spoof device development contractors (L3-IEC, Rockwell-Collins, and Raytheon) to participate in NAVFEST tests for eight years.

❋ ❋ ❋

The 746th Test Squadron and JNWC conducted JGPSCE and NAVFEST tests. These tests were usually conducted during the night from 10:00 p.m. to 4:00 a.m. The test site was in a high mesa, where one could see high mountain ranges running north and south. In between was a large tract of the white sand desert, the Tularosa Basin, where white sand dunes shimmered. The desert covered 300 square miles and formed the largest gypsum dune field in the world. The temperature in May was hot during the day but cooled off during the night. ONR contractors brought their recreational vehicles to stay in the test site, with equipment, food, and drink, since there were no restaurants near the test site. The range management warned visitors about rattlesnakes, which were most active in the warmer times of the year and nocturnal during the summer months. Indeed, whenever I heard rustling sound I reacted. At the NAVWAR test site, I saw the famous Trinity Site landmark in the middle of the desert, where the world's first atomic bomb was detonated.

PRECISION TERRAIN AIDED NAVIGATION (PTAN)

In 2006, I received a proposal for Tomahawk navigation from Dr. James Landon of Raytheon-Tucson. The title of the proposal was *An Alternative Navigation over Unstructured or Featureless Terrain.* In 1997, Raytheon Missile Division had adopted Precision Terrain Aided Navigation (PTAN) as the Tomahawk navigation system. Honeywell developed PTAN, which navigated Tomahawk by the radar-based Terrain Contour Matching (TERCOM) system. Before a platform launched Tomahawk cruise missiles, a mission planner had to make a map of the area over which the missile would travel. Jim Landon's Precision Terrain and Imagery Aided Navigation system were an extension of PTAN system

HIGH INTEGRITY GPS (HIGPS) PROJECT

In March 2007, I received an additional responsibility of managing a large project called the HIGPS program. The lock, stock, and barrel of the project funding was $165 million over three years. A month earlier, my department head, Dr. Bobby Junker, received an inquiry from Dr. John Stubstad, the Director of Space and Sensor Systems, at the Office of the Assistant Secretary of Defense for Research and Engineering (ASD-R&E), if ONR were interested in managing a GPS-related program. John Stubstad had already awarded the concept definition phase of the project to the Boeing Company. The Boeing project was initially called "iGPS." After an initial review of the document, I told Bobby Junker:

"Bobby, it might not be a good idea to build an alternate navigation system, iGPS, with the proposed satellite communications system."

"Why is that?"

"Well, they are proposing to use a commercial satellite communications system."

"What is wrong with that?

"John, we use them in several military systems."

"You may not like to use the one which Boeing is proposing.

"They propose to use the Iridium communications satellite system."

"Tell me more about it."

"O.K. In 1999, the Iridium Company invited me for a tour of the Satellite Network Operations Center in Leesburg.

"I knew that, in 1998, the Iridium communications system started its service.

"It had technical problems with handsets.

"They could not operate with partial satellite set in place.

"It also had financial problems as the user operating cost was very high."

"John, that doesn't sound good."

"The original company went into the bankruptcy."

"Oh, yeah."

"Listen, the restructured company provided better mobile telephone service to users like maritime platform, the petroleum industry, and Antarctic stations.

"Iridium provided good connectivity in remote places where terrestrial cell phone service was not available."

"John, so what happened?"

"They survived.

"I also knew that the Iridium communications system was being used by DoD, and the revenue from the government made up a significant portion of the company's sales."

The next day, Junker and I met again in his office.

"Bobby, what are you going to do with this project?"

"John, it is up to you. If you were not interested in it, ONR would decline to manage the program."

"Bobby, can I sleep on it?"

"Sure."

The next morning I went to Bobby's office. He said,

"Well, did you bite the bullet?"

"No, but I wanted to know how many choices do I have?"

"John, not many."

"That's what I thought. O.K. I will do it."

In December 2007, I received a briefing from the Boeing Co. on the next technology concept demonstration phase of the "iGPS." The first thing I did with the project was to change the title of the project to the High Integrity GPS (HIGPS). ASD R&E could have assigned this responsibility to the Air Force GPS Wing. But the program management responsibility came to ONR and then to me. HIGPS gave ONR high visibility in the Position-Navigation-Timekeeping (PNT) community. The Naval Research Laboratory, led by Jay Oaks of Space Application Branch (Code 8153), became the day-by-day manager of the HIGPS project. NRL awarded the prime contract to the Boeing Co. This project developed a GPS service that provided much faster position fix than the GPS Block II receiver. It improved accuracy for military users and was more resistant to jamming.

ONR Inertial Navigation System (INS) Programs

What is a gyroscope and what is an Inertial Navigation System (INS)?

"The gyroscope is like a spinning top; it maintains its rotational axis when it spins.

"The gyroscope can measure orientation, based on the principles of angular momentum.

"The gyroscope has a frame in which a rotor spins on an axle, mounted on gimbals.

"The rotary gyroscope has shortfalls due to its moving parts, rotors, and gimbals, which are subject to wear and tear, and limited by their physical size and weight.

"The state-of-the-art gyroscope uses fiber optics and MEMS."

I worked on the application of a gyroscope to the control system at Minneapolis-Honeywell MPG Research Laboratory and Aero Division. In the 1960s, Honeywell put much of its technology and business resources into gyroscopes. These instruments became one of the key items in the company's navigation, guidance, and control systems. Then Honeywell designed and developed a device called the Electrically Suspended Gyroscope (ESG). The key design feature of the ESG was a rotating ball suspended within a shell by an electric field. This rotating ball eliminated the mechanical bearings which cause drift of gyroscopes. In the 1960s, ESG provided the highest level of accuracy and durability, and the lowest level of drift or error over time. ESG does not have any wearing parts, which results in extremely long and reliable performance and a low drift rate.

In the late 1960s, Honeywell developed a third-generation gyroscope by using beams of light traveling in opposing directions, creating the Sagnac effect, which is the shift of the phase interference of the transmitted signals. These lights were sensitive to movement, like the spinning iron spheres in a traditional or ESG. This device became known as the Ring Laser Gyroscope (RLG).

Also, Sperry Marine Co., Charlottesville, Virginia, developed a competing RLG. This gyroscope replaced the rotary gyroscope for precision navigation applications for ships and submarines. The Sperry Marine RLG also had two lights traveling in the opposite directions in a fiber optic cable, creating the

Sagnac effect. As for the performance of the RLG, the longer the fiber optic cable, the more accurate the angle measurement. However, the length of the light path had a physical limitation as the instrument became heavier and consumes more power. RLG had a triangular light path with three mirrors at three corners of the triangle. The bias stability defined the grade of the gyroscope. Gyroscopes were categorized into four grades: the industrial grade (1-30 degrees per hour), the tactical grade (0.1-1), the navigation grade (0.01-0.1), and the strategic grade (0.0001-0.01).

In 2007, I initiated INS/gyroscope development and announced it on BAA on the Navigation and Timekeeping Program.

What is an Inertial Navigation System (INS)?
  "An INS comprises of the Inertial Measurement Unit (IMU) and the navigation computer.
  "An IMU contains gyros and accelerometers. The IMU measures the velocity and acceleration, and the angle.
  "The second part is the navigation computer.
  "The navigation computer takes measurements from the IMU and use them to solve a second-order differential equation to find the position, angle, and velocity of the platform."

In response to the 2007 BAA, I received ten INS proposals, five MEMS gyroscopes, and five optical RLGs, to meet the needs of future INS and gyroscopes. These proposals represented the best efforts from the industry and universities. The objective of my effort was the development of INS with a performance of 0.1 to 0.01 degree-per-hour drift rate. If successful, this new INS would replace thee xisting INS used in the fleet.

Honeywell HFOG INS

Dr. Glen Sanders of Honeywell developed a new gyroscope, known as the Hollow-core Fiber Optic Gyroscope (HFOG).[33] The limitation of conventional optical fiber was that the fiber requires a large diameter ring. The HFOG re-circulated the light many times. When light re-circulated many times in fiber, the effective length of fiber became longer, and the gyroscope, therefore, becomes more accurate. HFOG could also be bent and coiled in much smaller diameter than conventional optical fiber, which reduces the size of the equipment. (see photo 136)

The Navigation and Timekeeping Program Office sponsored Honeywell, Phoenix, Arizona to develop INS using HFOG. I considered Honeywell's HFOG INS as the leading candidate for our entry to replace the existing INS AN/WSN-7. NAVSEA needed to develop a new INS because of the following issues with AN/WSN-7: (1) the high maintenance cost, (2) the need to improve weapons alignment, and (3) the difficulty in supplying electronics components due to obsolescence.

Penn State University MEMS INS

My second INS project was a joint effort of PSU-ARL and Northrop-Grumman Corp. (NGC) using a MEMS gyroscope based on the Coriolis effect. PSU-ARL designed a MEMS gyroscope, and NGC manufactured an integrated circuit for the MEMS gyroscope and provided an off-the-shelf Silicon Accelerometer (SiAc) triad for INS.

Dr. Terry Roszhart of PSUARL designed a subharmonic, lateral mode, MEMS gyroscope using the Coriolis effect. The size of the INS was 70 cc, and the gyroscope bias stability was ten millidegree per hour. (see photo 142)

What is the Coriolis effect?
"You have seen a bathroom washbowl, which flushes counterclockwise in the Northern Hemisphere and flushes clockwise in the Southern Hemisphere.
"You also know hurricanes rotate counterclockwise in the

Northern Hemisphere due to the Coriolis force.

"An object moves in a spiral path while it is in a straight path about rotating surfaces such as the Earth.

"The Coriolis effect is the apparent deflection of objects on a rotating surface."

Johns Hopkins University (JHU) OPTIMUSS INS

My third INS project was the Optically Transduced IMU Sensor Suite (OPTIMUSS) by the JHU-APL team. The team members were JHU-APL, Sandia National Laboratory (SNL), and Systron-Donner Inertial (SDI). JHU-APL designed the OPTIMUSS, Sandia National Laboratories (SNL) provided the gyroscope chip from its foundry, and SDI integrated and tested OPTIMUSS. Dr. Robert Osiander of JHU-APL managed the project.

In January 2011, I conducted an IMU project review meeting of the JHU-APL team. Dr. Greg Nielson of SNL hosted the meeting at Microsystems and Engineering Scientific Application (MESA) Facility of SNL. The JHU-APL team produced OPTIMUSS, which fell far short of the goal set in 2006.

The University of Colorado Quantum Inertial Navigation System

All of the gyroscopes mentioned above and the INS relied on the theories of classical physics such as mechanical spinning, the Sagnac effect, and the Coriolis effect.

Next, I initiated a nonclassical physics-based INS. The new INS was a quantum-physics-based INS, which used an ultracold atom chip. The device incorporated an array of waveguides in which ultracold atoms move in a circular pattern on the array of waveguides, mimicking the optical ring. The ultracold atom chip produces the atom Sagnac effect. This device could perform a very accurate measurement of the rotational angle.

Professor Dana Anderson of the University of Colorado had been working on such a device and sent me the proposal "Ultracold Atom Chip Inertial Sen-

sor." Anderson developed and tested a prototype ultracold atom chip inertial system, which could become competitive to existing classical-physics-based INS. The goal of the prototype ultracold atom chip inertial sensor was to deliver accuracy of 2 millidegrees per hour drift rate. This research effort had the long-term potential for navigation-grade INS. (see photo 121)

Young Investigator Program (YIP)

DoD awarded most of its program grants and contracts to well-established scientists in the industry, Navy Warfare Centers, and universities. Younger scientists had fewer opportunities to obtain research funding, so DoD created the Young Investigator Program (YIP), which sought to support academic researchers who had received their doctorate within the previous five years.

In 2003, a visitor, Randy Bartels, came to my office unannounced. He was an assistant professor at Colorado State University. He wished to apply for the ONR YIP program and submit a proposal on *"Stable and tunable femtosecond optical combs through molecular modulation."* It was too late to be considered for FY2004, and I suggested he resubmits the proposalin the following year. When Bartels submitted it, I asked Professor Jacques Vanier of the University of Montreal to review the proposed research project. Prof. Vanier and I requested that Bartels address the following four questions:

> "(1) Clarify the objectives in a language common to the field in question, (2) outline clearly the problems in the present techniques using a comb for making optical measurements, (3) describe the exact techniques that are planned, and (4) describe how this is going to be an improvement over present measurements."

In his second proposal, Bartels answered these questions. Also, Professor David McLean, the Dean of the Engineering College of Colorado State University, supported the proposal by committing additional university resources. The university would return some of the indirect costs of travel and would reduce Bartel's teaching hours to one-half of the normal teaching load. The university

would pony up the funds by allowing discretionary funding to support his research activities in 2005. His proposal was accepted.

Each year, the government also selected several outstanding YIP scientists and awarded an additional prize called the Presidential Early Career Award for Scientists and Engineers (PECASE). Based on his successful three-year research project, I recommended Bartels for PECASE. Here is my letter informing him of the PECASE award:

Arlington, Virginia
June 4, 2008

Dear Dr. Randy Bartels,

Every year, two ONR Young Investigator award winners are selected to receive a Presidential Early Career Award for Scientists and Engineers (PECASE). You have won a PECASE award. As the PECASE winner, I invite you to submit a supplemental proposal for two additional years of research support at up to $100,000 annually. Your three-year YIP award ends May 30, 2008, so the proposal to supplement the YIP award should extend the award to May 30, 2010.

It might be best for you to wait until next summer before you submit the supplemental proposal. It would be an expansion to your YIP award.

Congratulations and Best Regards,
Dr. John C. Kim
Program Officer
Navigation and Timekeeping Program
The Office of Naval Research

Precision Celestial Navigation System (PCNS)

So far, I have explained navigation systems based on using GPS, bathymetry, gravity, inertial, and quantum mechanics. But there is one more navigation approach used by ancient mariners using celestial bodies. Celestial navigation uses "sightings," or angular measurements taken of celestial bodies (the sun, the moon, planets, or stars) and the visible horizon. A navigator uses a sextant to measure the angle of celestial bodies. The most commonly used body is the sun, but navigators can also use the moon, planets, Polaris, or 57 other navigational stars, which were published in the Nautical Almanac by the USNO. The *Nautical Almanac* tabulates the coordinates of celestial bodies. Here are two simple examples of celestial navigation.

Sailing from Honolulu to Papeete in Tahiti

The first example is that a mariner sailing from Honolulu to Papeete in the Tahiti Islands by sailboat, using a sextant for navigation. Before he leaves for Papeete, he makes a float plan. The latitude and longitude of Honolulu are 21.18 degrees N, 157.51 degrees W and those of Papeete are 17.6 degrees S, 149.42 degrees W. With these data, he calculates the distance between the two locations to be 2,730 nautical miles. Assuming his boat would sail at ten knots with a favorable wind, he would cover an average of 240 n-miles per day. Note that Honolulu and Papeete are not precisely on the same longitude. The difference of the longitude is 8.09 degrees. He assumes first that they are on the same longitude. Using this data, he calculates the triangle. The distance between Honolulu and Papeete is 2,730 n-miles, which would be the hypotenuse of the triangle. The difference of 8.09 degrees in longitude is significant enough that he decides to sail his boat first due south (or the bearing of 180 degrees) on the invisible meridian of 157.51 degrees W for 2,672 n-miles, which corresponds to the base of the triangle. He figures that it will take 11 days 3 hours to get there. After leaving Honolulu, for the next 11 days 3 hours he takes sightings of the sun at noon by a sextant, measures the elevation angle of the Sun, and calculates the distance traveled on his charts. After ten days of sailing, he would change course to the due east (or a bearing of 90 degrees). From there, he would

sail 557 n-miles due east and hope to find the Tahiti Islands. He may find seagulls coming from Tahiti, and follow them to the Port of Papeete.

Sailing from Honolulu to Tarawa Atoll

The second example is a mariner sailing from Honolulu to Tarawa Atoll. The latitude and longitude of Tarawa are 1.45 degrees N and 173.00 degrees E. With these data he calculates the distance between the two locations as 2,453 n-miles on the great circle. The longitude of two places is 29.49 degrees, or two time zones away. To calculate the position of the boat, he needs a clock to calculate the westward components of the distance traveled. The determination of westbound (or longitudinal) component was the quest of the Royal Navy for an accurate marine chronometer. In 1861, John Harrison invented Marine Chronometer H4, which can be used to determine any longitude from the prime meridian in Greenwich. John Harrison's Chronometer H4 could be used to determine a ship's location within 16,000 meters (or 10 n-miles).

The ONR's celestial navigation system, built by Mikhail Belenkii of Trex Technologies, Inc., was certainly more sophisticated and accurate than John Harrison's H4. I awarded a contract to Belenkii, who would go on to develop PCNS with the capability of determining a ship's location within 10 meters. PCNS could determine the ship's position with such accuracy by imaging stars and measure the local vertical using two optical horizon telescopes. He used the instrument for imaging or sighting stars by CCDs. I had been working on PCNS, which included a CCD camera with 6,000 x 6,000 pixels or 36 megapixels. Earlier I mentioned my visit to the Kitt Peak Astronomical Observatory, where the Nicholas Mayall telescope has a CCD with 67 megapixels. The average digital camera has about 2 megapixels of CCDs.

PCNS provides a solution for shipboard navigation in GPS-denied environments, although it would be limited to daytime. Belenkii, immigrated to America from Tomsk, Siberia, in 1986 during the Perestroika (Restructuring) movement, which allowed Glasnost (Openness). In the winter of 1985, he applied for an entry visa to America, and he and his family obtained an American visa ten days after Glasnost He told me he came to America with $100 in his pocket but thrived in the United States. I invited him to present the techni-

cal paper, *"Precision Celestial Navigation System,"* at the NATO SET Navigation Symposium, in Izmir, Turkey, in 2013.

ENVIRONMENTAL IMPACT ISSUE

In my ONR work, I occasionally ran into environmental impact issues, when I sponsored several sonar-related navigation projects which required the environmental impact statement. These sonar-related projects were:

    a.   PSU-APL, the "Geophysical Low Observable Bathymetric Estimator (GLOBE),"

    b.   PSU-APL, the "Broadband Navigation Sonar (BBNS),"

    c.   BBNT, the "Sonar-Aided Inertial Navigation Technology (SAINT)," and

    d.   BBNT, the "Adaptive Bathymetric Estimator (ABE).".

The ONR Legal Department scrutinized these projects for potential impacts on sea mammals. When a researcher proposes a sonar-related project, it triggers concerns of the environmental protection officials, and the principal investigator must answer environmental impact questions.

In 2012, PSU-ARL proposed the BBNS project to develop a velocity estimation device in GPS-denied deep-water operations in support of the Ohio Class Replacement (SSBN-X) Program. When I submitted the procurement request of BBNS, I received an inquiry from the ONR Contracting Office whether or not the proposed PSU-ARL project would cause any environmental impacts. I asked for advice of the ONR Legal Department. After the in-house counsel and I had reviewed the sonar experimentation portion of the project with the principal investigator, Cale Brownstead, I told them that this project would not have harmful impacts on marine mammals.

ALTERNATIVE POSITION NAVIGATION TIMING (APNT)

By 2007, both DoD and the FAA became interested in Alternative Position Navigation Timing (APNT) technology due to potential GPS vulnerability. I met with Dr. Wilson Felder, the Technical Director of the FAA Technical Center, Atlantic City, and shared technical information with him. He considered the ONR Navigation and Timekeeping Program as one of the vigorously pursued science and technology programs in the government, especially in the area of INS. Wilson Felder organized the First FAA APNT meeting at Stanford University in October 2010. He sent me a letter asking if ONR researchers were interested in participating in the conference.

> To: John Kim [john.c.kim1@navy.mil]
> From: Wilson.felder@faa.gov
> Cc: Mitchell Narins/AWA/FAA@FAA
> Subject: Stanford APNT meeting
> Date: 06/29/2010 05:27:45 AM

> John

> I strongly suggest you and your researchers try to lend your support to this meeting. (Information copied below.)
> Evolved INS is, in my opinion, the best answer to this problem and your program is at the forefront in this area. I know you spoke briefly to Dick Healing of L3-IEC, who is conducting an avionics study for Pax River under an ONR contract. I have suggested that he and Mike Contarino also attend the Stanford discussion.

> If you can't make it work, could you recommend someone who could speak to the technical challenges facing low-form factor and low-cost INS systems, particularly as it relates to the clock and accelerometer capabilities?

Thanks
Dr. Wilson Felder
Director, William J. Hughes Technical Center
Federal Aviation Administration
Atlantic City, NJ

In response to his request, I sent three of ONR's principal investigators to present the current status of APNT in ONR: Dr. Glen Sanders of Honeywell, Dr. Robert Osiander of Johns Hopkins University-APL, and Dr. Terry Roszhart of Penn State University-ARL. A few weeks later, I had lunch with Wilson Felder, who praised the three principal investigators.

EFFECTS OF WAVES AND WIND ON AIR CUSHION VEHICLE NAVIGATION

You probably heard about a wind tunnel, which is used for testing aerodynamics when aeronautical engineers design an aircraft. A model basin is used for testing hydrodynamics when naval architects design a ship. The University of Michigan-Naval Architecture and Marine Engineering Department, owned and operated a 360-foot model basin. The model basin had a water channel, on which ship models were tested their hydrodynamic performance. The carriage on a model basin was a wheeled bridge with a top speed of 10 miles per hour. In 2011, I visited the University of Michigan Model Basin, in Ann Arbor, where they were testing navigation errors due to the effect of waves and the wind on the Landing Craft Air Cushion (LCAC), which was one of the ONR projects.

The model basin operator invited me to ride on the carriage. But I was unprepared when the carriage started to move forward, and I momentarily lost my balance. However, I recovered and rode on it covering the full-length model basin. This model basin could make various types of ocean waves. One can make the simplest of waves by dropping an object into a calm body of water. The operator of the model basin could program his wave-maker computer and create a wave. For example, he can make a curling wall of water by moving in from one side and crashing on the simulated beach. Man-made waves were

produced with a plunger-type mechanism capable of generating regular and irregular waves, wave period, wavelength, and wave height.

I went to the Michigan Aerospace Corporation (MAC), Ann Arbor, Michigan, to review my "Wave-Wind" Project. MAC had been developing the "Wave-Wind" navigation system, which could correct navigation errors due to the action of waves and the wind on the LCAC. During landing operations, surf and wind would force LCACs to move like a crab, causing navigation errors. Dr. Dave Johnson developed a prototype sensor suite capable of measuring three-axis wind and wave motion by Light Detection and Ranging (LIDAR).[34] The final results of Johnson's project was a prototype sensor suite, successfully tested in a controlled laboratory environment. (see photo 128)

32

My Personal History of Electronic Computers and Moore's Law

Over the course of five decades, I have used a variety of computers. Some were one-of-the-kind computers, and others were mainframe computers, workstations, desktop computers, and laptop computers. During the period, the number of transistors per square inch on integrated circuits increased exponentially. This exponential growth was observed and quantified in 1965 by Gordon Moore, a co-founder of Intel Corporation. Moore found that transistor density doubled approximately every two years.

What about processor speed and memory? I have used 14 computers, starting from 1959 to 2018. Based on my personal experience, I calculated how the computer processing speed has increased over the years. The first electronic computer I had ever used was the Michigan State Instructional Computer (MISTIC), which measured 10 feet high, 11 feet long, and 2 feet deep, and occupied a 25-foot-by-30-foot room on the fifth floor of the MSU Electrical Engineering building.

Although the physical size of the computer was enormous, the computation speed was just 1 KHz, with a random access memory of 5 KBytes. The computation speed of a personal computer I used in 2018 increased to 3 GHz or 3,000,000 times of the MISTIC. Despite its small memory size and slow computation speed, the MISTIC was in high demand on the campus. It was used continuously by researchers in the Departments of Chemical Engineering, Agricultural Economics, Mathematics, and Electrical Engineering. MISTIC was functionally similar to the contemporary electronic computer, although it used 2,610 vacuum tubes in the computer processing unit (CPU) and electromechanical relays as the memory device. For the input unit, it used electrooptical paper tape and IBM punch card reader. A teletype printer was the output device.

In 1963, the second computer available to me was a Control Data Corp. (CDC) 160A. The Aerospace Research Laboratory at Wright-Patterson AFB installed the 160A computer in Building 450. I had access to this computer as part of the contract project for the Air Force Avionics Laboratory. CDC made the Model 160A using transistors instead of vacuum tubes. The computer used a magnetic core memory instead of electromechanical relays. The input and output devices were a photo reader of paper tapes, borrowed from the IBM electric typewriter using a telegraph ticker tape, or a card reader and a punch card. The CPU of the CDC 160A was much faster than the speed of its input and output devices. The CPU had to wait when the system handled the input and output data. To utilize the input-output processing more efficiently, CDC designed the 160A for handling the input-output device separately. The price of the 160A was $60,000. The processing speed of the CDC 160A was 18 KHz, and the magnetic core memory was 8 KBytes.

In 1965, at Raytheon-Melpar, I programmed mathematical problems by FORTRAN on the Scientific Data Systems (SDS) 910 computer. The processing speed of the SDS-910 was 60 KHz with a magnetic core memory of 65 KBytes. When I joined TRW, I used an expensive mainframe computer, the IBM 360. The TRW Computer Department provided an over-the-counter computing service. The TRW Computer Department would process submitted over-the-counter jobs in the batch processing mode. Each project I worked on I had to allocate and set aside a computation budget, as I must pay for my computer usage. The efficient utilization of the IBM 360 computer became necessary from the cost point of view. All users submitted their programming software on a deck of punched cards to the operator.

To overcome these problems, in 1976, a new computing method, called *Timeshare,* emerged to provide more efficient computing services. *Timeshare* provided access to a Digital Equipment Corp. (DEC) PDP-11 by an input teletypewriter (TTY). In the 1970s, the PDP-11/70 was one of the newest mainframe computers. The processing speed of a PDP-11 was 1 MHz with a processor RAM of 128 KBytes. The purchase cost of the PDP-11 was $10,000 per unit. By the 1980s, Personal Computers (PCs) started to compete with *Timeshare* service. In 1985, I bought an Apple II computer. The Apple and IBM Personal Computers(PC) became affordable. The processing speed of an Apple II computer was 1 MHz with a RAM size of 4 KBytes. Then, I

bought a Macintosh computer with a processing speed of 3 MHz and RAM of 60 Mbytes.

In 1997, several high-performance computer systems became available. I used such a computer system to simulate the Combat System LAN of the Next-Generation Attack Submarine (NSSN). The computer I used was the SunMicrosystem's SPARCstation, and the simulation tools were OPNET and Bones. These were event-driven simulation tools that required high-speed computation capability at a processing speed of 200 MHz. I made a firmware device using Digital Signal Processing (DSP),[35] which functioned as simulated hardware.

The ONR IT department provided me with a Gateway 2000 desktop computer running with the Windows operating system. The heart of the CPU was a Pentium III microprocessor, which ran at a speed of 880 kHz, using RAM of 680 Mbytes. In 2010, I bought a home desktop Dell computer, which was built with the fourth-generation Intel Core i5 processor; it had a RAM of 2 GBytes and a processing speed of 3.0 GHz.

The increase of the computer processing speed over the last six decades has been phenomenal. I plotted how the computer processing speed increased from 1958 to 2018 based on the 14 computers I had used in sixty years, including MISTIC, with which I had studied the computer hardware and software. (see photo 129)

In 1960, I remember I was holding a box of paper punch cards in my hands, crossing the campus from Armstrong Hall to the computer laboratory at the MSU campus. Now I can store the result of my work for a month on a small "thumb drive." Thomas Watson, Sr., the founder of IBM, who once sold punched card tabulating machines, allegedly forecasted that there was a world market for maybe five computers. He grossly underestimated the future of the computer industry, but still, IBM became one of the leading mainframe computer manufacturers.

33

Personal Miscellany V

In 2005, I reached the age of 70, which, in the old days, was a rare phenomenon. But thanks to modern medicine and healthcare, I reached the age of 70 with only few maladies along the way. I know the old Sage told us that:

"At 70, whatever I do, I do it as a human without violating moral codes."

What the old Sage meant was that with his morality firmly established and practiced within himself, he was able to live freely without committing wrong-doing. This lofty goal I do not think I could ever accomplish. The old Sage passed away at 72. Therefore, he left us without any musings for later milestones like 80, 90, or perhaps 100 years old.

YO-HAN CHU POETRY READING IN CHICAGO

I walked up to the podium and gave my cue to start the tape-recorded piano accompaniment.

"tic, tac, tic tac, tic, tac, tic, tac, tic-tic-tic-tic-tic—."

Then, I knocked rhythmically with the wooden bell, which I held in my hands. Then, I started to sing the song, *Moktak Sori (the Sound of the Wooden Bell)* in Korean.[36]

In November 2006, Rahn's family organized the "Yo-han Chu Poetry Reading Meeting" at the auditorium of Northeastern Illinois University in Chicago. About 100 people attended the meeting. A few months earlier, Dr. Tong-he Koh, who organized the meeting, asked me to sing a song called *The Sound of the Wooden Bell*. My father-in-law Yo-han Chu wrote the lyric in 1925. Here is an English translation of it:

The Sound of the Wooden Bell[37]

"If you give alms to this wandering monk,
I pray you would go to Nirvana.

"From eaves, dripping sounds of melting icicles,
On tree branches, I hear birds chirping.
Surely in the air, I smell the spring.
But the sound of a wooden bell is a surprise.
The southerly wind promises the warm spring air,
But my dearest has not kept her homecoming promise.

"If you give alms to this wandering monk,
I pray you would go to Nirvana.
I hear someone plays the flute
Hollowed from a willow tree branch,
And the sound of a wooden bell by a wandering monk.
"And returning swallows foretell the return of the spring air.
But the tidings of my dear lover are nowhere."

By Yo-han Chu, 1925
(Translated by John C. Kim, 2006)

To keep the tempo for my singing, I thought a wooden bell would be a good percussion instrument and asked my brother-in-law Tong-sul to buy me one. He bought one in Seoul and sent it to me to Washington. I also thought it would help my singing if I had a piano accompaniment. Doug helped me with that. His music tutor, Katie Reimer, a graduate of the Boston Conservatory, recorded "music minus one" on a CD. She recorded it at the Boston Conservatory studio. So, the day came for me to sing the song. Before my performance, I explained the lyric as follows:

"Korean people associate the wooden bell with Buddhist monks, but Yo-han Chu's poem had no religious connotation. When I was growing up in Korea, it was a familiar street

Map 3

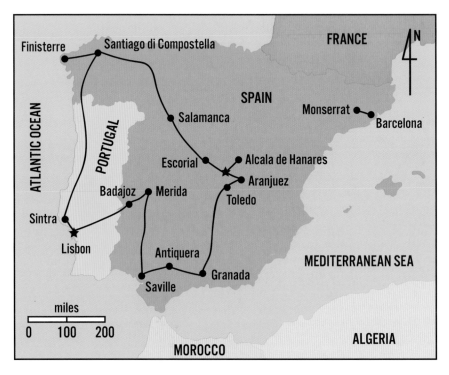

Rahn and I traveled through Spain and Portugal in 1993. Later, Rahn, Doug, and I traveled to Catalonia in 2010.

Map 4

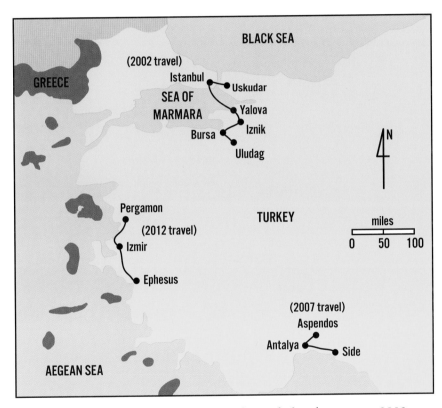

Map of Turkey; Rahn and I traveled through Istanbul and vicinity in 2002. Then, we traveled to Antalya and the region in 2007. In 2012, we traveled to Izmir and the surrounding areas.

117

I made this Canadian step-back cupboard using the cherry wood in 2005. The entire cupboard was made of the primary wood. Meredith L. Wilson, an industrial artist, appreciated the balance of the upper and lower portion of the cupboard.

118

Doug owns the Governor Winthrop secretary's desk. I made the desk using the cherry wood, 2007.

Rahn and I visited the Blue Mosque, Istanbul in November 2002.

Three brothers at the 2009 Kyunggi High School Alumni Christmas party in Washington. (From left) Moon-Kyu Kim, I, and Dong-Kyu Kim.

I was holding a prototype Miniature Ultracold Atom Chip Inertial Sensor, a Quantum Physics-based navigation device in 2009. Particles rotate in an array of the atom chips emulating an optical ring. Therefore, the device produces the atom Sagnac effect. The device performs a very accurate measurement of the rotational angle.

I was standing in front of the old ONR Building, 2002.

123

At the control room of the National Radio Astronomy Observatory, Green Bank, West Virginia in 2011.

124

Behind me is the 300-foot antenna at the National Radio Astronomical Observatory, Green Bank, West Virginia in 2011.

125

I toured the Old Melbourne Observatory, Australia in 2003. In the 1860's the observatory was used for the transit telescope as a time source for marine navigation and in the 1980's for inputs to the "Carte du Ciel" map-making by using photography for the first time.

126

My office in ONR in 2012.

127

I was touring the ONR Afloat Lab ship (YP-679), moored at the Gibb's Pier of NRL in June 2005. I became a "day sailor." The Afloat Lab operated by the ONR to demonstrate naval technologies in an "at sea" environment.

128

In 2011, I visited the model testing basin in the University of Michigan. Using the moving carriage, we tested the "Wave Wind" system which measured the sideslip caused by the wind and the wave of LCAC. While I stood on the carriage, it lurched suddenly, and I almost fell into the model basin. I only found out later that I was leaning on a life-buoy.

129

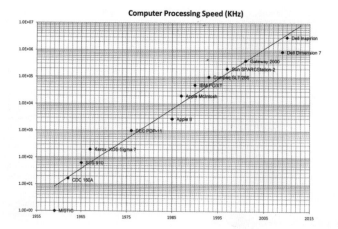

I plotted how the computer processing speed increased from 1958 to 2014, based on the twelve computers I had used in sixty years, including MISTIC the first Michigan State Instructional Computer, with which I had studied the computer hardware and software.

130

I was standing in front of Antoni Gaudi's Sagrada Familia Church in 2010. I saw the curvilinear architecture as in a Romanesque church but also the verticality of a Gothic cathedral. The exterior walls depicted the passion and teachings of Christ in the form of cubism and interior columns, beams, and ceilings with the light and optics of a prism.

The family gathered for taking a photo after Christopher was baptized in the Korean United Methodist Church, McLean; (from left, first row) Claire, and Matthew; (second row) Janet, Katie, Juli, Christopher, William, Rahn, and Doug; (third row) I, Tony, and Keaton in 2012.

132

My portrait in 2013.

133

The wedding photo of Doug and Jessica at Foundry United Methodist Church; (from left) I, Jessica, Doug, and Rahn in 2014.

134

Dr. Terry Roszhart was explaining about the newly developed gyroscope, being evaluated in the vacuum chamber at the IMU Test Facility, Penn State University-Applied Research Laboratory, Warminster, Pennsylvania in 2009.

135

Dr. Barry Tanju and I were standing on the flight deck of the USS George H.W. Bush (CVN-77); We were aboard CVN-77 to test the PASSION personal navigation system in Naval Station Norfolk in 2009. She was the tenth and the last Nimitz class supercarrier. I can proudly answer to the popular Naval motto of the day: "What have you done for the fleet today?" "Yes, I have installed and tested the PASSION personal navigation system on CVN-77.

136

Dr. Bobby Junker and I were standing in front of the C4ISR Department Technology Spotlight Booth, featuring the Honeywell Hollow-core Fiber Optic Inertial Navigation System, sponsored by the ONR Navigation and Timekeeping Program in 2012.

137

At the head table of my retirement luncheon of ONR; (front left) I and three Division Directors, Dr. Mike Pollock, Dr. Joseph Lawrence, Dr. Chip Grounds, and Department Head Dr. Bobby Junker in April 2013, 2013.

138

Rear Admiral Matthew Klunder, Chief of Naval Research, pinning the Navy Distinguished Civilian Service Medal on me, April 24, 2013. He read the citation: "… Dr. Kim's pioneering research directly transformed Global Positioning System technologies from a commercial system into a robust military system highly resistant to jamming, spoofing, and tampering. His work on ultra-miniature tactical grade atomic clocks and compact inertial navigation systems serve as critical enabling technologies for small autonomous unmanned platforms with linear scalability to aircraft, submarines and surface ships with projected cost savings of over $75 million. Dr. Kim's superb program management and technical expertise paved the way for HIGPS which will deliver improved navigation, higher signal integrity, precision accuracy and more jam-resistant capabilities directly to the warfighter…"

139

Rahn and I at our golden anniversary party held at Lockmeade Court, Great Falls in September 2015.

140

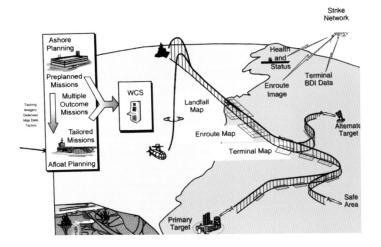

Mission planning using diverse navigational approaches

141

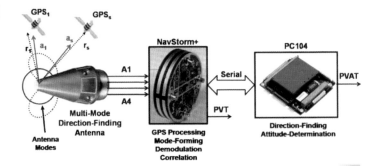

GPS antenna for small, less than 5-inch diameter airborne system.

142

Navigation-grade MEMS inertial sensor assembly.

143

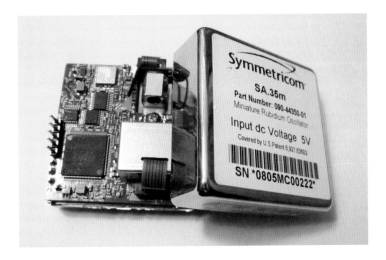

Tactical-grade atomic clock, volume <3cc, power <100 Mw.

144

Shipboard, Precision celestial navigation system.

scene to see Buddhist monks, begging for alms to show their humility."

I sang the song, and my performance was amateurish, but I did my best. (see photo 104)

✿ ✿ ✿

One day in 2011, I received a letter from Young-hwan Koh, my KHS classmate. In his letter, he sent me a copy of a Yo-han Chu's poem, *The Unforgettable*.[38] *The Unforgettable* was one of my favorite poems written by my father-in-law.

The Unforgettable[39]

"I cannot forget even now the boat
Passing through the fog with its sails unfurled.
"No waves on the morning water
It vanished without a splash.
"Though the boat and those years have faded
My childhood dreams are hazy in fog.
"Like that boat which sailed by long ago
Has gone in the fog forever."

By Yo-han Chu
(Translated by Tong-he Koh.)

DOUG'S WEDDING

In March 2014, Doug told Rahn and me that he had met his girlfriend, Jessica Pollock, at the Foundry UMC. Shortly after that, they got engaged, and in July 2014, family and friends gathered at Brio Restaurant in Tyson's Corner and celebrated their engagement.

Rahn and I ordered the "hahm" (wedding gift chest) this time on the Internet in June 2014 to be delivered to McLeanf rom Seoul. Rahn also ordered traditional "hanbok" (Korean garments) for the bride, the groom, and herself.

The wedding ceremony was on October 25, 2014, at Foundry UMC, Washington, D.C. Pastor Dawn Hand of the Foundry Church officiated the wedding ceremony. Stanley Thurston, the Director of Music, played the organ. William, the best man, and Laurie Hoble, the matron of honor, entered the sanctuary with a processional, Bach's *Sheep May Safely Graze*. The bride walked down the aisle with her father and mother, Daniel and Pamela Pollock, while Thurston played Herbert Perry's *I Was Glad When They Said Unto Me*. Doug told me Perry's organ music was performed in 2011 at the wedding of Prince William and Duchess Catherine as the processional song. It was beautiful. Janet read Scripture lessons from Jeremiah 29:11, Psalm 103, and Philippians 1:6. After Doug and Jessica exchanged their marriage vows, Pastor Hand declared them man and wife. Doug and Jessica selected as a recessional, Karg-Elert's *Nun Danket Alle Gott (Marche Triomphale)*.

The Kim and Pollack families and, the guests attended the wedding dinner party held at Cabell's Mill in Elizabeth C. Lawrence Park in Centreville. During the dinner party, I delivered a wedding toast to Jessica and Doug and introduced my family members.

"Thank you and welcome you all, who came to this dinner party. I am at the stage of my life when I have to write notes for everything. Where did I put my speech? Ah, here it is.

Before I make a toast, I would like to introduce my family. From the Los Angeles area, my brother-in-law, Dr. Bill Chu, a physicist at Lawrence Livermore National Laboratory, and his wife In-soo, and their two daughters, Joan Reese, a Stanford MBA and Partner of Monitor Group and Jean Dalton, an architect. Also from Los Angeles, my nephew, Dr. David Kim, teaching OB-GYN at UCLA, and his mother, Jung-sook Kim. From Syracuse, New York,

my brother, Professor Moon-kyu Kim of Syracuse University, and his wife, Jung-hee, a computer scientist, and their son, Peter Kim, also a computer scientist from Atlanta. Mike Lee, a nephew, who runs an international trading company in Baltimore. My brother, Daniel, an architect, and his wife Ki-nam, a nurse. Also their two daughters, Julia, a Presidential Innovation Fellow at Veterans Affairs and Joyce, who has an MBA degree from U. Penn. Our son, William, aeronautical engineer, our own rocket scientist, and his wife, Juli, Legal Counsel at IRS. Our daughter, Dr. Janet Lee. Did I miss anyone? I also thank all of you who came to celebrate Jessica and Doug's marriage. Now I propose a toast to Jessica and Doug. (see photo 133)

"May your marriage and life be full and happy together.

"Thank You."

34

My Retirement from ONR

After 12 years of ONR employment, I decided to retire—again! I was finding my job increasingly burdensome to perform, caused by the defense budget cuts, the sequestration of federal budgets, never-ending continuing resolutions, and occasional government shutdowns.

BEYOND GPS: FUTURE PRECISION NAVIGATION AND TIMEKEEPING FOR NAVAL FORCES

A few months before my retirement, I contributed the article, "Beyond GPS" to the ONR Journal *Innovation*.[40] This article presented my views on the future of navigation and timekeeping for the U.S. Naval forces. Also, one day in 2012, Joe Lawrence had asked me if I could recommend a reference article on GPS. He was by then a research fellow at Defense University. I showed him three papers of mine, but he liked this article "*Beyond GPS*," which summarized the future of GPS and navigation and timekeeping technology.

By John Kim, Ph.D. - ONR Program Manager, Navigation, and Timekeeping

The ONR Navigation and Timekeeping Technology Program is investing in new and innovative navigation technologies that will provide more accurate, reliable, maintainable and affordable systems for Naval Air, Surface, Subsurface, and Ground Platforms and Forces. Precision navigation and timekeeping are essential functions of many modern naval and maritime

systems. It is critical that navigation and timekeeping services are available to platforms and weapons at the highest level of accuracy and with the highest possible confidence while being at a reasonable cost. Lack of precise navigation and timekeeping technologies may jeopardize the success of military operations. For example, GPS provides highly accurate position/time information at low cost, and as a result, GPS has become the technology of choice for many users. Unfortunately, GPS signal is a low-power signal that is susceptible to interference. Therefore, there is a need for affordable and dependable precision navigation/timing alternatives to GPS.

Up until the 1980s, naval platforms navigated using spinning mass gyroscopes and inertial devices: aircraft used strap-down gyroscopes and altimeters; ships and submarines used INS and Loran Radio Navigation, and vehicles and weapons used spinning mass gyroscopes. In the past, naval platforms obtained time references from onboard organic frequency standards as well as by a radio broadcasted time source. Since the 1990s, with the advent of the GPS system, most naval platforms have relied on GPS for navigation and for providing precision time. The success of GPS for navigation and timekeeping (PNT), however, puts too much responsibility on one system for these operationally critical functions. The PNT community, both the user and the acquisition communities, have spent the last fifteen years researching and developing methods that mitigate GPS interference. Some approaches have utilized antenna nulling and antenna electronics to suppress interference. The ONR PNT Program has been one that employs diversified approaches in a balanced program plan with an emphasis on making non-GPS PNT readily exploitable and operationally available. In the future, a commercial transport aircraft could navigate from Dulles International Airport (IAD) to Charles de Gaulle Airport (CDG) via an inertial navigation system and an associated atomic clock, completely without a GPS sys-

tem. To accomplish this one may need a half dozen waypoint corrections, using landmarks, or updating clock functions using RF sources. This approach will undoubtedly allow a pilot to find Paris, and with high probability, the appropriate runway at CDG. ONR has been investing in various non-GPS navigation and small, accurate atomic clocks. Specifically:

a. Tactical-grade atomic clock; volume (300, power < 100 mW) (see photo 143)

b. Celestial navigation, starting initially with 10-meter positional accuracy and extending that to 3-meter accuracy, equivalent to present GPS capability; (see photo 144)

c. Advanced Technology Inertial Navigation employing Fiber Optics, MEMS, and Quantum Mechanical approaches; (see photos 136, 142, and 121)

d. Advanced Technology Magnetic Navigation (using Superconducting Devices);

e. Bathymetric navigation of the seafloor using sonar imaging;

f. Gravimetric navigation using seafloor mass density differences;

g. Image-based terrain feature-following Navigation. (see photo 140);

h. GPS antenna for small, less than 5-inch diameter airborne system. (see photo 141)

Naval forces need to know where they are; they need to be aware of precision time to be on-location. GPS, by itself, can provide this necessary information. However, a range of interference methods could deny satellite-based GPS information. The Navigation and Timekeeping Program has improved GPS's resistance to intentional interference by more than three orders of magnitude in the last decade. Although this effort to increase robustness continues, other initiatives, which are stand-alone/stand-apart on GPS, have been pursued to ensure

that one's position is always precisely known. They explored every useful navigational metric. The best were undergoing multiple-pass performance refinement efforts. Knowing one's position to three meters and knowing the universal time to less than a microsecond are possible even for the smallest of naval platforms and the most isolated individual warfighter. Robust GPS systems affiliated with backup systems of equivalent performance provide the operational confidence that our forces require. The ONR effort continues to introduce and refine technologies for this critical function.

I received comments on this article from the navigation community. My old friend Johnny Johnson sent me the following comment.

"Great article, John. That's a neat looking sextant. Lots of ship movement to counteract at that level on the superstructure. Had not thought about navigating using ocean bottom features; did not realize that they defined data so well."

Johnny Johnson

FUNDING CUTS IN SCIENCE AND TECHNOLOGY

For several years, there had been a steady decrease of the ONR budget, which began to impact my basic and applied research projects. Also, the Obama Administration had frozen federal employee's pay for several years. The science and technology community hoped that the Congress and the Administration would cut the ONR budget wisely, but the budget matters were at the whim of Congressional politics.

Any budget cuts in basic research now would have adverse effects on applied science and technology a decade and beyond. For basic science to mature into applied science and technology requires the gestation period of many years. History has shown this well. At the turn of the 20th century, Germany arguably led the world in science. Germany contributed to the advancement of modern

physics such as quantum mechanics. Several decades later, German basic science declined with the lack of funding and the exodus of her leading scientists. After World War I, Germany could not afford basic science due to the country's ensuing economic hardship. Also, politics intervened in the scientific community, which resulted in the migration of many scientists.

In earlier chapters, I have mentioned Norm Augustine's assertion about the decline of American science at the Brookings Institution. He and others were concerned by the next shift of scientific excellence. There is the likelihood of a future shift of the center of scientific excellence from the United States to elsewhere, even though American science remains predominant in the contemporary world.

MY RETIREMENT PARTY AT ONR

In March 2013, I closed another chapter of my professional career. In my previous job at TRW, I held a dozen positions in the company during my 32-year tenure. At ONR, I held one position as a Program Officer for the Navigation and Timekeeping science and technology program, and I managed 30 technically diverse projects each year. My professional career was never dull.

On March 19, 2013, I attended my ONR retirement luncheon at Union Jack's Restaurant in Ballston. (see photo 137)All former and current C4ISR department leadership came to the luncheon. The leadership included Bobby Junker, Joseph Lawrence, Preston Chip Grounds, Mike Pollock, Wen Masters, and Robert Medve. There were many colleagues from ONR. My family members also attended, who supported me all through my tenure at ONR. Several former colleagues from Melpar and TRW days came to the luncheon as well. I was surprised to see six Principal Investigators, some of whom came from as far as Los Angeles and Phoenix. At the end of my farewell speech, I quoted the following poem by Cervantes:[41]

"No hay pájaros en los nidos de antaños;
There are no birds this year in last year's nest."

Bobby Junker said, "That is true."

Wen Master commented, "I didn't know you speak Spanish."
I replied, "Me neither."

Passing of Dr. Bobby Junker

Bobby Junker (1944-2014) passed away in June 2014. As Rear Admiral Matthew Klunder said in his announcement:[42]

> "There was no finer or dedicated star in the Information Sciences and C4I community than Bobby Junker. He has been a national treasure. I will miss him dearly as a professional colleague, a trusted advisor, and most importantly a true friend. Bobby was a hero of the scientific and research communities."

The Junker family held a memorial service at Fairfax Christian Church. After the Junker family delivered eulogies, Bill Phillips went to the podium and told the family and guests a brief personal story about Bobby Junker and ONR atomic clocks. After the service, I ran into Pastor Bob Kennel, who conducted the funeral service. I said, "Did you know the last speaker, Dr. Bill Phillips, is a Nobel laureate."

> "I knew he was from the National Institute of Science and Technology, but I did not know that. Why didn't you tell me earlier?"
> "You didn't ask me, but I am telling you now."

I Receive a Navy Medal

A few days after my retirement, I received an e-mail from Mike Pollock that I would be a recipient of the Department of the Navy Meritorious Civilian Service Medal. My family members, Rahn, William, Juli, and Douglas, attended the awards ceremony held in the auditorium of ONR. First, Command Master Chief Charles Ziervogel escorted the family members to their seats and then the recipients. Captain Douglas Marble, the Assistant Chief of Naval Research, was the master of ceremonies. Rear Admiral Matthew Klunder, the Chief of Naval Research, pinned the decoration on my lapel while Captain Marble read the following citation. (see photo 138)

The Citation for the Meritorious Civilian Service Award.

The Chief of Naval Research takes pleasure in presenting the DEPARTMENT OF THE NAVY MERITORIOUS CIVILIAN SERVICE AWARD TO: Dr. John C. Kim

For service as set forth in the following

CITATION:

For meritorious civilian service as Program Officer for Navigation and Timekeeping, Command, Control, Communications, Computers, Intelligence, Surveillance, and Reconnaissance Department, ONR, from February 2001 to March 2013. Dr. Kim's pioneering research directly transformed Global Positioning System technologies from a commercial system into a robust military system highly resistant to jamming, spoofing, and tampering. His work on ultraminiature tactical grade atomic clocks and compact inertial navigation systems serve as critical enabling technologies for small autonomous unmanned platforms with linear scalability to aircraft, submarines and surface ships with projected cost savings of over $75 million. Dr. Kim's superb program management

and technical expertise paved the way for HIGPS which will deliver improved navigation, higher signal integrity, precision accuracy and more jam-resistant capabilities directly to the warfighter. The impact of these achievements will be seen and appreciated throughout the Department of Defense for decades to come. The contributions of Dr. John Kim reflect great credit upon himself, ONR, and the Department of the Navy.

Matthew L. Klunder
Rear Admiral, US Navy
Chief of Naval Research

In the past, Bobby Junker and a few others in our department have received this medal. This award was a surprise to me. As a response to my medal award, I delivered the following short speech, which represented my sentiment.

"One month ago at my farewell luncheon, I heard a mariner's proverbial farewell message. 'Fair Winds and Following Seas.' I thought that was my last gathering in ONR. It was not the case. Two weeks ago, Mike Pollock called me about my award of the Navy Meritorious Civilian Service Medal. I was pleasantly surprised.

"Admiral Klunder and Dr. Junker and friends. Thank you very much for this award. I will cherish it."

Indeed, I took a victory lap that afternoon.

Alfred Schuler, Eugene Kaiser, and I have been friends for almost 50 years. I told Al about my Navy medal, and he wanted to know more about it. I sent a photo of the decoration medal and the above citation. When three of us met again several months later, Al told me, "You are a shining example of

immigrants contributing to this nation." I appreciated his remark. Way back in 1965, when I became a naturalized U.S. citizen at the U.S. District Court for the Eastern District of Virginia, I remembered a Bible verse, "I was a stranger, and you took me in." However, I have a more inclusive view now, as former President Obama said, "My fellow Americans, we are and always will be a nation of immigrants. We were strangers once, too." Indeed, I was a stranger once, but no more.

GOLDEN ANNIVERSARY PARTY

In September 2015, the family celebrated our Golden Wedding Anniversary party. (see photo 139) Doug made a slideshow of our life together, and wrote a poem to commemorate our anniversary:

> In 1965, it all began.
> A sweet, romantic voyage that grew
> Into deep love between a young man,
> Dr. Kim, and the lovely Miss Chu.
>
> From the Midwest to DC they went,
> They dated and followed love's road,
> From her Capitol Hill apartment,
> To his fair, Fairfax abode.
>
> Trips to the park, music, and chess,
> Then a proposal and she said, "Yes!"
> Engagement, a shower, and gifts rained down.
> Pretty soon some family came to town.
>
> They gathered together for a time to remember,
> Bride and groom, wed that day in September.
> Their marriage celebrated with so many folks,
> Overjoyed for the couple in their *hanboks*!

Festivities continued after the wedding,
On Connecticut Avenue at Restaurant Yenching.
Half a world away, brothers, sisters, parents as well,
Rejoiced and feasted at the Chosun Hotel.

The parties subsided in the late afternoon,
Off went the couple to their Williamsburg honeymoon.
Now many memories they've made since that day,
Three children, grandchildren, a home on Snowpine Way.

We gather together to celebrate what they've seen
On their golden anniversary in 2015!

Doug Kim
September 11, 2015

We are Fruitful and Multiply (Genesis 1:28)

In June 1958, when I stepped out of the Greyhound bus in Angela, Indiana, I was alone carrying with me a Northwest airlines travel bag, in which I carried a toothbrush and underwear and T-shirts. Other than my cousin Phillip Myong in Champaign-Ubrana, and a dozen of my KHS high school classmates networked in the Midwest, I was a lone foreign student. Then, my four siblings came to America. By 1973, there were five of us, mighty Kims, each of them supported by the finance of my parents. Phil, Moon-kyu, Dong-kyu, and Kyung-sook all went to colleges in the Midwest states of Indiana, Ohio, Missouri, Michigan, and Illinois. They all made our house in Fairfax and McLean as their home base.

By 1973, my sister Kyung-sook was alone with my parents in Seoul. She was the last child in my parent's nest. Sure enough, she also wished to come to America to study pharmaceuti-

cals. She is a graduate of Sook-myung Girl's High School in Seoul and studied pharmaceuticals at Ehaw Women's University. In 1972, she was one of the Homecoming Queens representing the School of pharmacy. In 1973, she enrolled at the University of Illinois, majoring in Nutrition Sciences and received her M.S. degree. Then she worked one year as a research assistant at Johns Hopkins University, Toxicology Department. She is a licensed pharmacist. She was married to Dr. Ted Sung-kook Won, who was her brother Dong-kyu's high school classmate. Ted received his doctorate in Material Science from the University of Utah, and has been working at Honeywell Company in Tucson, AZ. She and Ted raised three children. (see photo 114)

I came to this country alone, but I have multiplied now 14 second generation (sons, daughter, nephews, and nieces), and 16 third generations (grandchildren, grand-nephews, and grand-nieces). Rahn and I showed the Malthusian theory of population is working, not quite exponentially as he predicted. But we are fruitful and multiply. (see photo 131)

CONNECTING TO A LONG-FORGOTTEN COUSIN VIA FACEBOOK

In 2016, I too got wrapped up with social media. In May 2016, I saw a story posted by my long-forgotten cousin, Dr. Myung-joon Kim. I heard about him from my son Doug, who had met him when he attended a Korean-American summer intern program in SNU-Suwon in 1996. Myung-Joon and I got connected by Facebook, and he sent me the following message.

Seoul
May 3, 2016

Dear Cousin John,

Thank you for the telephone call this morning. I heard about you from my mother in the past. I am delighted to get connected to you by Facebook. I am pleased to hear that your family is well. You told me you are writing a memoir. As you have suggested, I opened your memoir website, http://johnck-imstem.com, where I found your short biography, by which I could visualize your life and your accomplishments in America.

In the summer of 1996, your son Douglas and I have met once when he came to Seoul, to participate in a Ministry of Education internship program for overseas Korean students. You told me that he is now a neuroscience researcher. I would like to meet with him again as I am interested in neuroscience.

I remember your benevolent father and gentle mother, who lived in Dong-soon Precinct, not far from our house. My mother always told me about her, your father, Ke-jun, and the family with deep affection.

Recently I attended a lecture on the brain research. In that lecture, I learned that a neuron is the working unit of thec entral nervous system and the memory. I hope that our family's collective memory will be connected again and fill the missing pieces of the family memories.

My email address is: xxx@gmail.com and can be reached by telephone at 82-10-xxxx-8001. Please send me Douglas's Facebook and/or email addresses.

With Warm Regards,
Myung-joon Kim

My cousin Myung-joon Kim had an exciting career. In 1999, he received his doctorate in Public Policy from Seoul National University-School of Public Administration. He was appointed as the Deputy Director, Ministry of Planning and Budget, South Korean Government. He spent two years working as the Sales Tax Specialist at the Department of Revenue, the State of Minnesota. He then returned to Seoul and became the Director of the Keun Hwa Fur Company, Seoul, at the helm of a prosperous family business with over 20 franchise fur outlets in South Korea.

35

Positively Final Retirement

When I retired from TRW in 2001, it had not really been a retirement, but a change of employment. I have stayed at home for only seven days before I reported to work at ONR. Then again, when I retired from ONR in 2013, I had been employed as a consultant by the Institute for Defense Analyses. But now I have reached the last chapter of my memoir, and I would like to call it positively final retirement.

My memoir is about my life's journey, guided by my belief in the power of Science, Technology, Engineering, and Mathematics (STEM). Looking back over the last 60 years of my professional life, I sometimes ask myself, What have I accomplished during that time? I indeed pursued STEM and accomplished a few things. My answer is, "I also ran." That is, 30 projects to which I contributed while at TRW and more than 100 projects which I managed at ONR. I nibbled a bit here and there, yet it hung together with a few central themes. I have devoted my time and energy to the themes in the best way I could.

When I began this memoir, I thought it would have a definitive beginning and an end, like two bookends, between which my memories were captured and chronicled. The beginning of my memoir was marked definitely, but the end may be like a movable bookend.

I wish that I could include in this memoir one more excursion as yet unfulfilled, which would be a visit to my ancestral home in Pyongyang and Yongbyon. The homeland of the Kim's became a frozen wasteland, and our clan was shackled by the oppressive North Korean regime. It has been more than 70 years since I left Pyongyang and Yongbyon. Would I even find living relatives if I traveled there? If they were all deceased, would I find tombs with the name of my cousins, uncles, and aunts? Would I find any tombs at all? Their tombs might be submerged into the lagoon of the Yongbyon Nuclear Research Facil-

ity. Many questions will remain unanswered.

I have seen in my lifetime the incredible progress made in science and technology. It has been more than 60 years since I entered SNU Engineering College. Over those six decades, I have seen progress made in science and technology at a breathtaking pace. I have mentioned Moore's law, that is, of computers doubling their capabilities every eighteen months. In 1959, when I arrived at the campus of MSU, I remember MISTIC's size and processing capability. Sixty years later, I own a computer, which is 1/10,000 smaller in size and 10 million times faster than those of MISTIC.

I also mentioned the progress made in communications technology. Way back at the beginning of my journey in science and technology, a teletypewriter sent typed words between two locations separated by a few tens of miles at 150 bits per second. Today, fiber optic communication links send images and words across the continent at a speed of 1 terabit-per-second. This is the progress of technology, thanks in part to the development for military use, which are then applied to broader civilian applications. In the last twelve years of my career at ONR, I oversaw the development of atomic clocks with the accuracy of one nanosecond per day, which can be used to improve the efficiency of weapons systems. The accuracy of the clock of 10^{-12} onboard a weapons system corresponds spatially to a one-foot accuracy, which significantly eliminates collateral damage through surgical bombing. Naval science and technology and in the broader sense military application prompted that innovation. Now, capabilities of these clocks can also be applied to commercial systems. For example, navigation technology using such an atomic clock and an inertial navigation system can be used in commercial airline flights from Washington Dulles Airport to Paris Charles de Gaulle Airport. A pilot using such instruments will find France and Paris easily, or locate the runway, by using an accurate atomic clock and an inertial navigation system. One or two decades from now, what will science and technology bring to our civilization? I regret that I cannot push my closing bookend into the future.

Acknowledgments

The author wishes to express his appreciation for reviewing excerpts of my manuscript for public release by David Smalley and Robert Freeman of the ONR Corporate Strategic Communications; Dr. Wen Masters, Head of ONR C4ISR Department; and Lt. Matthew Stroup, Deputy Director of the Naval Information Office-East.

Thanks to Prof. Dana Anderson of the University of Colorado for reviewing the section on the quantum mechanics-based inertial navigation system. Hwan-soo Kim provided helpful information about the Korean Contemporary Printmakers' Association, and the correction on my characterization of Yoong Bae's printing technique from "woodcut etching prints" to "etching print." He also suggested several improvements in the manuscript regarding the Korean art collections of Arthur McTaggart, Marcus Scherbacher, and Greg Henderson. My brother-in-law Dr. Bill Chu and my brother Dr. Moon-kyu Kim read a draft of this memoir and gave me useful comments. My daughter, Dr. Janet Lee, helped me with social media applications, and my son, William Kim, gave critiques on the sections about hypothetical Honolulu-Papeete-Tarawa Atoll sailing scenarios and the Stanford satellite-related project. My son, Dr. Douglas Kim, gave me reviews and suggestions. My niece, Julia Kim, read an earlier version of the manuscript and encouraged me to write more on our family history. My grandson, Keaton Lee, was my sounding board, reflecting a younger generation's view on my memoir, and I appreciated Keaton's comments.

I want to thank several people at Mascot Books, who have helped me to publish this book: Naren Aryal, and Maria Abrams for their interest and support; Kristin Perry, Kiley Garrett, and Dennis Kouba for their editorial efforts; Jasmine White for graphic design. It took almost three years for Mascot Books primarily because of the size of the book. In the words of Paul Valery: a poem is never finished, only abandoned. Like Valery's poem, I, too, have frozen my memoir as suggested by one of my editors. It appears at this moment that Lauren Magnussen will be the last editorial baton carrier in this four-year book

publishing relay. She has done an excellent and professional job of carrying the baton to the finish line.

I included several personal letters sent to me from my friends and business associates. They are:

1. Letters from Dr. Chan-mo Park, dated Feb. 13, 1973, & Oct. 14, 1973;

2. Letters from Dr. Sook-il Kwun dated Jan. 30, 1966, April 18, 1966, & Jan. 22, 1968;

3. Letter from my cousin, Dr. Myung-joon Kim, dated May 3, 2016;

4. Letter from my father-in-law, Yo-han Chu, dated March 12, 1973;

5. Letters from Jerry Scharzbach of TRW, dated Jan. 23, 1972, Feb. 14, 1972, & Nov. 21, 1972;

6. Letters from Maynard Fader of TRW, dated March 10, 1972, March 15, 1972, & March 17, 1972;

7. Letter from RADM Dave Gove of the Oceanographer of the Navy/the Navigator of the Navy, dated Aug. 6, 2007;

8. Letter from Dr. Wilson Felder, Technical Director of FAA William J. Hughes Technical Center, Atlantic City, NJ, dated June 9, 2010;

9. Letter from the friend Dr. Edward King and Phylis King dated Jan. 17, 2012;

10. Letter from Professor Dr. Vincent Icke of Leiden University, dated March 21, 2012; Report of the Yearly Appraisal Review of my performance by Dr. Joe Lawrence, ONR Division Director of Electronic Systems, dated Sept. 9, 2003.

In this memoir, I also included several poems and articles. They are:

1. A poem, *Unforgettable*, by Yo-han Chu, Feb. 1, 1932;

2. Poem *Commemorating our golden anniversary*, by Douglas Kim, Sept. 11, 2015;

3. Lyric *Mother's Love*, in Korean by Yo-han Chu, 1967;

4. Lyric *Mother's Love*, in English, translated by John Thomas Underwood, 1988, which became part of *the Korean English*

Hymnal, published by the Christian Literature Society, Seoul, 1991;

5. Newspaper article, *A letter from an Overseas Korean Scientist*, which was published in the *Seoul Daily Newspaper*, on March 28, 1967;

6. News release *the ONR Rb atomic clock* by the Public Affairs Office of the ONR on Sept. 3, 2003.

I have included 144 illustrations. All, except nine items listed below, are from the John C. Kim collection. For those nine illustrations, I express my gratitude to the individual and organization for allowing me to reprint in this memoir. The nine photos/illustrations are;

29. Portrait of Rahn Kim, Seoul, Korea, 1956 (Courtesy of Rahn C. Kim);

41. Yo-han Chu's linear writing of Han-Gul, January 1, 1946 (Courtesy of Tong-Sul Chu);

85. Sang-beom Lee, Asian watercolor on rice paper painting, *Four Nobles, Autumn*, c. 1962 (Courtesy Rahn C. Kim);

103. Photo of Basho's Poem, Leiden, the Netherlands, 2000 (Courtesy Vincent Icke of Leiden University);

140. Mission planning, 2013, *Beyond GPS* (Courtesy the Office of Naval Research);

141. GPS antenna for small diameter airborne system, *Beyond GPS* (Courtesy the Office of Naval Research);

142. Navigation-grade MEMS inertial sensor assembly, *Beyond GPS* (Courtesy the Office of Naval Research);

143. Tactical-grade atomic clock, *Beyond GPS* (Courtesy the Office of Naval Research); and

144. Shipboard, Precision celestial navigation system, *Beyond GPS* (Courtesy the Office of Naval Research). Finally, this book would not be possible without my wife Rahn's meticulous editing and sharing her diaries and memorabilia, diligently cataloged and stored for over a half-century of our married life together.

This book could not have been possible without my wife Rahn's meticulous editing and sharing her diaries and memorabilia, diligently cataloged and stored for over a half-century of our life together. Looking back on our life, I can say that Rahn was my conscience and helped me in the matters of moral standards and kept me on an even keel on occasional perturbations in my life. She came from a family where Christian ethics were tacitly assumed. She was naturally a caring person. She had learned to survive and thrive in a large family of eight siblings. She had a good head on her shoulders and always the top drawer academically. I was a lucky man to have her provided peace and harmony in our home.

My life was defined by people, like family members, friends, teachers, and colleagues of the past and present. Therefore, they became part of my memoir. I have given credits for those who deserve credits as much as I could. But, in my autumn of life, my memory failed to remember those people dear to me. But when my memory recalls those people, I will remember them in my heart.

APPENDIX
LIST OF GLOSSARIES AND ACRONYMS

A

ABE	Adaptive Bathymetric Estimator
ABM	Anti-Ballistic Missile
ACM	Association for Computing Machinery
ACS	Alternative Community Service
ACU	Assault Craft Unit
ACY	Airport Call Letter for Atlantic City-International
ADA	Air Defense Artillery
AFB	Air Force Base
AFIPS	American Federation of Information Processing Societies
AFOTEC	Air Force Operational Test & Evaluation Center
AH-1F	Bell Cobra Combat Helicopter
AHA	American Heart Association
AJ	Anti-Jam
AM	Amplitude Modulation
AMRL	Air Force Medical Research Laboratory
AN/PRC-68	Hand-held tactical radio for ground-to-ground voice communications
AN/ARC-134	Airborne radio for air-to-ground voice communications
AN/BPS-16	Submarine X-band navigation radar
AN/BQN-17	Submarine sonar depth sounder
AN/BQQ-10	Submarine undersea sensing sonar
AN/BSY-1	Los Angeles class submarine integrated ASW combat control system
AN/BSY-2	SSN-21 submarine combat system
AN/SPA-25	Marine radar indicator
AN/SQS-23	Long-range sonar system for DDG-2 and DDG-16 classes
AN/SQS-4	Long-range sonar system for Fletcher class destroyer

AN/USC-32	HF digital transceiver
AN/WRN-6	Shipboard GPS receiver
AN/WSC-3	Shipboard UHF FLTSATCOM satellite communication radio
AN/WSC-6	Shipboard SHF DSCS satellite communication radio
AN/WSN-7	Shipboard ring laser gyroscope inertial navigation system
APL	Applied Physics Laboratory
APNT	Alternative Position, Navigation, and Timing
ARL	Applied Research Laboratory
ARPANET	Advanced Research Projects Agency Net
ARTS	Automated Radar Terminal System
ASCC	Automated Sequence Controlled Calculator
ASD-R&E	Assistant Secretary of Defense for Research and Engineering
ASME	American Society of Mechanical Engineers
ASW	Anti-Submarine Warfare
ASWOC	Anti-Submarine Warfare Operations Center
ATCA	Air Traffic Control Association
ATM	Asynchronous Transport Mode
AWACS	Airborne Warning and Control System

B

B&B	Bed and breakfast
B&P	Business and Planning
B-1B	Rockwell Lancer long-range bomber
B-2	Northrop Grumman Spirit stealth bomber
B-26	Martin Marauder bomber
B-29	Boeing Superfortress bomber
BAA	Broad Agency Announcement
BAE	British AErospace

BB	Bottom Bounce
BBNS	Broad Band Navigation Sonar
BDA	Airport call letter for Bermuda
BDM	Braddock Dunn McDonald Company
BEC	Bose-Einstein Condensate
BGM-3	Bell Aerospace se gravity meter
BLM	Bureau of Land Management
BMC3	Ballistic Missile Command Control and Communications
BMD	Ballistic Missile Defense
BMDO	Ballistic Missile Defense Organization
BOQ	Bachelor Officer Quarters
bps	bits-per-second
BRAC	Base Closure and Relocation
BSO	Boston Symphony Orchestra
BT	British Telephone Co.
BT-431A	U.K. phone jack
BTL	Bell Telephone Laboratory
BuShips	Bureau of Ships
Byte	8-bits
BZ	Naval signal, meaning "Well done."

C

C&O	Chesapeake and Ohio
C/A	GPS code
C-17	Boeing Large Transport Aircraft Globemaster
C3	Command, Control and Communications
C4I	Command, Control, Communications, Computers, and Intelligence
C4ISR	C4I Surveillance and Reconnaissance
CALSPAN	New York corporation
C-Band	Frequency band from 4 to 8 GHz

CBD	Commerce Business Daily
CBNE	Chemical, Biological, Nuclear, and Explosive
CBR	Chemical, Biological, and Radioactive
CCD	Charge Coupled Diode
CCS	Combat Control System
CD	Compact Disk
CDC	Control Data Corporation
CDG	Call sign for Paris Charles de Gaulle International Airport
CEO	Chief Executive Officer
CETI	Communication with Extra-Terrestrial Intelligence
CH-47	Boeing Chinook helicopter
CI	Counter Intelligence
CINCPAC	Commander-in-Chief, Pacific
CINCUSNAVEUR	Commander-in-Chief, Navy, Europe
CNO	Chief of Naval Operations
COMDAC	Command, Display and Control
COMSAT	Communication Satellite
COTS	Commercial-off-the-shelf
CPI	Consumer Price Index
CPT	Coherent Population Trapping
CRA	Continuing Resolution Authorization
CRPA	Controlled Radiation Pattern Antenna
CRT	Cathode Ray Tube
CSAC	Chip Scale Atomic Clock
CSC	Corporate Strategic Communications
CSCI	Commercial Satellite Communication Initiative
CTA	Chicago Transit Authority
CubeSat	A miniaturized satellite for space research
CV-3332	A voice digitizer
CVN-68	USS Nimitz
CVN-77	USS George H.W. Bush
CZ	Convergence Zone

D

DARPA	Defense Advanced Research Projects Agency
Datanet-355	Honeywell computer front-end processor
dB	deci-Bell
DC-6	Douglas propeller aircraft
DCA	Defense Communications Agency
DCA	Reagan National Airport Call Letter
DDT	Insecticide – Dichloro Diphenyl Trichloroethane
DEC	Digital Electronic Corporation
DICOSE	Digital Communication System Evaluator
DIFAR	Directional Frequency Analysis and Recording
DISA	Defense Information System Agency
DMZ	DeMilitarized Zone
DNA	Deoxyribonucleic Acid
DoD	Department of Defense
DOMSAT	Domestic Satellite
DOS	Department of State
Double-E	Electrical Engineering
DP	Direct Path
DSCS	Defense Satellite Communication System
DSN	Defense Switch Network
DSP	Defense Support Program
DTIC	Defense Technical Information Center
DVD	Digital Video Disk

E

E-2C	Northrop Grumman Hawkeye early warning and control aircraft
EB	Electric Boat Company
ECCM	Electronic Counter-Counter Measures
ECM	Electronic Counter Measure
EE	Electrical Engineering
EKG	Electrocardiogram
ELI	English Language Institute
ENIAC	Electronic Numerical Integrator and Computer
EPA	Environmental Protection Agency
ER	Emergency Room
ESD	Electronics System Division
ESG	Electronics and Space Group
EU	European Union
EW	Electronic Warfare
EXCOM	Executive Committee

F

F-117	Lockheed Nighthawk stealth fighter aircraft
F-15	McDonnell Douglas Eagle fighter aircraft
F-16	General Dynamics Fighting Falcon fighter aircraft
F-4U	Vought Corsair fighter aircraft
F-80	Lockheed Shooting Star fighter aircraft
FAA	Federal Aviation Administration
FBO	Federal Business Opportunities
FCC	Federal Communications Commission
FCVC	Fairfax County Volunteer Center

FDS	Fixed Distributed System
FedBizOpps	Federal Business Opportunities
FEI	Frequency Electronic Inc.
FICA	Federal Insurance Contribution Act
FLTSAT	Fleet Satellite
FM	Frequency Modulation
FMS	Foreign Military Sales
FORTRAN	A general-purpose programming language for scientific computing
FOUO	For Official Use Only
FOV	Field of View
FSS	Fixed Satellite Service

G

G&A	General and Administrative
G-1 Spec	Military flight jacket
GAS-1	GPS Anti-jam Antenna-1
GBT	Green Bank Telescope
GDP	Gross Domestic Product
GE	General Electric Co.
GFE	Government Furnished Equipment
GHz	1,000,000,000 Hz
GI	Soldier
GIUK	Greenland-Iceland-U.K.
GLOBE	Geo-Low OBservablE
GPS	Global Positioning System
GPSMAP-195	Garmin aviation GPS receiver
GS	General Service
GWOT	Global War On Terror
GWU	George Washington University

H

H-6000	Honeywell general-purpose computer, WWMCCS computer
HF	High Frequency
HFOG	Hollow-core Fiber Optic Gyroscope
HHMI	Howard Hughes Medical Institute
HIGPS	High Integrity GPS
HQ	Headquarters
HR	Human Resources

I

IBM	International Business Machine Co.
ICBM	Inter-Continental Ballistic Missile
ICO	Intermediate Circular Orbit
IEC	Interstate Electric Company
IEEE	Institute of Electrical and Electronic Engineers
IGG	Interferometric Gravity Gradiometer
iGPS	Boeing GPS Program
ILLIAC	Illinois Automatic Computer
IMU	Inertial Measurement Unit
INMARSAT	International Maritime Satellite
INS	Inertial Navigation System
INTELSAT	International Telecommunication Satellite
IOC	Initial Operational Capability
IPS	Improved Processing System
IR&D	In-house Research and Development
ISM	Industrial Scientific and Medical radio band
IT	Information Technology

ITAR   International Traffic and Arms Regulation
ITASS   Interim Towed Array Surveillance System
IXS   Information Exchange Subsystem of FLTSATCOM

J

JACTS   Joint Air Combat Training System
JAMFEST   GPS Anti-Jam Test
JCS   Joint Chiefs of Staff
JGPSCE   Joint GPS Combat Effectiveness
JHU   Johns Hopkins University
JIA   Japanese Imperial Army
JNWC   Joint Navigation Warfare Center
JTIDS   Joint Tactical Information Distribution System
JTMD   Joint Theater Missile Defense

K

K-1   Yeouido Air Base
K-18   Gangneung Air Base
K-2   Taegu Air Base
K-3   Pohang Air Base
KAIST   Korean Advanced Institute of Science and
             Technology
KAL   Korean Air Lines
KCIS   Korean Counter Infiltration System
KHS   Kyunggi High School
KOC   Korean Olympic Committee
KPNO   Kitt Peak National Observatory
K-ration   Individual daily combat food
Ku-Band   A radio band: 11.7-12.7GHz and 14-14.5GHz

KUMC   Korean United Methodist Church

L

L1	GPS Frequency at 1575.42 MHz
L-1011	Lockheed-Martin TriStar commercial aircraft
L2	GPS frequency at 1227.60 MHz
LAAS	Local Area Augmentation System
LAN	Local Area Network
LAX	Airport call sign for Los Angeles
LCAC	Landing Craft Air Cushioned
LEO	Low Earth Orbit
LHA	Landing Helicopter Assault
LHD	Landing Helicopter Dock
LIDAR	Light Detection and Ranging
Link-11	HF tactical data link
Link-16	VHF/UHF tactical data link
LN-66	Marconi of Canada navigation radar
LOFAR	Low-Frequency Array
LOFARgram	LOFAR sonar spectrum chart
Loran	Radio navigation system
L'OTAN	L'Organisation du Traité de l'Atlantique Nord
LP	Long-Playing phonograph record
LSD	Landing Ship Dock
LTV	Ling-Temco-Vought

M

M-1	Springfield carbine rifle
MAC	Michigan Aerospace Corporation
Mark-1	An IBM-Harvard computer ASCC, model

	number Mark-1
MARS	Military Auxiliary Radio Station
MBA	Master of Business Administration
MCI	A telephone company
M-code	A GPS code
M-CRPA	Miniature-Controlled Radiation Pattern Antenna
MCTL	Military Critical Technologies List
MEMS	Micro-Electro-Mechanical System
MEO	Medium Earth Orbit
MESA	Microsystem and Engineering Sciences Application in Sandia Laboratory
MILCOM	Military Communication
MISTIC	Michigan State Integral Computer
MIT	Massachusetts Institute of Technology
MOD	Ministry of Defense
MOU	Memorandum of Understanding
MPG	Military Product Group
MS	Master of Science
MSS	Mobile Satellite Service
MSU	Michigan State University
MTONN	Multilayered Third Order Neural Network
MTS	Member of Technical Staff
MUE	Modernized User Equipment
MYCA	GPS M-Y-C/A code

N

NADC	Naval Air Development Center
NAS	Naval Air Station
NASA	National Air and Space Administration
NATO	North Atlantic Treaty Organization
NAVCAMS	Naval Communication Master Station
NAVCOMMSTA	Naval Communication Station

NAVELEX	Naval Electronics Command
NAVFAC	Naval Facility
NAVFEST	Navigation Anti-Jam Test
NAVSEA	Naval Sea Systems Command
NAVWAR	Navigation Warfare
NEXCOM	Next Generation Aviation Communication
NGC	Northrop Grumman Corporation
NIH	National Institutes of Health
NIST	National Institute of Science and Technology
NMCC	National Military Command Center
NMCS	National Military Command System
NMD	National Missile Defense
NMOS	NATO Maritime OPINTEL System
NORAD	North American Air Defense Command
NRAO	National Radio Astronomy Observatory
NRDC	Navigation Research and Development Center
NRL	Naval Research Laboratory
NSO	National Symphony Orchestra
NSSN	Next Generation Attack Submarine
NUWC	Naval Underwater Warfare Center

O

OBU	OSIS Baseline Upgrade
OIP	Operational Incentive Plan
OJT	On-the-Job Training
ONR	Office of Naval Research
ONRA	ONR Code A
OP-09N	CNO staff for warfare systems
OPINTEL	Operational Intelligence
OPNET	Simulation software program
OPTIMUSS	Optically Transduced IMU Sensor Suite
OSCI	Open Systems Critical Item

OSIS — Ocean Surveillance Information System

P

P(Y)	GPS code
P3-C	Lockheed Orion ASW Patrol Aircraft
PAC-3	Patriot Advanced Capability-3
PASSION	Precise At-Sea Ship Indoor-Outdoor Navigation
Paveway	A Raytheon laser-guided bomb
PAX	Patuxent River
PCNS	Precision Celestial Navigation System
PDP-11	General purpose computer by DEC
PE	Program Element
PECASE	Presidential Early Career Award for Scientists and Engineers
Pentium	An Intel computer processor
PEO	Program Executive Officer
PINS	Precision Inertial Navigation System
PLA	People's Liberation Army
PME	NAVELEX Program Office
PMS	NAVSEA Program Office
PNT	Position, Navigation, and Timing
POT	Plain Old Telephone
POW	Prisoner of War
PPD-40	Russian submachine gun
PR	Procurement Requisition
PRN	Pseudo Random Noise
PSRCP	Public Service Radio Communication Program
PSU	Penn State University
PTAN	Precision Terrain Aided Navigation
PTTI	Precise Time and Time Interval
PUMA	Precision Underwater Mapping
PUST	Pyongyang University of Science and Technology

R

R&D	Research and Development
R/M	Reliability and Maintenance
RA	Resident Assistant
RADC	Rome Air Development Center
RADM	Rear Admiral
RAF	Royal Air Force
RAM	Random Access Memory
Rb	Rubidium
RDT&E	Research, Development, Test and Engineering
Red Flag	Air Force air combat training operation
RF	Radio Frequency
RFOG	Resonant Fiber Optic Gyroscope
RFP	Request for Proposal
RICE	Reitaku Institute of Cultural Exchange
RJ11	US phone jack
RLG	Ring Laser Gyroscope
RLV	Reusable Launch Vehicle
ROK	Republic of Korea
ROTC	Reserve Officer Training Corps
RSNF	Royal Saudi Navy Force
RTA	Research and Technology Agency
RTCA	Radio Technical Commission for Aeronautics
RTO	Research and Technology Organization

S

S&T	Science and Technology
SAIC	Science Application International Company
SAINT	Sonar Aided Inertial Technology
SAM	Surface-to-air Missile
SAO	Smithsonian Astrophysics Observatory
SAPPHIRE	Stanford Audio Phonic Photographic IR Experiment
SAR	Search and Rescue
SATCOM	Satellite Communication
SBIR	Small Business Innovation Research
SC-159	RTCA Special Committee on Navigation Equipment Using GPS
SC-172	RTCA Special Committee on Future VHF A/G Communications
SC-198	RTCA Special Committee on Next Generation A/G Communication
SDS	Model name for the Scientific Data System computer
SEBIT-24	Bunker-Ramo digital vestigial sideband modem
SET	NATO RTA Panel on Sensors and Electronics Technology
SETA	Systems Engineering and Technical Assistance
SETAD	Secure Transmission of Acoustic Data
SHF	Super High Frequency
SHR	Super Heterodyne Radio
SiAc	Silicon Accelerometer
SIG	Systems Integration Group
SIGINT	Signal Intelligence
SLAM	Simultaneous Localization and Mapping
SNCF	French Railroad Company

SNFEP	Shipboard Network Front End Processor
SNL	Sandia National Laboratory
SNU	Seoul National University
SONET	Synchronous Optical Network
SOSUS	Sound Surveillance System
SOW	Statement of Work
SPARCstation	A Sun Microsystem workstation computer
SPAWAR	Space and Naval Warfare Systems Command
SQUIRT	Satellite Quick Research Testbed
SRL	Systems Research Laboratory
SSB	Single Side Band
SSBN-X	An experimental fleet ballistic missile submarine
SSC	SPAWAR Systems Center
SSC-SD	SPAWAR Systems Center, San Diego
SSN	Attack submarine
SSN-21	USS Seawolf submarine
SSTP	Submarine Sensor Test Platform
STEM	Science, Technology, Engineering, and Mathematics
SU	Automobile part manufacturer Skinner Union
SURC	Syracuse University Research Center
SURTAS	Surveillance Towed Array Sonar System
SVGC	Secure Voice and Graphics Conferencing
SVP	Sound Velocity Profile
SWaP	Size Weight and Power
SWATH	Small-Waterplane-Area Twin Hull

T

T&E	Test and Evaluation
T-40	Czechoslovakian Skoda medium tank
TACTS	Tactical Air Combat Training System
T-AGOS-20	USNS Able oceanographic survey ship
TCP/IP	Transmission Control Protocol/Internet Protocol

TCXO	Temperature Control Crystal Oscillator
TDY	Temporary Duty
Tera	One million million
TERCOM	Terrain Contour Matching
TGAC	Tactical Grade Atomic Clock
Thomson-CSF	French electronics and defense company; now Thales Group
TIS	Tower Information System
TRACON	Terminal Radar Approach Control Facilities
TRW	Thompson Ramo and Wooldridge
TSC	Tactical Support Center
TSPI	Time Space and Position Information
TTY	TeleTypewriter
TWSTT	Two-Way Satellite Time Transfer

U

U-2	Lockheed high-altitude reconnaissance aircraft
UARC	University Affiliated Research Center
UAV	Unmanned Aerial Vehicle
U-Class	University-class spacecraft
UH-1D	Bell Huey military helicopter
UH-1H	Bell Huey military helicopter
UHF	Ultra High Frequency
UI	University of Illinois
U.K.	United Kingdom
UMC	United Methodist Church
UNCTAD	United Nations Conference on Trade and Development
UNESCO	United Nations Education, Scientific and Cultural Organization
UNIVAC	UNIVersal Automatic Computer by Eckert-Mauchly Computer Corp.

UNIX	Computer operating systems by AT&T
URI	The University of Rhode Island
USAF	US Air Force
USIA	US Information Agency
USIS	US Information Service
USKOPS	U.S. Korean Operational Planning Staff
USN	US Navy
USNKCOM	US Navy Command in Korea
USNO	US Naval Observatory
USNS	US Navy Ship
UTC	Universal Coordinated Time
UUV	Unmanned Underwater Vehicle
UVA	University of Virginia

V

VADAC	Voice Analysis Data Converter
VCSEL	Vertical-Cavity Surface-Emitting Laser
VHF	Very High Frequency
VJ Day	Victory over Japan Day
VMEbus	Versa Module Europa bus, a computer bus standard
VOA	Voice of America
VP	Vice-President
VTC	Vehicular Technology Conference

W

WAAS	Wide Area Augmentation System
WPAFB	Wright-Patterson AFB
WPRB	An FM radio station in Princeton, New Jersey.
WSMR	White Sands Missile Range

WVA	Washington, VA airport call name
WWMCCS	World Wide Military Command and Control System
WWV	NIST radio station broadcasting time and frequency information

X

| X-34 | Technology demonstrator for future low-cost, reusable launch vehicles. |
| X-band | A frequency band from 8 to 12 GHz |

Y

Y2K	Year 2000
YIP	Young Investigator Program
YMCA	Y M and C/A code
YP-679	ONR afloat laboratory
YWCH	Young Woman's Christian Home

# #

| 427M | Cheyenne Mountain Complex Improvement Program |

ENDNOTES

Part One

1. Images approved for media use by the Office of Naval Research; See ONR permission letter: From David C. Smalley (ONR, BDCSC), To John Kim, CC: Robert S. Freeman, JR (ONRA, BDCSC), Subject: *Memoirs from ONR PM*, Dated January 12, 2016.
2. http://introgps.uga.edu/course/Satellites_AtomicClocks.html
3. Frank Vizard, "Safeguarding GPS," *Scientific American*, April 14, 2003.
4. Ronald Beard, J. Murray, and J. White, "GPS Clock Technology and the Navy PTTI Program at the U.S. Naval Research Laboratory, " NRL Technical Report, *Proceedings of the Eighteenth Annual Precise Time and Time Interval (PTTI) Applications and Planning Meeting*, 1986.
5. Nuclear Threat Initiative, *Yongbyon Nuclear Research Center*, Washington, Sept. 2011.
6. Kang Cheol-hwan, "People in Bunganjigu, Yongbyon, the Mecca of Nuclear Development," *Chosun Ilbo*, November, 2001.
7. Sherwood Hall, *With Stethoscope in Asia: Korea*, MCL Associates, McLean, VA, 1978, p. 196.
8. Kerry O'Shea, New Irish-Korean historical links are uncovered, *Irish Central*, June 18, 2012, 875 Avenue of the Americas, Suite #201, New York, NY 10001.
9. Kirsty Taylor, Web project reveals Korean-Irish history, *The Korea Herald*, June 17, 2012, Seoul, Korea, (kirstyt@heraldcorp.com).
10. Yongbyon County Historical Association, Soong-Deok Mission School, *Records of Yongbyon County*, Seoul Hwal-pan-sa Publishing Co., Seoul, Korea, 1971, p.223.
11. American Security Projects, "*North Korea's Nuclear Program*," *Fact Sheet*, Aug. 2012, www.americansecurityproject.org
12. Soon-yo Lee, *My Memoir*, Ko-Un Publisher, Seoul, Korea, 2007, p.221.
13. Sherwood Hall, *With Stethoscope in Asia: Korea*, MCL Associates, McLean, VA, 1978, p. 313.
14. Ibid, p. 314
15. In 2016, my cousin Jae-jeon Park confirmed that he also has an identical photograph of Governor Luther Park. Luther Park was his uncle.

16. Ibid., p. 314.

17. The Little Diamond Mountains is located near Haeju, in Hwanghae Province, North Korea.

18. Geol-Jeong Hong Park, the wife of Governor Luther Park.

19. Sherwood Hall, *With Stethoscope in Asia: India*, MCL Associates, McLean, VA, 2007, p. 1.

20. 荒城 の 月
    春　高樓の　　花の宴
    めぐる盃 かげ　さして
    千代の　松か枝　わけ 出でし
    昔の光　今　いずこ

21. Masatoshi Mitsumoto was a graduate of Tokyo University of Fine Arts and a former student of Piatigorsky.

22. Army Map Service, US Army, *Pyongyang*, G7900, A2, 1947, Map Room, General Library, PCL 1,305, the University of Texas, Austin, TX.

23. George Sansom, *A History of Japan: 1334-1615,* Stanford University Press, p. 249.

24. https://en.wikipedia.org/wiki/Choyang_Tangwang_Line; https://en/Wikipedia.org/wiki/Gaecheon_Light_Railway

25. D. Gillin and C. Etter, "Staying On: Japanese Soldiers and Civilians in China, 1945-1949," *The Journal of Asian Studies*, Vol. 42, No. 3 (May, 1983), Published by Association for Asian Studies, pp. 497-518.

26. "*Sensei*" means teacher in Japanese and is used as an honorific.

27. "朔風은 나무끝에 불고 . . ." 金 宗瑞

28. Suk-Rai Cho received his M.S. in Chemical Engineering from Illinois Institute of Technology. His family owns the Hyo-seong Group, one of the ten largest conglomerates in Korea. In 1966, he became COO of Tong-yang Nylon Co. In 1982, Suk-rai Cho became CEO of the Hyo-seong Group, when his father retired from active management of the Group. In 2011, he was elected to President of the Federation of Korean Industries.

29. James Legge, *Analects of Confcius,* Pantianos Classic, Book II-Wei Chang, Chapter IV, ISBN 97815355002630.

30. 送元二 安西使　王維 作"
    渭城朝雨浥輕塵　客舍青青柳色新
    勸君更進一盃酒　西出楊關無故人

31. 春 望　杜甫
國破山河在 城春草木深 感時花濺淚 恨別鳥驚心
烽火連三月 家書抵万金 白頭搔更短 渾欲不勝簪

32. Frederick E. Terman, *Electronic and Radio Engineering*, Fourth Edition, McGraw-Hill Book Company, New York, 1955.

33. Carter J. Eckert, *Park Chung Hee and Modern Korea: The Roots of Militarism-1866-1945*, Marxism and Ethnic Nationalism, pp. 200-201, Belknap Press of Harvard University Press, Boston, MA, 2016, ISBN-9780674659865.

34. Spencer Tucker (Editor), *The Encyclopedia of the Cold War: A Political, Social, and Military History*, Park Chung Hee.

35. Ung-Soo Kim, "Private conversation with Major General Ung-soo Kim and John C. Kim," June 1985.

36. History.com staff, *Korean War*, http://www.history.com/topics/korean-war, A&E Networks, 2009.

37. Richard M. Miller, Jr., *Funding Extended Conflicts: Korea, Vietnam, and the War on Terror*, Praeger Security International, 2007, Chapter 3-Korean War: Fiscal Years 1951-1953, pp 10-41, http://www.koreanwar-educator.org/topics/p_cost_war.htm

38. Alexandre Micha, *Verlaine et Les Poetes Symbolistes*, Libraire Larousse, Paris VI, 1943, p. 15.

39. http://www.lirecreer.org/biblio/classiques/la-mort-des-oiseaux0

40. Sezuzou Takeyama, *Theory of Electromagnetic Phenomena*, Maruzen Publishing Co., Tokyo, 1944.

41. *Private correspondence,* from Ung-Soo Kim to John C. Kim, December, 1962

42. Ung-Soo Kim, *Memoirs of Ung-soo Kim-From the Songhua River to the Potomac River*, SSBooks Publishing Company, Seoul, Korea, 2007, ISBN 978-89-8120-338-2(03810).

In Pursuit of Science and Technology

Part Two

1. Judy Tatham, "Maroa honors Doc for 49 years of service," *The Herald & Review Newspaper*, Decatur, Ill., July 17, 1995; Decatur Herald-Review's permission letter; email from Chris Coates to John C. Kim on July 7, 2017.

2. Jusang Kang, *Biography of Benjamin W. Lee*, Luxmedia Publishing Co., Seoul, 2006, ISBN 978-89-89822-99-03812, p. 107; His doctoral dissertation was "Study of K-N Scattering in the Double Dispersion Representation." Benjamin worked at the Institute for Advanced Study and Fermi National Accelerator Laboratory.

3. Yong-Po Lee, *Biography of Whi So Lee*, Jageun-si-at Publishing Co., Seoul, Korea, 2006, ISBN 89-90787-43-2 03810.

4. Norbert Wiener, *I am a mathematician*, MIT Press, 1956, pp 72-73.

5. Hodgman, Charles (editor), *CRC Standard Mathematical Tables*, Eleventh Edition, Chemical Rubber Publishing Company, Cleveland, Ohio, February 1957.

6. Department of State, "Foreign Relations of the United States, 1969-1976," Document 114.

7. Untermeyer, Louis, *Modern American Poetry*, New York: Harcourt, Brace and Howe, 1919; Bartleby.com, 1999. www.bartleby.com/104/June 4, 2012; Joyce Kilmer 119, *Trees*; see permission letter 7.

8. Michigan State University Electrical and Computer Engineering Department, News, *In Memoriam: Herman Koenig*, August 2010, East Lansing, MI, http://www.egr.msu.edu/ece/news/2010/08/memoriam-herman-koenig.

9. Martin Davis, *Computability and Unsolvability*, McGraw-Hill Book Co., 1958.

10. The Weinstein Co., *The Imitation Game*, 2014.

11. Amiel Feinstein, *Foundation of Information Theory*, McGraw-Hill Co., 1952

12. R. Filpowsky and E. Muehldorf, *Space Communication System*, Prentice-Hall, 1965.

13. R. Filpowsky and E. Muehldorf, *Space Communication Technique*, Prentice-Hall, 1965.

14. Jeff Chanley, Lawrence von Tersch, *Transcript of Interviewing Dr. Lawrence Von Tersch for the MSU Oral History Project for the Sesquicentennial*, University Archives & Historical Collections, Michigan State University, East Lansing, MI, 2001.

15. The Runge–Kutta method is an iterative method for the approximation of solutions of ordinary differential equations.

16. Harvey Garner, "The Residue Number System," *IRE Transactions on Electronic Computers*, Volume EC-8, June 1959.

17. The binary number system represents a number by n-bits. The residue number is a q-tuples representation, in which each tuple is the remainder of the radix r. It is a well-known theorem in number theory, which the Chinese mathematician named Sun invented. *Sun Zi Suan-Ching or Master Sun's Arithmetic Manual*, in the fourth century AD.

18. The Disk Operating System (DOS) is a meta-language, which instructs the computer by commands like DIR, COPY, and DEL. For example, the command DIR is used to list files specified in a drive and a directory. Howard Aiken developed this concept in 1962. Decades later computer manufacturing companies adopted the idea of the meta-language.

19. RADC Contract AF 30(602)-2741, Project 5581, Task 02.

20. Patrick Purcell, *Congressional Research Service Report for Congress*, 7-5700, "Federal Employees: Pay and Pension Increases Since 1969," Congressional Research Service, 2010.

21. US Office of Personnel Management, Salary Table 2013-Washington-Baltimore-Northern Virginia, January 2013.

22. *My Memoir*, Soon Yo Lee, Ko-Un Publisher, Seoul, Korea, 2007, pp 220-221.

23. Alice R. Burks, *Who Invented the Computer?*, Chapter 5 (Larson from the Bench), p. 145, Prometheus Books, Amherst, NY, 1996.

24. Ibid.

25. Yo-Han Chu, *Chu Yo-Han Mun Jip – Sae Byuk*, Yo-Han Memorial Foundation, Seoul, Korea, 1982, p. 11 "A Memoir: My Resume."

26. *The Creation* was the first Korean language literary magazine published in Tokyo in 1919, which started a new movement of Korean. In 1919 Kim Tong-in and Kim Hyok founded a literary magazine, The *Creation* (Changjo 창조), marking the starting point of contemporary Korean literature. The magazine was followed in 1920 by *Kaebyok* (개벽), and *The Ruins* (Pyeho 廢墟) by Hwang Song-u and Yom Sang-sop. https://en.wikipedia.org/wiki/Korean_literature

27. Yo-Han Chu, "Chapter 1 – Tokyo and Shanghai", *Collected Work of Yo-Han Chu – Sae-Byeok*, Published by Yo-Han Ki-Nyeom-Sa-Eob-Hoe, Seoul, Korea, 1982, p. 27.

28. Patent No. 2,625,251, Korean typewriter, Application July 2, 1949, Serial No. 193,570 in Korea May 18, 1948.

29. As an example, a word 삶 is written in a 2x2 matrix. Its single line construction is ㅅ ㅏ ㄹ ㅁ.

30. Yo-Han Chu, "Chapter 7 - Mechanization of Hangul, electric teletypewriter, and Computer input-output device," *Collected Work of Yo-Han Chu – Sae-Byeok*, Published by Yo-Han Ki-Nyeom-Sa-Eob-Hoe, Seoul, Korea, 1982, p. 113.

31. See Chapter 20, Section 6 Yo-han Chu and Korean typewriter, Part 2, p. 93.

32. *Korean English Hymnal*, Published by the Christian Literature Society, Seoul, 1984.

33. John T. Underwood in Korean; Christian Literature Society of Korea, permission letter of *The Mother's Love*, Korean and English Hymnal No. 304.

34. D'amico, Angela, and R. Pittinger, "A Brief History of Sonars," Aquatic Mammals, 2009, pp. 414-426.

35. Every military equipment and system has an annotated name by alphanumeric symbols; for example the first letter S for ship, the second letter Q for sonar or sound, the third letter S for detection, range and bearing and search and the number for serial number.

36. Robert Urick, *Principles of Underwater Sound for Engineers*, McGraw-Hill Publishing Co., 1967.

37. Ivan Tolstoy and C. Clay, Ocean Acoustics: Theory and Experiment in Underwater Sound, McGraw-Hill Book Co., 1966.

38. http://www.fedbizopps.gov

39. The proposed HF channel simulator must be able to simulate up to five multipaths caused by dispersive ionospheric refraction. It must simulate slowly-time-varying frequency and phase attenuation distortion. The simulated signal is subject to the Doppler shift & time-delay. The simulator must inject controlled Gaussian noise and impulse noise. This simulator will be part of the testbed of HF modems and various error detection and correction methods.

40. DICOSE – Digital Communications System Evaluator.

41. A profit center is a part of a corporation with assignable revenues and costs and hence ascertainable profitability. A profit center is responsible for generating its own earnings and its manager has the decision-making authority related to costs and expenses.

42. Igor Ansoff, "Strategies for diversification," *Harvard Business Review*, Vol. 35-5, 1957, pp.113-124.

43. "Obituary – Dr. Thomas F. Curry," by Pete Sypher, Scanner Editor-in-Chief, published in the *IEEE National Capital Area Scanner*, Vol. 20, No.1, Jan.-Feb. 2005. IEEE Fellow citation and article from the Northern Virginia Section newsletter 2nd of 3 issues (spring 1978).

44. *Seoul Daily Newspaper*, March 28, 1967.

45. Lincoln Spector, "The IBM Personal Computer's 25th Anniversary," *PCW orld*, Aug 11, 2006.

46. United Nations Conference on Trade and Development (UNCTAD) is an organization of the United Nations Economic and Social Council (ECO-SOC). The objective of the UNCTAD is to formulate policies relating to all aspects of development including trade, aid, transport, finance and technology.

47. College of Business, the University of Illinois, Champaign-Urbana: Ph.D. in Finance in 1974; http://business.illinois.edu/finance/phd/alumni.aspx

48. Bellman, Richard, *Dynamic Programming*, Princeton University Press, Princeton, NJ, 1957.

49. Andre Agassi, *Open – An Autobiography*, Alfred A. Knopf Publishing Co., pp. 329-330.

50. Ung-soo Kim, *Memoirs of Ung-soo Kim-From the Songhua River to the Potomac River*, SSBooks Publishing Company, Seoul, Korea, 2007, ISBN 978-89-8120-338-2 (03810), p.250.

51. Korean spoken with a heavy accent, typically by foreign missionaries.

52. Arthur McTaggart, Sing-mo Hwang, et al, *Dr. Arthur McTaggart: Life and Anecdotes*, Donga Publishing Co., Seoul, Korea, 1985 OCLC Number 17225278.

53. The National Museum of Korea, Artifact Management Department, Catalog No. 398-5103, 2000/03/29.

54. Sotheby's Catalog of Auction, *Korean Art from the Estate of Marcus W. Scherbacher*, Sotheby's New York, 1997.

55. Henderson, Gregory, *Korea: The Politics of the Vortex*, Harvard University Press, Cambridge, MA, 1968, Library of Congress Catalog Card Number 68-25611.

56. *Korean Ceramics, An Arts Variety*, by Gregory Henderson, Ohio State University Press, 1969, p. 25, illustration caption 20.

Part Three

1. USAF, Fact Sheet, *Defense Support Program, Post date May 14, 2015,* http://www.losangeles.af.mil/library/factsheets/factsheet.asp?id=5323

2. https://en.wikipedia.org/wiki/MM-104-patriot

3. *National Geographic Magazine,* "Dangerous Divide," July 2003, pp. 8-9.

4. CRT stands for Cathode Ray Tube.

5. Travel category by government airplane or authorized commercial airplane.

6. Bong-Seo Lee was Special Assistant to the Prime Mister Jong-Pil Kim. He worked at the World Bank (1965-1971) in Washington. In 1988, he became Minister of the Energy Ministry.

7. It was established by the ROK Presidential Order 28.

8. Camp Casey, was the home of 2nd Infantry Division in Dong-Du-Cheon, Korea.

9. Camp Red Cloud, was the home of 1st Brigade, 2nd Infantry Division Command in Ui-Jeong-Bu, Korea.

10. Camp Page, was the home of 2nd Aviation Regiment, US Army in Chun-Cheon, Korea.

11. During the Korean War, Korean airfields were designated by Identification Codes, e.g., K-1 for Pusan-West Airbase. Starting with K-17, there are air-fields in North Korea that were assigned K numbers. The reason is that some or all of these airfields were, for a period of time, under the control of United Nations forces and some were actually used for allied air operations.

12. The KCIS project office booked a room for me and the family in Chosun Hotel.

13. The USAF Electronics System Division Program to improve NORAD Computer System in Cheyenne Mountain Complex, Colorado.

14. The stone table of our ancestor's tomb was 450 years old. What had been carved in the stone table was identical to the records in our genealogy book; I visited the grave, which was located at Ma-u-gok Village, Jeon-ui District, Yeon-gi County, North Chung-cheong Province, South Korea.

15. The memorial park is located at No. San-9, Suk-gok Village, Sungnam District, Cheong-won County, North Chung-cheong Province, South Korea.

16. An Asian philosophical system of harmonizing everyone with the surrounding environment.

17. Korean United Methodist Church, *60 Years History of KUMC (1951-2011) - Fountain of Life*, 2011.

18. See Ed and Phyllis King in Chapter 2.

19. Sherwood Hall, *With Stethoscope in Asia: Korea*, MCL Associates, McLean, VA, 1981.

20. The New Testament, John 11:25.

21. The *Saint* is a British mystery spy thriller TV series.

22. *Caillou* was a popular kid's Public Broadcasting System (PBS) television program.

23. Steven R. Strom, "A Stellar Rendezvous," Crosslink, Winter 2002/2003 Vol. 4 No. 1, Aerospace Corporation, p. 12.

24. John Kim and Juanita Ford, "BMDO Virtual Data Center (VDC) Network Traffic Analysis," *Proceedings of IEEE 1998 MILCOM Conference*, Boston, 1998, pp. 951-960.

25. DCA became DISA in 1991.

26. Thomas C. Lassman, *Sources of Weapon Systems Innovation in the Department of Defense: the Role of Research and Development, 1945-2000*, Center of Military History, US Army, Washington, DC, 2008.

27. MTONN stands for Multilayered Third Order Neural Network.

28. Tong-He Koh (ed), *Selected Writing of Soon-Deok Koh*, the University of Illinois at Chicago Publication Service, 1991.

29. This is a two-volume, 1,806-page book; Yo-Han Memorial Foundation, *The Collected Literary Works of Yo-Han Chu – The Dawn*, 1982.

30. Young-Seop Chu, *Introduction to Scenario Writing*, In-Min Publishing Company, Pyongyang, 1948.

31. NAVCAMS were located in Norfolk, Hawaii, London, and Naples.

32. H. Graham, J. Kim, E. Band & A. Fowler, "Air Cushion Landing Craft Navigation," *Naval Engineers Journal, May 1985, pp 248-260.*

33. Ronald L. Rusing, MAJ, USAF, *Prepare the Fighter Force-Red Flag/Composite Force*, Thesis, Master of Military Art and Science, US Army Command and General Staff College, Ft. Leavenworth, Kansas, 1980, http://www.dtic.mil/dtic/tr/fulltext/u2/a094982.pdf

34. Stephen Law Company, *Fighter Pilot: Operation Red Flag*, Directed by Stephen Law, 2004.

35. J. Kim and P. Girardi, "Application of the ATM-SONET to New Attack Submarine (NSSN) Radar Subsystems," *1997 IEEE MILCOM Proceedings*, Vol II, pp 1003-1010, Nov. 2-5, 1997.

36. EUROCONTROL is the European Organization for the Safety of Air Navigation.

37. J. Kim, "A Review of Enabling Technologies for the Next Generation Aviation Communications System," *American Institute of Aeronautics and Astronautics (AIAA)/ Society of Automotive Engineers (SAE) World Aviation Congress Proceedings*, Oct 19 - 21, 1999, San Francisco.

38. Andrew C. Nahm, A History of the Korean People: Tradition and Transformation, Hollym Publishing Co., Seoul, 1988, p. 274.

39. Hyeong-Seok Noh, "Discovery of Hidden Art Work by Kwe-dae Lee," *The Hankyoreh Newspaper,* October 1, 2010, Seoul, Korea.

40. Young-ran Lee, "The Exhibition of South Korean Pioneer Screen Printing Artist – Yoong Bae on April 12, 2015 at Asian Art Museum, San Francisco, " *Joong-ang Daily Newspaper*, Published in San Francisco, April, 8, 2015.

41. Sotheby's Catalog of Auction, *Korean Art from the Estate of Marcus W. Scherbacher*, Sothey's New York, 1997.

42. Can Shen (715-770) was a Tang Poet, who served as military commander in Northwest frontier of China.

43. Can Shen (715-770) was a Tang Poet, who served as military commander in Northwest frontier of China.

44. Staff Writers, "History of the CubeSat," *Space Daily*, Bethesda MD (SPX), Aug 23, 2016, http://www.spacedaily.com/reports/History_of_the_CubeSat_999.html

45. Kitts, Christopher A., and William H. Kim, "The Design and Construction of the Stanford Audio Phonic Photographic Infrared Experiment (SAPPHIRE) Satellite", May 25, 1994, Proceedings of the 8th Annual AIAA/USU Conference on Small Satellites, Logan, Utah, Aug. 29 – Sep. 1, 1995.

46. NASA, "X-34: Demonstrating Resuable Launch Vehicle Technologies," *Fact sheet*, FS-1999-10-137-MSFC, 1999.

47. William Kim, "Design of the X34 Speedbrake Mechanism Under Volume, Stiffness, Cost and Schedule Constraints," *Proceedings of the 35th Aerospace Mechanisms Symposium*, at NASA Ames Research Center, Mountain View, CA, May 9 - 11, 2001. This symposium was hosted by National Aeronautics and Space Administration (NASA) and Lockheed Martin Space Systems Company, and organized by the Mechanisms Education Association.

48. J. Kim and E. Muehldorf, "Naval Shipboard Communications System," Prentice-Hall Pub. Co., 1985.

49. Reprinted from *Proceedings* with permission; Copyright © 1995 US Naval Institute/www.usni.org; Lieutenant Commander Thomas J. Cutler (ret.), USN, *Proceedings of Naval Institute*, Books of Interest, September 1990.

50. "Keeping up with shipboard communications," TRW Magazine, *Spectrum,* July 1994.

51. In 1996 TRW Magazine, *Spectrum*, "five TRW Technical Fellows selected."

52. John C. Kim, "Simulation and Analysis of GPS LAAS Interference Mitigation," *1998 TRW IR&D Project Reports*, TRW, Redondo Beach, CA.

53. The C-band is the electromagnetic spectrum in the frequency of 4-8 GHz; Ku-band is in the frequency of 11.2-14.5 GHz.

54. The three codes are the Reed-Solomon code, convolution code, and interleaving, which can detect and correct multiple random errors.

55. The antenna beam forming method suggested was a shaped (depressed cardioids) antenna pattern for lower orbit LEO satellites, by which the received signal level could be maximized at very low elevation angles.

56. This project was reported in the proceedings: J. Kim and D. Schall, "On the Improvement of Low Elevation Angle Satellite Communications Impaired by Tropospheric Fading Effects," *IEEE 1999 MILCOM Conference, Atlantic City, NJ*, Proceedings, pp. 603-607.

57. The photo of "Basho in Leiden": Courtensy of Prof. Vincent Icke, Leiden University, The Netherlands.

58. 荒海や　佐渡に　よこたふ　天の川 -- 芭蕉 Basho (1644 - 1494).

59. Decca Recording Company, Mahler Das Lied von der Erde, Los Angeles Philharmonic, 2009.

送別王維　作

下馬飲君酒　問君何所之　君言不得意

歸臥南山陲　但去莫復問　白雲無盡時

60. W. S. Hyun, Anthology of Tang Poems, Hyung-Am Sa Publishing Co., 1971

61. Category - Telegraph; Subject – Equipment; Date of picture - c 1900; Details of picture - Single Current Key; Location or place: BT Archives, GO9, Telephone House, 2-4 Temple Avenue, London EC4Y 0HL; Negative reference - E50.

62. Category - Telegraph; Subject – Equipment; Date of Picture – 29/07/1921; Details of Picture - Standard Relay "B"; Location: BT Archives, GO9, Telephone House, 2-4 Temple Avenue, London EC4Y 0HL; Negative reference - E50.

63. ICO is the terminology used in the U.K. for Medium Earth Orbiting (MEO) satellites.
64. William Barrett, *Irrational Man*, Random House Publishing Co., 1958.

Part Four

1. Eric M. Weiss and Lori Montgomery, "Relocation of DARPA," Washington Post, August 26, 2005.

2. ONR, *A Biography of Senior Executives: Bobby Junker*, January 2013.

3. Dr. Bobby Junker's introduction of Nobel Laureate William Phillips.

4. William D. Phillips, "Laser cooling and trapping of neutral atoms," *Reviews of Modern Physics*, Vol. 70, No. 3, July 1998.

5. Hung Ly, et al, "Design, Simulation and Testing of a Miniaturized GPS Dual-Frequency (L1/L2) Antenna Array, *Proceedings of ION GPS 2002*, Portland, Oregon, Sept 24-27, 2002.

6. See ONR permission letter: From David C. Smalley (ONR, BDCSC), To John Kim, CC: Robert S. Freeman, JR (ONRA, BDCSC), Subject: *Memoirs from ONR PM*, Dated January 12, 2016.

7. A flat radio antenna designed to follow a prescribed shape.

8. Ron Walsworth et al, "The Story Behind Stopped Light," *Optics & Photonics News*, May 2002, pp. 51-54.

9. Lockman, F.J. et al (ed.), *But it was Fund-The first forty years of radio astronomy at Green Bank*, National Radio Astronomy Observatory, 2007.

10. http://www.seti.org/seti-institute/project/details/seti-observations.

11. Douglas Kim, et al., "Ultrasensitive fluorescent proteins for imaging neuronal activity," *Nature*, 18 July 2013, Volume 499, pp. 295-304.

12. Jacques Vanier, Marty Levine and John Kim, "Recent Advances in Atomic Clock Development: Coherent Population Trapping (CPT) Rubidium Atomic Clock Research," *Proceedings of NATO Navigation Symposium*, 14 – 16 Oct. 2002, sponsored by NATO Sensors and Electronics Panel, No. 168, at Istanbul, Turke.

13. John Kim, Charles Falchetti, Eric Evans, and Bareket Tanju, "Link 16/GPS Integrated Enhancements – A Robust Navigation Resource For Military Applications," *Proceedings of NATO Navigation Symposium, 14 – 16 Oct. 2002*, sponsored by NATO Sensors and Electronics Panel, No. 168, at Istanbul, Turkey.

14. Sophia Hagia was originally built as a Greek Christian Basilica in 575 by Emperor Justinian.

15. J. Kim and D. Lewis, "MEMS IMU and Temperature Controlled Crystal Oscillator (TCXO) Effect on Ultra-Tightly Coupled GPS-INS Tracking Performance," *Proceedings of the Sixth International Conference on Satellite Navigation Technology Including Mobile Positioning & Location Services*, Melbourne, Australia, 22–25 July 2003.

16. Tony Abbott (Aerospace Corporation), "GPS/IMU Ultra-Tight Integration," *Presentation at GPS User Equipment Modernization and Advanced UE Technology Industry Days*, October 23-24, 2001.

17. http://en.wikipedia.org/wiki/Cavendish_Laboratory.

18. The vibration noise is less than 10^{-8}g/Hz$^{1/2}$.

19. Naval Research Advisory Committee, Damage Control and Maintenance Panel, *Report on the Damage Control and Maintenance*, NRAC, Washington, DC, 1996; See ONR permission letter: From David C. Smalley (ONR, BDCSC), To John Kim, CC: Robert S. Freeman, JR (ONRA, BDCSC), Subject: *Memoirs from ONR PM*, Dated January 12, 2016.

20. John Castagna, *ONR Corporate Communications*, Mar. 16, 2010; See ONR permission letter: From David C. Smalley (ONR, BDCSC), To John Kim, CC: Robert S. Freeman, JR (ONRA, BDCSC), Subject: *Memoirs from ONR PM*, Dated January 12, 2016.

21. Andrew McBarnet, "Gravity Gradiometer Has Graduated," *Offshore Engineering*, June 1, 2013.

22. ONR Yearly Appraisal Report for John Kim by Joseph Lawrence, Director, Code 321, Sept. 12, 2003; See ONR permission letter: From David C. Smalley (ONR, BDCSC), To John Kim, CC: Robert S. Freeman, JR (ONRA, BDCSC), Subject: *Memoirs from ONR PM*, Dated January 12, 2016.

23. General Dwight Eisenhower's speech, "*D-Day*." D-day statement to soldiers, sailor, and airmen of the Allied Expeditionary Force, June 1944, Collection DDE-EPRE: Eisenhower, Dwight D: Papers, Pre-Presidential, 1916-1952; Dwight D. Eisenhower Library; National Archives and Records Administration.

24. Eisenhower's Famous Other Message on D-Day, a memo in the event of failure, Letter from Washington, Lessons Learned From Eisenhower, By Albert R. Hunt and Bloomberg News, Published: June 3, 2012.

25. National Academy of Science, *Rising Above the Gathering Storm*: Engineering and Employing America for A Bright Future, National Academies Press, 2006.

26. Michael Teitelbaum, *Falling Behind - Boom, Bust & the Global Race for Scientific Talent*, Princeton University Press, 2017

27. M. King Hubbert, *Nuclear Energy and the Fossil Fuels*, Shell Development Company, Publication Number 95, Houston, Texas, June 1956.

28. Paul Benshouf, "JAMFEST, A cost effective solution to GPS vulnerability testing," *GNSS*, Nov 2005.

29. The FedBizOps (FBO), formerly known as the Commerce Business Daily (CBD), is the source for federal procurement bidding opportunities, contracts awarded, special notices, and surplus government sales.

30. Michael D. Shear. "Budget Deal Reached to Avert Shutdown: Vote Set Next Week After 6-Day Bridge," *The New York Times*, April 8, 2011.

31. Pronounced as "gypsy.

32. Angelo Trunzo, et al., "JAMFEST - Testing Your Way Out of a GPS Jam," *Inside GNSS*, Jul/Aug 2003.

33. G. A. Sanders, L. K. Strandjord, and T. Qiu, "Hollow Core Fiber Optic Ring Resonator for Rotation Sensing," in *Optical Fiber Sensors*, Optical Society of America, 2006.

34. LIDAR is a remote sensing technology that measures distance by illuminating a target with a laser and analyzing the reflected light.

35. Digital Signal Processing (DSP) is used as a quick prototyping hardware device for any digital devices for communications system transfer of firmware program to an embedded memory called a Programmable Read-Only Memory (PROM). This process is called "burning" PROM.

36. "목탁소리" - 주 요한

"이중한푼 주시오면 극락세계 가리오다."
어름녹아 락수소리　　가지우에 꾀꼴소리
봄날이 완연컨만　　목탁소라 윈일인고
갓던봄 왓건만은　　오마던님 웨 안오고

"이중한푼 주시오면 극락세계 가리오다."
버들줄에 피릿소리　　중치는 목탁소라
강남제비 왓건만은　　님의소리웨 안오고

37. Translated by John C. Kim on May 13, 2006; Lyric and music of "The Wooden Bell" *Cho Doo Nam Music Book* , ISBN 89-03-92102-X93670, published by Sekwang Music Publishing Co., Seoul, South Korea.

38. Lee Kwang Soo, Chu Yo-Han, Kim Dong Hwan and Kim Eok, *Shiga Dong In Jip*, Shiga Dong In Sa Publishing Co., Feb. 1, 1932.

39. 지금에도 못 잊는 것은   주 요한 작
    지금에도 못 잊는 것은
    안개 속에 돛 달고 가던배.
    바람도 없는 아침 물결에
    소리도없이 가 버린 배
    배도 가고 세월도 갔건마는
    안개 속 같은 어릴적 꿈은
    옛날의 돛달고 가던 배같이
    안개속에 가고 오지 않은 배 같이

40. ONR, *Innovation*, Vol. 9, Fall Issue, 2012, pp 6-8; See ONR permission letter: From David C. Smalley (ONR, BDCSC), To John Kim, CC: Robert S. Freeman, JR (ONRA, BDCSC), Subject: *Memoirs from ONR PM*, Dated January 12, 2016.

41. Cervantes, *Don Quixote* ii. lxxiv.

42. Rear Admiral Matthew Klunder, CNR, "Bobby Junker - National Treasure Remembered," email dated June 15, 2014; See ONR permission letter: From David C. Smalley (ONR, BDCSC), To John Kim, CC: Robert S. Freeman, JR (ONRA, BDCSC), Subject: *Memoirs from ONR PM*, Dated January 12, 2016.

INDEX

A

B

C

D

E

F

G

H

I

J

K

L

M

N

O

P

Q

R

S

T

U

V

W

Y

C000061482